The Quantum Challenge

The Jones and Bartlett Series in Physics and Astronomy

Astrophysics I: Stars
Richard Bowers and Terry Deeming

Astrophysics II: Interstellar Matter and Galaxies
Richard Bowers and Terry Deeming

The Quantum Challenge: Modern Research on the Foundations of Quantum Mechanics
George Greenstein and Arthur G. Zajonc

Physics for Scientists and Engineers
Lawrence S. Lerner

Modern Physics
Lawrence S. Lerner

Physics for Scientists and Engineers, Volume 1
Lawrence S. Lerner

Physics for Scientists and Engineers, Volume 2
Lawrence S. Lerner

ZAP! Experiments in Electrical Currents and Fields
Jerry Pine, John King, Philip Morrison, and Phylis Morrison

The Quantum Challenge

Modern Research on the Foundations of Quantum Mechanics

George Greenstein
Arthur G. Zajonc
Amherst College

Jones and Bartlett Publishers
Sudbury, Massachusetts

Boston London Singapore

To A.G.W. Cameron and Ernst Katz
our most important teachers

Editorial, Sales, and Customer Service Offices
Jones and Bartlett Publishers
40 Tall Pine Drive
Sudbury, MA 01776
(508) 443-5000
info@jbpub.com
http://www.jbpub.com

Jones and Bartlett Publishers International
Barb House, Barb Mews
London W6 7PA
UK

Library of Congress Cataloging-in-Publication Data
Greenstein, George (George S.)
The quantum challenge : modern research on the foundations of quantum mechanics / George Greenstein, Arthur G. Zajonc.
p. cm.
Includes bibliographical references and index.
ISBN 0-7637-0216-1
1. Quantum theory. I. Zajonc, Arthur. II. Title.
QC174.12.G73 1997
530.1′2—DC21 96-36637
CIP

0-7637-0216-1 (Paperback)
0-7637-0467-9 (Casebound)

Printed in the United States of America
01 00 99 98 97 10 9 8 7 6 5 4 3 2 1

The Challenge Series

> I was inspired by the remarks in those books; not by the parts in which everything was proved and demonstrated [but by] the remarks about the fact that this doesn't make any sense....
>
> So I had this as a challenge and an inspiration.*

The Challenge Series invites undergraduate science, mathematics and engineering majors to investigate the most important unsolved scientific problems of our day. Each book of the series will explore a particular problem in depth, doing full justice to the difficulties and subtleties involved. The aim of the series is to equip readers to think about these problems for themselves.

Each book will be written at the advanced undergraduate level. Each will be relatively brief and more or less self-contained. Great attention will be paid to the quality of the writing and the honesty of the presentation. Rather than relying on jargon, which often obscures fundamental difficulties, each book will squarely confront crucial problems facing scientists today.

The great problems of science, like great works of art, challenge us radically. But the exhilaration of actually grappling with such issues is usually reserved for practicing scientists. Undergraduate students, on the other hand, are often insulated from these deeply unsettling but exciting questions. The Challenge Series aims to remove this insulation.

A textbook instructs its readers in the methods and techniques of a field. The Challenge Series, by tightly focusing attention on important unsolved problems, intends to inspire. As Richard Feynman testified in his Nobel Prize acceptance speech, a wonderful exhilaration comes from holding in the mind the deepest questions we can ask. Such questions are what animate

---

*R. P. Feynman, "The Development of the Space–Time View of Quantum Mechanics," Nobel lecture, in *Les Prix Nobel en 1965*, the Nobel Foundation, Stockholm, 1966.

all scientists. Many students of science were first attracted to the field by popular accounts of important unsolved problems. They have been waiting ever since to begin working on these mysteries. The books of this series will allow them at last to begin.

These books will have three quite different uses: (a) as supplements to the textbooks in undergraduate courses offered within traditional departments; (b) as stand-alone texts designed for courses, often of an interdisciplinary nature, devoted to particular issues; and (c) as informative reading for practicing scientists. Jones and Bartlett Publishers welcomes communications from authors with suitable manuscripts.

George Greenstein and Arthur G. Zajonc
Series Editors

Contents

Acknowledgments

Throughout the writing of this book, we have benefited immeasurably from the assistance of colleagues and friends. We particularly wish to thank Daniel Greenberger, David Mermin, Abner Shimony and Daniel Velleman, who read portions of the manuscript and gave us valuable advice. We are also happy to thank Herb Bernstein, Kannan Jagannathan and Anton Zeilinger for help—and many others for innumerable fascinating and stimulating conversations. We also thank Ellen Feld and Paolo Carini for their patient and unflagging assistance in producing the manuscript.

Prologue

Not long ago, the authors of this book decided to organize a conference on the foundations of quantum mechanics.

Conferences are the staff of life to the working scientist. The lectures presented at conferences provide an in-depth view of the latest advances in the field: often these lectures are collected and published as a book, which stands as an invaluable summary of the current state of the art. Paradoxically, however, what participants often find most valuable in a conference is not these lectures. Rather, it is what happens in the nooks and crannies lying between the formal presentations: the brief conversation over coffee, the chance encounter in the hallway, the scientific argument that erupts over dinner. We decided to organize a conference that would consist of *nothing but* these informal chats.

The meeting that we envisaged was to be a week-long conversation, tightly focused on the issue at hand. Attendance was to be kept low: in addition to the local physicists from the host institutions, only a limited number of the world's foremost workers in the field would be invited. Total immersion, we decided, was an important consideration: the conferees would sleep under the same roof and eat all their meals together. It was essential that the accommodations be comfortable and the meals tasty. We decided to hold it at Amherst College, our home institution.

After eight months of planning and preparation, the conference began with a cocktail party on the back porch of what had, until recently, been a college residence hall. The school year had just ended; hard upon the heels of the departing students, a small army had descended on the building—cleaning up the mess, moving in new furniture, and putting fresh sheets on the beds. The sun shone brightly down, puffy white clouds marched across a sky of perfect blue, and the meeting's participants enthusiastically pumped one another's hands. Some had flown in from Europe or across the United States, others had driven for hours, and yet others had walked over from their offices. Although some collaborated regularly, others had not seen one another for years; indeed, a few had known each other only as names on scientific publications, and were meeting for the first time. Suitcases stood around unattended as their owners, not bothering to carry them up to their rooms, fell deep into conversation.

The next morning, after a gourmet breakfast, we gathered around a large table downstairs. One of the participants stood to deliver a brief talk. He had not spoken for five minutes before someone interrupted him with a comment. Someone else then chimed in with a comment on the comment—and we were off.

For the rest of the week, participants gathered around the table to discuss some of the most fascinating and profound problems of modern physics—problems that are the subject of this book. But the conference did not take place only around that table. It also took place out in the garden, and on the streets of Amherst, as two or three participants would break away from the group and wander off for a stroll. It took place over meals, which were invariably huge and invariably delicious. The conversation would zip from topic to topic with astonishing rapidity—from the implications of a recent experiment to the standings of the New York Mets, from culinary delights to a possible new theorem four of the participants thought they had just discovered (these four skipped going out to a movie with the rest of us one evening, stayed up to all hours, and eventually decided that their promising new approach was probably no more than a dead end).

Late one afternoon, we all repaired to the Greensteins' back yard for a picnic. There Abner Shimony, who has Ph.D.'s in both physics and philosophy and whose name will appear often in these pages, propounded on the rules and strategy of croquet with the same thoroughness he has brought to the study of quantum mechanics. David Mermin, some of whose work we will describe in Chapter 5, played piano four hands with Victor Weisskopf, former director-general of CERN. Later in the evening, Weisskopf teamed up with Barbara Greenstein, a violinist, to play Beethoven sonatas. Wafting in through an open window came the protests of Heide Zajonc as one of her sons prepared to whack her croquet ball out of the court: "But I'm your *mother*," she remonstrated, as the ball bounded off into the bushes.

At one point, Greenstein spotted John Bell and Kurt Gottfried off in a corner. As the reader of this book will shortly see, the problems posed by quantum mechanics are as difficult as they are profound. There is no consensus among workers in the field as to how to solve them. At times the disagreements that surfaced during the conference became severe. One such moment had occurred just that afternoon, when Bell and Gottfried squared off. For years Bell has probed with astonishing brilliance and depth the foundations of quantum theory, and he has argued that the theory is plagued by fundamental inadequacies. Gottfried, in turn, has argued with great subtlety that the mysteries of quantum mechanics have been widely exaggerated, and that in reality the theory poses difficulties no deeper than those raised by many other branches of physics. That afternoon, their debate had risen to a passionate intensity.

Greenstein grew perturbed. Bell and Gottfried stood with heads together, isolated from the rest of the throng. Were they at it again? Had emotions risen so high that they had grown furious at one another? Greenstein sidled unobtrusively over to eavesdrop—and found them quietly comparing their cameras.

Both of us look back on that conference as a peak experience. We were taking part in one of the deepest pleasures the practice of science can bring—a week-long debate, on issues as important as they are mysterious; a debate that was tightly focused, passionate, and regularly punctuated by bursts of laughter. Throughout that conference, the historic arguments that had so gripped the founders of quantum mechanics took new guise, as recent exciting developments were discussed.

Since its inception in the early decades of the twentieth century, quantum mechanics has joined Einstein's theory of relativity and Darwin's theory of evolution as a dominating scientific presence. There is hardly a single facet of physical science that it has not transformed beyond recognition. Nevertheless, the theory has steadfastly resisted interpretation. It gives a detailed set of instructions for calculating submicroscopic processes, while at the same time failing to provide the usual comprehensive picture of how these processes take place.

Indeed, it seems possible that such a picture may never be reached. Quantum mechanics seems to teach, for example, that a particle can pass through two different slits at the same time to produce an interference pattern. It teaches that measurements can never be perfectly accurate, but rather are beset by a fundamental uncertainty. It teaches that the very concepts of cause and effect must be rethought. What can we make of these lessons?

The battle over the interpretation of quantum mechanics raged until the early 1930s. The inventors of the theory, well realizing the magnitude of the dilemma, devoted considerable energy to its mysteries. Two gigantic figures presided over this debate.

Niels Bohr, on the one hand, originated the so-called Copenhagen interpretation, according to which all hope of attaining a unified picture of objective reality must be abandoned. Quantum theory, he held, would provide predictions concerning the results of measurements—but, unlike all previous theories, it was incapable of providing a full account of "how nature did it." Indeed, Bohr argued that the very desire to seek such a complete account was misguided and naive. All human understanding takes place in terms of the classical concepts fashioned from direct experience, he maintained. But the quantum world is demonstrably nonclassical. Therefore the quantum universe cannot be understood in the old sense of the term—not even in principle.

Albert Einstein, on the other hand, never abandoned his dissatisfaction with quantum mechanics. In his famous dictum that "God does not play dice with the universe," he expressed his opposition to the probabilistic nature of the theory. In 1949, responding to the accolades lavished in honor of his seventieth birthday, he emphasized that the theory had relinquished precisely what has always been the goal of science: "the complete description of any (individual) real situation (as it supposedly exists irrespective of any act of observation or substantiation)."[1] He emphasized that for centuries science had viewed its aim as the discovery of the *real*. This entailed creating new concepts to correspond with that reality, and so scientific ideas such as force, energy and momentum were hammered out over decades of struggle and debate. They corresponded to important features of the physical world, and so could be used productively to understand it. Yet the Copenhagen interpretation insisted that this tradition, which defined the very nature of the scientific enterprise, had now to be abandoned.

This debate never reached a satisfactory conclusion. Rather, with a few signal exceptions, it was simply relegated to the back burner. After the 1930s there followed a long period in which most physicists turned their attention elsewhere, and progress in understanding the foundations of quantum mechanics attracted only the attention of the relatively small number of people who continued to seek an understanding of these matters. During this period, the wonderful difficulties of quantum mechanics were largely trivialized, swept aside as unimportant philosophical distractions by the bulk of the physics community. This did not mean, however, that these issues of interpretation had been solved. Indeed, the interpretation of quantum theory remained as unclear as ever: in his book *The Character of Physical Law*, Richard Feynman unabashedly declared that "nobody understands quantum mechanics."

Recently, however, renewed efforts to explore these puzzles have gained momentum—and hence our decision to organize a meeting. A complex skein of developments, ranging across fields as diverse as physics, mathematics and philosophy, has led to this development; but in this history two important advances stand out. The first was a theorem published in 1964 by John Bell, which shed an extraordinary new light on quantum theory. Bell's Theorem showed that questions pertaining to the foundations of quantum mechanics were not purely matters of interpretation and philosophical argument. Rather, they actually had physical implications. One consequence was that experiments could be performed that would shed light on these questions, experiments that ultimately were carried out. Bell, in fact, played a central role in our conference's discussions; tragically, he was to die unexpectedly a mere few months after returning home from the conference.

The second great advance has been the enormous technological strides that have occurred in recent years. These now permit us to perform single-quantum experiments of every type. Until recently, the manipulation of individual particles had been little more than a theorist's dream. Experimenters commonly dealt with millions to trillions of particles at the very least. But now our latest techniques bring to the lab methods that permit us to manipulate and measure individual atoms, individual electrons, individual photons. Using such methods, experiments have recently been performed that the founders of quantum theory only dreamed about. In our roundtable discussions these beautiful experiments surfaced again and again, transforming what for decades had been an abstract discussion into the stuff of everyday life. In this book we will describe many of them in detail—they show quantum effects with a vengeance.

But they do not solve the problems that so perplexed the creators of quantum theory. Indeed, in our view, modern research has only made the theory's paradoxical nature more evident. Our thesis in this book is that the quantum universe forces upon us a radical revision in our conception of the physical world, a revision that has by no means been achieved. Our aim is not to accomplish this task, for we have no idea how this could be done. Rather, our aim is to make as vivid as possible the difficulties of interpretation posed by quantum mechanics.

In the past, books dealing with these issues have been constrained by two complementary difficulties. At the instructional level, the theoretical apparatus of quantum theory is complex and unfamiliar; textbooks are therefore forced to concentrate heavily on the technical aspects of the theory. Most texts, if they discuss issues of interpretation at all, do so only briefly. At the popular level, in contrast, considerable attention is often devoted to these questions; but owing to their nontechnical nature, such presentations are necessarily limited in the understanding they can convey.

The Quantum Challenge is explicitly intended to fill the gap between these two approaches. We believe that the material can be presented with reasonable rigor and intellectual honesty in a presentation accessible to undergraduate physical science, mathematics and engineering students. In particular, neither a presentation of Hilbert space nor of quantum electrodynamics is required for this purpose. Rather, we concentrate on developing insight by means of simple calculations using only nonrelativistic quantum mechanics. A unique feature of our presentation is that we have taken care to present conceptual issues in an experimental context, in which the difficulties of interpretation are dramatized by means of reference to actual contemporary experiments.

In addressing our intended audience, our aim has been purely pedagogical. The goal has been to reach as many readers as possible. We have therefore rigorously adopted the policy of introducing a topic only to the extent that it illustrates one or another of the overarching themes of quantum theory: squeezed states as exemplars of the uncertainty principle, quantum beats as exemplars of complementarity. In contrast, we have made no attempt to survey the field in its entirety and we have found ourselves forced to pass over in silence much fine work and many wonderful subjects.

We have also paid only brief attention to a variety of alternative interpretations of quantum theory, and of entirely new theories that have been proposed to take its place. Brevity, we are convinced, is a great virtue.

We also hold it to be a virtue that a book speak the language of its intended readers. In this case our readers are scientists, engineers and mathematicians; and we suspect that most hold a view of the nature of physical reality shaped by their ordinary daily experience. It will become evident as this book proceeds, however, that the challenges to our understanding posed by quantum theory extend all the way to our conceptions of the nature of physical reality, and of the proper function of science itself. The research we describe has made abundantly clear that the conventional view is entirely inadequate. While a full discussion of these issues would carry us far beyond the scope of this book, we should alert the reader to the fact that modern research on the foundations of quantum mechanics has generated an extensive philosophical literature, as people struggle to find a way of thinking that can do justice to the remarkable situation that research has revealed.

No longer does it make sense to ignore the more bizarre phenomena of quantum physics. Atom-by-atom, instant-by-instant, we can probe them with fascinating results. As a consequence, contemporary research has moved far beyond the original concerns of quantum theory's founders, into such issues as quantum beats and quantum non-demolition measurements, quantum non-locality and quantum erasers. A burgeoning new mood is on the rise, in which the contradictory features of quantum phenomena are enjoyed in their own right. Seen in this light, the mysteries of quantum mechanics can enchant us, as they encourage us to ask ever-deeper questions. Perhaps by thinking long enough about these effects we will come to a new way of seeing, to a new idea that will allow us to understand the quantum world after all.

In every textbook we know, quantum mechanics has been largely sanitized of these beautiful enticements and their implications. This book is intended to complement these accounts with a broader range of considerations. With even a modest mastery of the technical side of quantum mechanics, many of its mysteries can be appreciated. Each new problem delights, through the confusion it sows in our otherwise straightforward mechanical picture of the world. We hope that every reader finds, as we do, that the puzzles of quantum theory are plums to be savored, and returned to again and again; and we write this book in the hope that our readers will join in the burgeoning discussion of these wonderful mysteries. The enjoyments they offer are both lasting and profound.

Chapter 1

Matter Waves

The concept of matter waves is central to quantum theory. Ever since 1924, the year Louis de Broglie introduced the notion, physicists have learned to live with its strange duality between particles and waves. But learning to live with something is not the same as fully coming to terms with it. In this chapter we will explore some of the curious ramifications of this concept.

1.1 An Experiment

In 1989 an experiment was reported that dramatizes de Broglie's matter wave conundrum in particularly striking terms.[1] In this experiment, A. Tonomura, J. Endo, T. Matsuda, T. Kawasaki and H. Exawa, working at the Hitachi Advanced Research Laboratory and Gakushuin University in Tokyo, positioned a source of electrons to fire the particles through a barrier pierced by the equivalent of a pair of slits. After passing through the barrier, each electron fell upon a sheet of fluorescent film, which emitted a brief burst of light at the point at which it had been struck. By recording each burst, the experimenters were able to document the arrival of each electron.

The experimental design was as follows. Following an earlier design by Moellenstedt and Druecker,[2] the experiment of Tonomura et al. used an electron biprism to simulate a double-slit geometry. Similar in operation to an optical biprism, the device deflected the electrons as they passed between a charged wire and grounded electrodes. Figure 1–1 diagrams their apparatus. Its effects on the electrons were identical in kind to those that would be produced by the two slits of Figure 1–2.

After passing the electrons through a system of electrostatic lenses, Tonomura and collaborators used a state-of-the-art position-sensitive electron-counting system to image the arrival of electrons one by one.

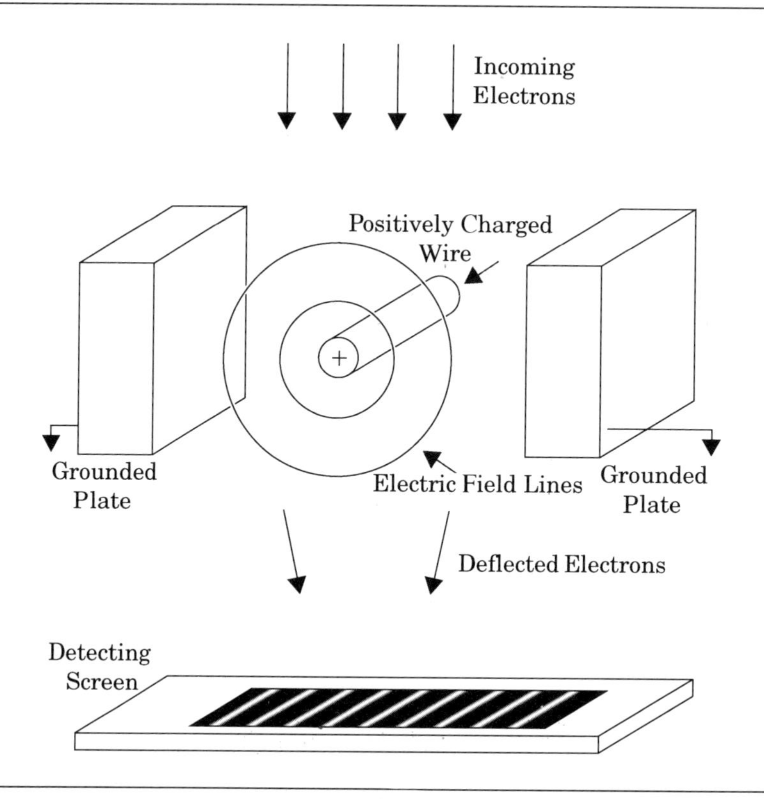

Figure 1–1 *An Actual Realization of a Classic Thought-Experiment.* The experimental design used by Tonomura et al. in their demonstration of the interference of matter waves. Incoming electrons pass between two parallel grounded plates, and are deflected around a thin wire maintained at positive potential midway between them. SOURCE: Adapted with permission from A. Tonomura, J. Endo, T. Matsuda, T. Kawasaki and H. Exawa, "Demonstration of single-electron buildup of an interference pattern," *Amer. J. Phys.*, vol. 57, p. 117 (1989).

When a single 50-kV electron struck the fluorescent film, about 500 photons were produced. Abutting the film was a plate of optical fibers that captured these photons and carried them without image degradation to a photocathode. Here each weak light pulse produced a corresponding pulse of electrons. These few electrons were multiplied enormously in number by passing them through a honeycomb of tiny electron-amplifying tubes, termed a "multichannel plate," to the image sensor. The end result was an exact image in the sensor plane of the events on the fluorescent film. Data from the image sensor were processed and displayed on a video monitor, such that a pixel on the monitor lit up in a position that corresponded to the places where the primary 50-kV electrons had originally struck the film.

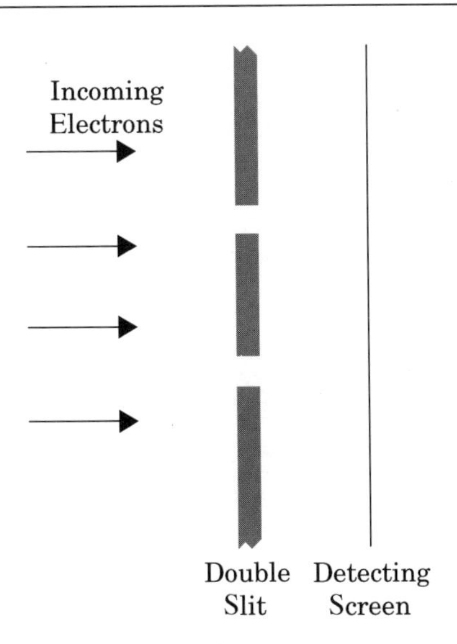

Figure 1–2 *The Thought-Experiment of which Figure 1–1 is the Realization.* Note the resemblance of this diagram for electrons to Figure 1–11 below, the classic double-slit experiment by which the existence of waves is demonstrated.

Sparkles appeared upon the video monitor, each recording the arrival of an electron. At first glance, these tiny bursts of light appeared to be distributed more or less evenly over the film. But as time passed, hints of a pattern began to emerge. The bursts appeared to be preferentially occurring in certain regions, and to avoid others altogether. Tonomura and colleagues employed a scheme whereby these patterns of preference and avoidance could be documented. They recorded the position of each sparkle with a photon-counting image acquisition system, ran the experiment for progressively longer and longer periods of time, and displayed the final results on a TV monitor. The technique was analogous to positioning a camera so as to photograph the fluorescent film, and setting it to take time exposures. A brief exposure would record the locations of a small number of flashes of light, but a long time exposure would show the pattern of arrival of enormous numbers of electrons.

Figure 1–3 shows a sequence they obtained of five such "time exposures" of successively longer and longer duration. In the initial frames of this figure, which document the arrivals of a relatively small number of electrons, little can be discerned. But by the third frame, hints of an orderly pattern are beginning to emerge. By the final frame, in which fully 70 000 arrivals have been documented, a pattern has become evident: an alternating series of parallel bands.

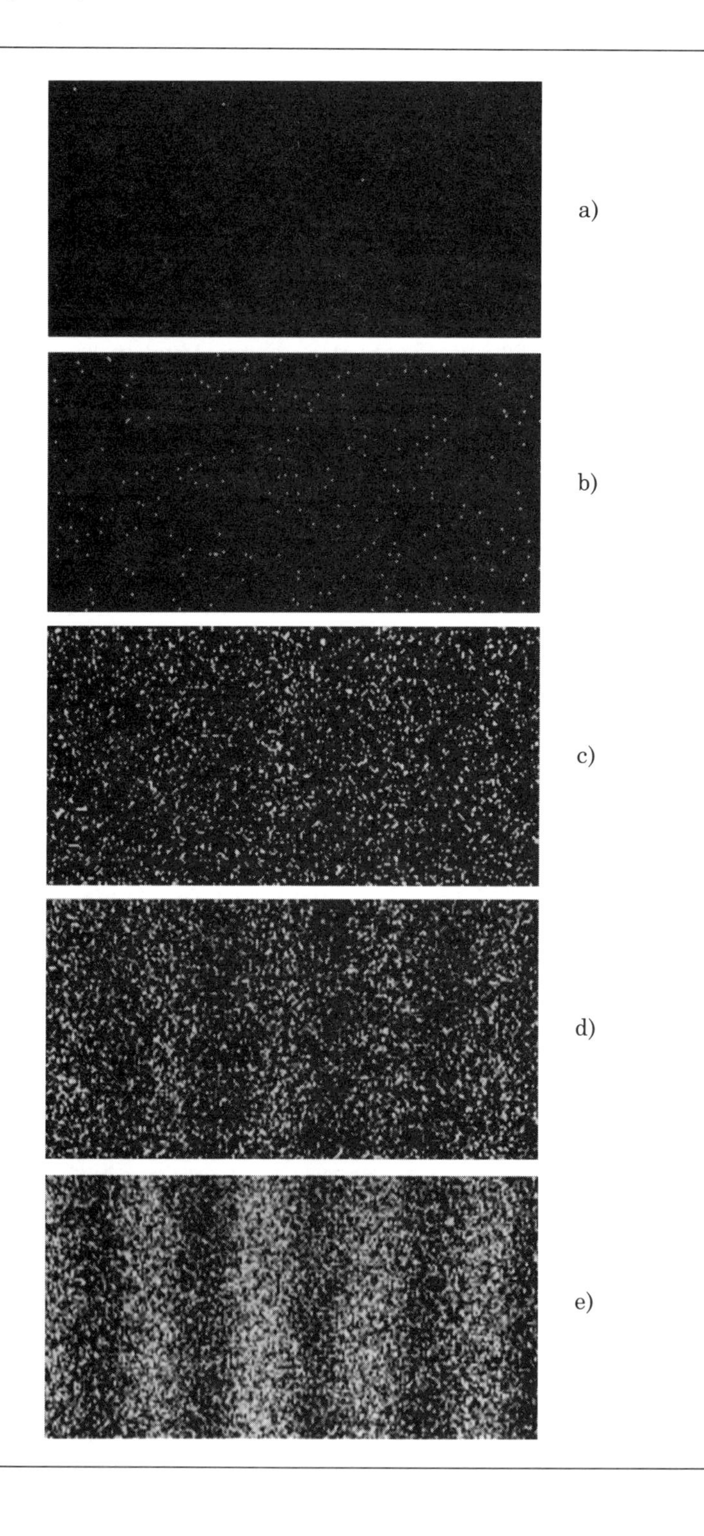
a)
b)
c)
d)
e)

1.2 A Second Experiment

The experiment of Tonomura et al. describes an intriguing phenomenon, and the urge is great to seek an explanation for it. But it will pay to delay this task, and describe now a second experiment. It is but a minor modification of the first: we plug up one of the two slits and run the experiment over again.

We begin by plugging up slit *A*. Although Tonomura et al. did not happen to perform this variation, there is not the slightest doubt as to what the result would have been; it is diagrammed in Figure 1–4. In this figure the same number of arrivals as the last frame of Figure 1–3 have been recorded. But it is evident that we are now witnessing an entirely different pattern of preference and avoidance of arrivals. The alternating sequence of light and dark bands has been replaced by a single band. This band turns out to be positioned directly across from the open slit, slit *B*.

What are we to make of this fact? It implies that, in the original experiment, the electrons must have been passing through slit *A*. After all, had they not been passing through this slit, plugging it up would have made no difference. But if we now unplug that slit, and block the other, we obtain yet a third pattern—one centered across from slit *A*. In this way, we can show that in the original experiment, the electrons must also have been passing through the other slit.

By this series of operations, we have shown each electron to have been passing through both slits in the experimental apparatus. But this is utterly impossible. The electron is a particle, and by the very meaning of this term we mean something that is at a particular point in space. A particle can be "here" or "there," but never in two places at once. But the electrons in the experiment of Tonomura et al. have apparently managed to do just that.

One might imagine that these results can be understood in a relatively prosaic way. Perhaps a sort of "traffic jam" of electrons had developed as they passed through the two slits. Suppose that each electron is indeed an indivisible, elementary particle, and that each passes through one and only one slit—but that, in this passage, each collides and jostles against others, which themselves have passed through the other slit. If this were the case, the pattern of arrivals of electrons at the screen might be expected to depend on whether one or both slits were open.

Figure 1–3 (left) *Experimental Demonstration of Matter Waves.* Each dot records the arrival of an electron at the detecting screen. In (a) 10 electrons have been recorded, in (b) 100, in (c) 3000, in (d) 20 000 and in (e) 70 000. The banded pattern is the classic signature of interference. SOURCE: Reproduced with permission from A. Tonomura, J. Endo, T. Matsuda, T. Kawasaki and H. Exawa, "Demonstration of single-electron buildup of an interference pattern," *Amer. J. Phys.*, vol. 57, p. 117 (1989).

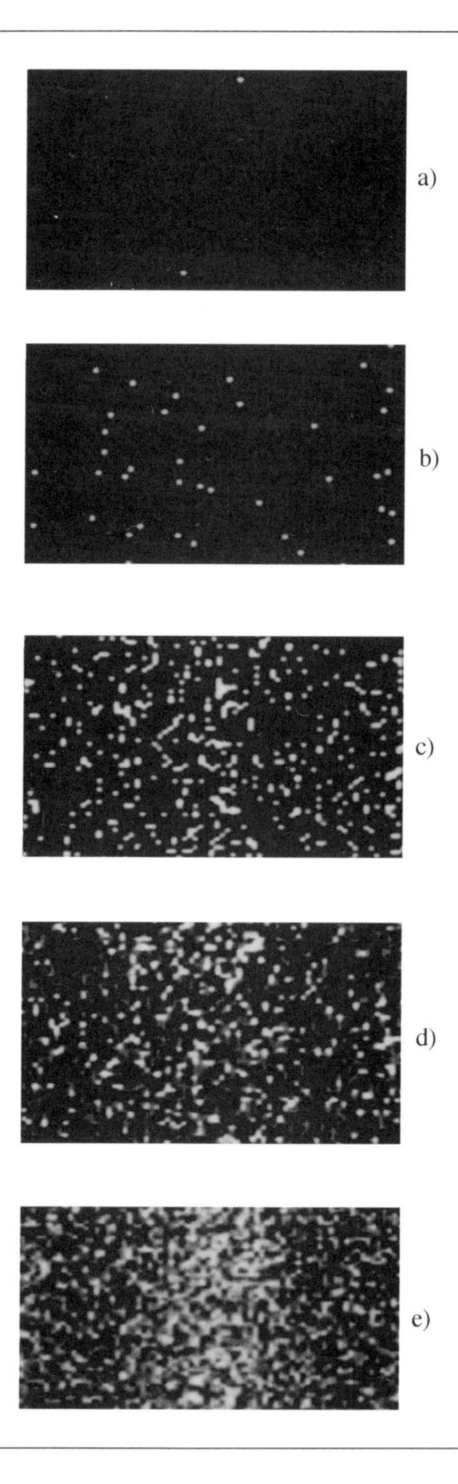
a)
b)
c)
d)
e)

But this possibility is not available to us. Tonomura et al. demonstrated that it was untenable by turning down the intensity of the source producing their electrons. They arranged for their source to be so weak that one electron at a time was in the apparatus. Specifically, they adjusted their electron flux to be about 1000 electrons/second. At 50 kV, electrons have a velocity of about 10^8 m/s. Assuming them to be emitted in a roughly uniform way, the electrons were therefore separated from one another by 100 kilometers! In this way the likelihood of a "traffic jam" in their experiment was eliminated. But no matter how much they turned down the source intensity, reducing further and further the probability that more than one electron was present in their apparatus, their experimental results remained unchanged.

The logic seems irrefutable. Tonomura's electrons were at two places at the same time.

1.3 Locality

Or were they? The conclusion *seems* irrefutable: indeed, this is the standard interpretation of this and other similar experiments. But this interpretation is not the only possible one. In recent years, interest in another interpretation has grown.

Recall the logic we employed in the preceding section. We noticed that plugging up one slit influenced the pattern of arrivals, and we concluded that this proved the electrons to have been originally traveling through that slit. "After all," we wrote, "had they not been passing through this slit, plugging it up would have made no difference." But this is not necessarily true. It would only be true if we were to make an assumption: that plugging one slit has no effect on the electrons passing through the *other* one.

This is known as the assumption of *locality*. The locality hypothesis is that things done at one location only have effects at that location. But if we drop the locality hypothesis, and allow for the possibility that plugging one slit might alter the paths of electrons passing through the other slit, we would no longer be forced to conclude that electrons can be in two places at once.

Locality has long been a guiding principle of physics. But it is not inviolate. Recent years have seen a growing interest in the consequences of dropping the hypothesis. In Chapter 6 we will recount the nonlocal interpretation of David Bohm, which accounts for the results of the double-slit experiment in entirely different terms.

Figure 1–4 (left) *Data with One Slit Closed.* The interference pattern has disappeared.

1.4 Neutrons and Atoms

One might imagine that these strange results point to some bizarre property of electrons. But the electron experiments have been replicated using neutrons[3] and, most recently, atoms.[4] Zeilinger and collaborators have performed experiments with neutrons of very low velocities (around 2 km/s), which are collimated and guided to a double slit made from a neutron-absorbing material. The double slit itself is formed by a 104 micrometer diameter boron wire placed in the middle of a larger slit formed from absorbing glass. The spacing between the two slits was 126 μm. Downstream a BF_3 proportional counting chamber detected the neutrons that passed through a 20-μm-wide exit slit. Scanning the slit allowed the group to spatially image the neutron flux emerging from the double slit. Once again, neutron by neutron, a pattern gradually emerged with the same detailed structure we have seen for Tonomura's electrons (Figure 1–5).

Finally, we turn to the case of atoms. Here an important step is made from simple to composite systems. The electron is thought to be a truly elementary particle, and while the neutron is thought to be composed of

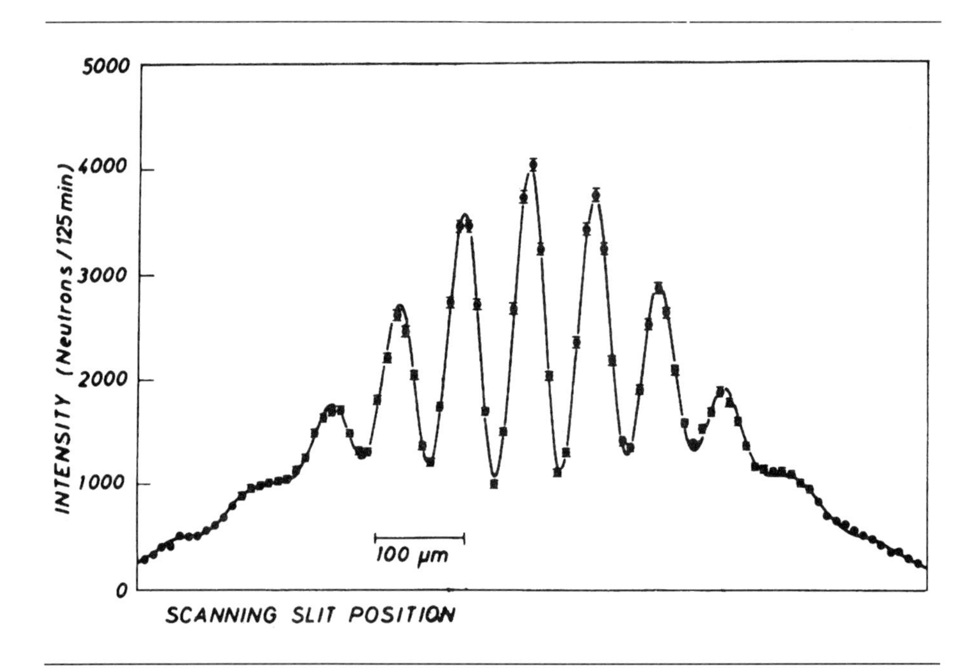

Figure 1–5 *Interference of Neutrons.* The interference pattern obtained by Gähler and Zeilinger, demonstrating neutron interference. SOURCE: Reproduced with permission from R. Gähler and A. Zeilinger, "Wave-optical experiments with very cold neutrons," *Amer. J. Phys.*, vol. 59, p. 316 (1991).

Figure 1–6 *A Picture of Atoms.* An array of xenon atoms on a nickel surface, as imaged by a scanning tunneling microscope. They certainly *look* like particles! SOURCE: Reproduced with permission from D.M. Eigler and E.K. Schweizer, "Positioning single atoms with a scanning tunneling microscope," *Nature*, vol. 344, p. 524. Copyright 1990 Macmillan Magazines Limited. The image shown was provided by IBM Corporation, Research Division, Almaden Research Center.

quarks, these quarks apparently cannot exist in isolation. Atoms, in contrast, are quite complex. Two elements often used in these experiments are helium and sodium: helium is composed of six particles (two protons, two neutrons and two electrons), whereas sodium possesses fully thirty-three constituents. By being composite, atoms constitute a bridge between the microscopic world of elementary particles and the macroscopic world of everyday objects.

Furthermore, the evidence that atoms are corpuscular in nature appears overwhelming. For example, in a recent technological breakthrough, it has become possible actually to image atoms, as illustrated in Figure 1–6. Furthermore this image, generated using scanning tunneling microscopy, was not only obtained, but was actually constructed by adapting the microscope for micro-manipulation. Images of this sort are not optically generated, but reflect the changes in tunneling current between the microscope's tip and the surface as it "feels" its way about. The group that obtained this image used the Van der Waals and electrostatic forces between the tip of their microscope and the xenon atoms to act like the hand on a robotic arm to grasp and drag atoms over the surface into position. Figure 1–7 is from the same group,[5] and shows stages in the assembly of a linear array of xenon atoms on an ultracold surface of nickel. Such atom manipulation promises to become the hallmark of a new nanotechnology, in which the assembly of increasingly complex structures takes place on the atomic scale.

Atoms are, at present, the smallest building blocks we can get our hands on, and they certainly seem solid. But in 1991, Mylnek and Carnal[4] performed the first of many similar experiments in which atoms were

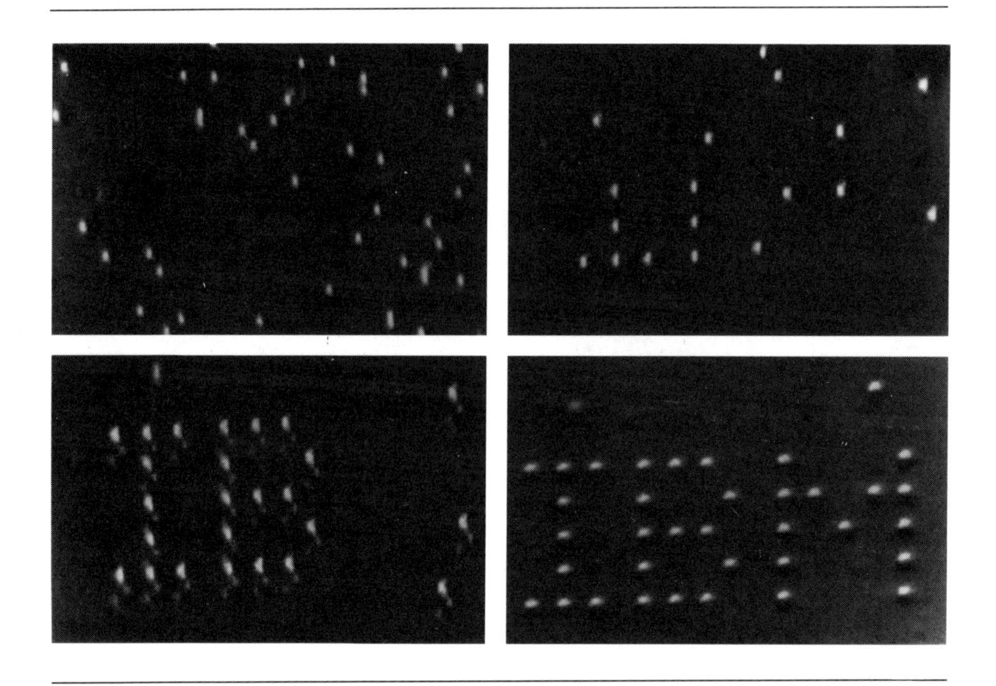

Figure 1–7 *Moving Atoms Around with a Scanning Tunneling Microscope.* Illustrating stages in the construction of an "atomic logo." SOURCE: Reproduced with permission from D.M. Eigler and E.K. Schweizer, "Positioning single atoms with a scanning tunneling microscope," *Nature*, vol. 344, p. 524. Copyright 1990 Macmillan Magazines Limited. The image shown was provided by IBM Corporation, Research Division, Almaden Research Center.

passed through a double-slit apparatus and their apparent solidity evaporated. Again the experiment was a *tour de force* of experimental techniques. Tiny micro-fabricated transmission structures were produced in gold films by a photolithographic technique. These were even tinier than the slits used in the neutron experiments: 1 μm wide and 8 μm apart. As with the neutrons and electrons, a position-sensitive single-atom detector (a secondary electron multiplier) could be scanned to show the downstream structure in the atomic beam after the double slits. The results are shown in Figure 1–8. Again, the characteristic banded pattern is evident.

1.5 Quantum Theory of Two-Slit Interference

Every physicist will immediately recognize the patterns revealed in the experiments we have been recounting. They are interference patterns, and they are identical to that produced by passing light waves—or indeed,

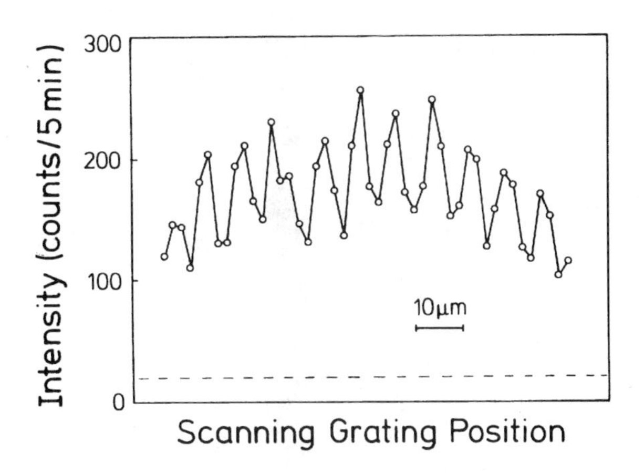

Figure 1–8 *Interference of Atoms.* The interference pattern obtained by Mlynek and Carnal, demonstrating atom interference. SOURCE: Reproduced with permission from O. Carnal and J. Mlynek, "Young's double-slit experiment with atoms: A simple atom interferometer," *Phys. Rev. Lett.*, vol. 66, p. 2689 (1991), published by The American Physical Society.

any wave—through the two slits. Every physicist also knows that quantum mechanics can account for this phenomenon. We now turn to a description of this account.

Quantum mechanics treats the motion of an electron, neutron or atom by writing down the Schrödinger equation:

$$-\frac{\hbar^2}{2m}\frac{\partial^2\psi}{\partial x^2} + V\psi = i\hbar\frac{\partial\psi}{\partial t} \tag{1.1}$$

where m is the particle mass and V the external potential acting on the particle. As these particles pass through the two slits of any of the experiments we have been discussing, they are moving freely: we therefore set $V = 0$ in the Schrödinger equation.

Let us seek a solution of the form of a traveling wave

$$\psi = A\exp\left[i(kx - \omega t)\right] \tag{1.2}$$

where A is the amplitude of the wave, and k and ω are constants to be determined. Taking the derivative with respect to the time of our trial solution, we find

$$\frac{\partial\psi}{\partial t} = -i\omega\psi \tag{1.3}$$

Taking two derivatives with respect to x, we find

$$\frac{\partial^2 \psi}{\partial x^2} = -k^2 \psi \tag{1.4}$$

Thus Equation (1.2) will be a solution of the Schrödinger equation if

$$-k^2 \psi = \left(-\frac{2mi}{\hbar} \right)(-i\omega)\psi \tag{1.5}$$

i.e., if

$$k = \sqrt{\frac{2m\omega}{\hbar}} \tag{1.6}$$

Thus we see that Schrödinger's equation leads us quite naturally to think of quantum particles in terms of waves, but only through the wave function.

This solution can be re-cast in a more intuitively satisfying form by rewriting it in terms of the wavelength λ and period P of the wave. To do this, we take a "snapshot" of the wave at some instant, say $t = 0$. At this instant, the wave function has the form

$$\psi(t = 0) = A\, e^{ikx} \tag{1.7}$$

At the origin, $x = 0$, ψ has the value A; by the wavelength we mean the distance we must progress before ψ returns to this value. From the theory of complex numbers, we know that $e^{2\pi i} = 1$, from which we can see that ψ returns to A when $kx = k\lambda = 2\pi$. Thus the wavelength λ is related to k by

$$k = \frac{2\pi}{\lambda} \tag{1.8}$$

By a similar argument, we can show that the period P of the wave is related to ω through

$$\omega = \frac{2\pi}{P} \tag{1.9}$$

Thus we obtain as an alternative form of the solution to the Schrödinger equation in empty space

$$\psi = A \exp\left[2\pi i \left(\frac{x}{\lambda} - \frac{t}{P} \right) \right] \tag{1.10}$$

We now turn to a discussion of interference. It is a property of every wave. Figure 1–9 illustrates a rope that has been stretched tight between

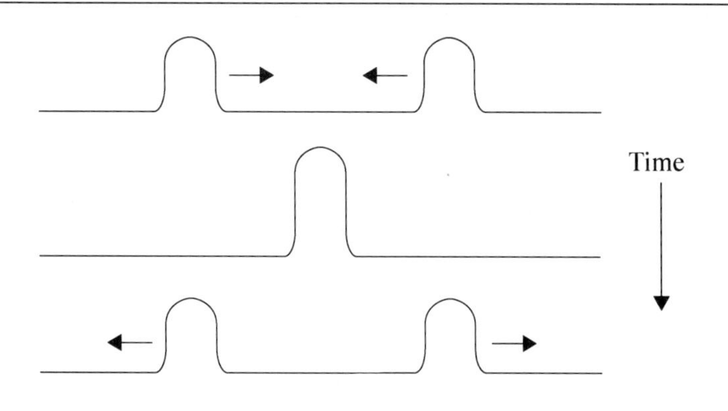

Figure 1–9 *Constructive Interference.* Waves add to produce a larger wave.

two people. They have shaken the ends in such a way as to produce two waves traveling toward one another. As illustrated, when the waves meet they combine to produce a resultant that is greater than would have been produced by either wave acting alone. This is constructive interference; it arises when the two oscillations are in phase with one another. Figure 1–10 illustrates the opposite case of destructive interference, which arises when the combining waves oscillate out of phase. In this case the wave amplitude upon combination is zero.

Figure 1–11 diagrams a generic version of the double-slit experiment we have been recounting. Interference effects arise here too. In all these

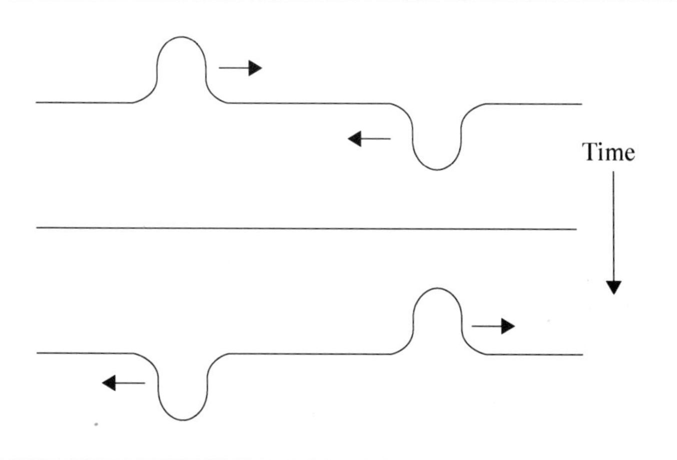

Figure 1–10 *Destructive Interference.* Waves subtract to produce a smaller wave. In the case illustrated, the subtraction is perfect.

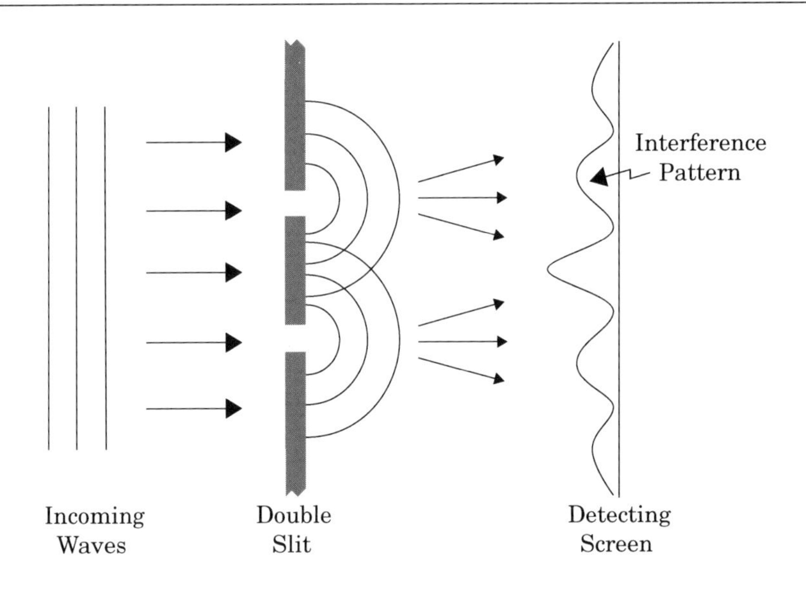

Figure 1–11 *The Two-Slit Interference Experiment for Waves.* Each slit acts as a source of waves; along the detecting screen, both constructive and destructive interference result. Note the striking resemblance of this diagram to Figure 1–2—but note also that Figure 1–2 referred to particles, whereas this figure refers to waves.

experiments, each slit each acts as a source of waves, which propagate toward the detecting screen. At some points along this screen the waves add, as in Figure 1–9, to give constructive interference; at other points, they subtract, as in Figure 1–10, to give destructive interference. Running along the screen, therefore, is an *interference pattern* exhibiting alternate maxima and minima. It is just this pattern that the experiments have revealed.

We now turn to a mathematical treatment of these general principles. The wave at the point of combination will be the sum of those from each slit. If ψ_1 is the wave from slit 1 and ψ_2 that from slit 2,

$$\psi = \psi_1 + \psi_2 \tag{1.11}$$

where

$$\begin{aligned} \psi_1 &= A_1 \exp\left[2\pi i\left(\frac{x_1}{\lambda} - \frac{t}{P}\right)\right] \\ \psi_2 &= A_2 \exp\left[2\pi i\left(\frac{x_2}{\lambda} - \frac{t}{P}\right)\right] \end{aligned} \tag{1.12}$$

where A_1 and A_2 are the amplitudes of the two waves. Each term in this sum has the same time behavior, which can be factored out to yield

$$\psi = f(x_1, x_2) \exp\left[-\frac{2\pi i t}{P}\right] \tag{1.13}$$

where

$$f(x_1, x_2) = A_1 \exp\left[\frac{2\pi i x_1}{\lambda}\right] + A_2 \exp\left[\frac{2\pi i x_2}{\lambda}\right]$$

According to quantum theory, $|\psi|^2$ at each point in space gives the probability of finding the particle there. We write

$$\begin{aligned} |\psi|^2 &= \psi^* \psi \\ &= f^* \exp\left[\frac{2\pi i t}{P}\right] f \exp\left[-\frac{2\pi i t}{P}\right] \\ &= f^* f = |f|^2 \end{aligned} \tag{1.14}$$

where an asterisk denotes the complex conjugate. Thus we see that $f(x_1, x_2)$ contains the information we seek describing the interference pattern. Since the amplitudes A_1 and A_2 are real, we get (writing $\theta_j = 2\pi x_j/\lambda$)

$$\begin{aligned} |f|^2 &= [A_1 e^{i\theta_1} + A_2 e^{i\theta_2}][A_1 e^{-i\theta_1} + A_2 e^{-i\theta_2}] \\ &= A_1^2 + A_2^2 + A_1 A_2 \{e^{i(\theta_2 - \theta_1)} + e^{i(\theta_1 - \theta_2)}\} \end{aligned} \tag{1.15}$$

Note, however, that the term in curly brackets represents a quantity plus its complex conjugate; this equals twice the real part of this quantity, or

$$\begin{aligned} |f|^2 &= A_1^2 + A_2^2 + 2A_1 A_2 \cos[\theta_2 - \theta_1] \\ &= A_1^2 + A_2^2 + 2A_1 A_2 \cos\left[\frac{2\pi(x_2 - x_1)}{\lambda}\right] \end{aligned} \tag{1.16}$$

This result gives the predicted interference pattern. Its first term, A_1^2, is just what we would expect if slit 1 alone were emitting waves. Similarly, A_2^2 is the term arising from slit 2. The last term in Equation (1.16) gives the effects of combining the two waves. As we progress up along the screen, this term oscillates, yielding the characteristic maxima and minima of the interference pattern.

How is this theory to be compared with the experiment? The light bands that we saw in Figure 1–3 represent areas of the detector upon which electrons are falling with a relatively great frequency—that is, areas in which the probability of finding a particle is greatest. Conversely, the dark bands are regions of low probability of finding a particle. The density of experimental points should therefore be proportional to $|\psi|^2$. Similarly, the peaks in Figures 1–5 (neutrons) and 1–8 (atoms) should also fall at locations at which $|\psi|^2$ is greatest. When the experimental data is compared to this prediction, the agreement turns out to be excellent in all three experiments.

1.6 Critique of the Quantum-Mechanical Account

Take a step backwards now, and survey the above account. Quantum mechanics has correctly reproduced the results of experiment. But has the theory explained to us how indivisible particles manage to pass through two slits at once?

It has not. Nothing in the preceding section gives us the slightest insight into how a particle manages to do this. On the one hand, the quantum treatment deals primarily with waves rather than particles. Indeed, a quick glance over the above section will reveal that the very word "particle" plays little part in the discussion. Aside from a few introductory appearances, the word does not appear until the very close, where the principle was used that $|\psi|^2$ measures the probability of finding "the particle" at a given point. On the other hand, at no place did the theory attempt to analyze the particle's path through space. Indeed, as we will discuss in Chapter 3, quantum mechanics regards the very concept of a trajectory as deeply suspect.

The connection between interference as a characteristic of waves and particles was noticed by de Broglie. He connected particle to wave mechanics through a generalization of Equation (1.8) above. In Equation (1.8) the wavelength is inversely proportional to the wave number k. De Broglie proposed that particles behave as if they possessed a wavelength that was inversely proportional to their momentum, mv, and that the constant of proportionality was Planck's constant, h:

$$\lambda = \frac{h}{mv} \tag{1.17}$$

With this simple relationship and the quantum-mechanical treatment of interference, we can precisely predict the outcomes of the matter wave experiments described above. Electrons at 50 kV have an associated de Broglie wavelength of 0.0054 nm. Depending on the temperature of the helium gas source (which determines the mean velocity of the helium), the de Broglie wavelength of the atoms in Mlynek et al.'s experiment ranged between 0.056 nm and 0.103 nm. By using extremely cold beams with corresponding low velocities, Zeilinger et al. could produce neutrons with de Broglie wavelengths of the order of 2 nm. Given these data and a knowledge of the slit separation, it is trivial to calculate a predicted interference pattern. The correspondence between experiment and theory is very impressive. The solid curve through the neutron data points in Figure 1–5, for example, has no adjustable parameters, but it fits the data perfectly.

Quantum theory has therefore succeeded in *reproducing* the results of experiment. But has it provided us with any *understanding* of the results? It has not. Indeed, it is quite impossible to visualize what has been going on in these experiments. They present us with an intolerable state of affairs, one which appears to violate the very principles of elementary logic. Whether the beam is one of electrons, neutrons or atoms, the kind of complex structure evidenced downstream from a pair of slits confounds our intuitive understanding of particles.

Historically, particles and waves have formed the two poles between which the imagination of physics has worked. During the three centuries from 1600 to 1900, a long struggle had taken place in physics, sometimes acrimoniously, over how to think of the world. Isaac Newton, for example, thought of the universe in terms of particles:

> It seems probable to me, that God in the Beginning form'd matter in solid, massy, hard, impenetrable, movable Particles, of such Sizes and Figures, and with such other Properties, and in such proportion to Space, as most conduced to the End for which he formed them . . .[6]

On this model, everything was particle dynamics. In opposition, other physicists felt that parts—and perhaps all—of the world could not be so described. They developed a model that emphasized the smooth, unbroken character of nature, creating a continuum mechanics in which wave phenomena find a natural account. Light above all, with its host of interference effects, seemed especially amenable to a continuum treatment. Through the efforts of the French scientist Augustin Fresnel and others, light came quite naturally to be understood as a wave-like disturbance in the "ether," analogous to sound waves in air, or water waves on a pond.

By 1900 the world of physics was neatly divided into two domains, particle dynamics versus continuum dynamics: particles versus waves, for short. Baseballs and pebbles, on one hand, were particles, obeying the laws of discrete mechanics. Light and sound, on the other, were waves, running through the unfragmented media of ether and air. In skipping pebbles at the beach, particles meet waves—but a much more significant meeting between them took place at the dawn of the twentieth century, with the birth of quantum mechanics.

With this theory, the clean division between wave and particle was spoiled. The initial steps were taken by Planck and Einstein, who suggested that blackbody radiation and the photoelectric effect were better explained if one thought of light as particulate in character. But the real shock came later, when Louis de Broglie made the even bolder suggestion that particles could behave like waves. During the early decades of this century, when the quantum theory was being developed, the evidence for matter waves was meager. But by today, with experiments such as those we have recounted in this chapter, the evidence has become utterly compelling.

We are left in a remarkable state of affairs. Normally, once we have developed a theory of a phenomenon, we have also reached some sort of understanding of that phenomenon. Newtonian mechanics allows us to comprehend the orbits of the planets about the sun in terms of the response of material bodies to mechanical forces. While the details of the theory may be complex, the underlying insight is straightforward. Similarly, thermodynamics yields the insight that heat is a form of energy.

But what is the insight provided by quantum mechanics? The quantum-mechanical account we have given of particle interference has managed to avoid asking the very question we would most like to see answered. Furthermore, it has avoided the question by the very nature of the terms of analysis it employs. By the structure of this theory, by the manner in which it proceeds, quantum mechanics evades the inconceivable.

What are we to make of this strange state of affairs? Different views are possible. Throughout his life, Albert Einstein never accepted the quantum theory. He consistently argued that the theory has failed us in an essential respect. Surely *something* is going on in these experiments, he would have claimed, some remarkable process that accounts for each particle's strange behavior. Quantum theory has not told us what that process is, and it is our wish to search for an understanding of this "something." According to Einstein's view, quantum mechanics, while perfectly adequate so far as it goes, simply does not go far enough. It is not telling us everything we demand of a good theory. The theory is incomplete.

Niels Bohr championed an opposing view. According to him, particle interference experiments present us with a state of affairs that is quite literally incomprehensible, at least if we are restricted to conventional ways of thinking. While we naturally wish to build in our minds a picture of the behavior of the particles used in the experiments, we are not going to get our wish—not because we have not yet found the right means, but because the atomic world simply cannot be approached in this manner. Mental pictures draw their elements from our sense world, but nothing like the quantum world has ever appeared to our senses, so how can we expect to make a suitable image of it?

Up to this point in the development of scientific knowledge, it has always been possible, to a greater or lesser degree, to build in our minds a visualizable image of the workings of the world. But, according to Bohr's view, we are now presented with a situation in which such visualization is impossible. In entering the atomic realm, we have entered a world in which our very ideas of what human knowledge can achieve need revision. Reality can no longer be thought of in the terms we have become used to;

new terms need to be invented. Any theory that seeks to comprehend in classical terms what has been going on in our experimental apparatus is guaranteed to fail. Quantum mechanics' avoidance of this question, far from being a defect, is actually the theory's greatest virtue. By its very structure, it avoids using those terms of analysis that are inadequate to describe the atomic realm.

The debate over the completeness of quantum theory continued throughout Bohr's and Einstein's lives, and the issues they raised will surface again and again in this book. For decades most physicists regarded the debate as essentially philosophical in nature, but with little empirical content. In 1965, however, Bell's Theorem succeeded in transforming the issue into an experimental one. We will recount this remarkable story in Chapter 5. For now, however, we turn to light. Long considered a wave, it too has shown a paradoxical face.

Chapter 2

Photons

Electrons are obviously discrete; they are the epitome of "particleness." Light, in contrast, is most naturally thought of as a wave, and for over 200 years has been known to exhibit the phenomena of interference and diffraction associated with waves. In Chapter 1, the force of experiment drove us to accept the existence of matter waves, introduced by Louis de Broglie in 1924. Historically, however, de Broglie's hypothesis was preceded by another daring suggestion: that of photons. In 1900, Max Planck proposed that an atomic oscillator could exchange energy with a radiation field only in discrete units. In 1905, through his analysis of the photoelectric effect, Einstein broadened this suggestion to the notion that light itself consists of a collection of particles with wave-like properties.

Thus, ever since the early days that saw the creation of quantum theory, physicists have tended to regard matter and light as essentially equivalent: particles show wave-like properties and light shows particle-like properties. Recent work, however, has revealed the actual situation to be a good deal more subtle than this. In 1969, it was shown that the photoelectric effect could be understood without invoking the concept of photons at all. Furthermore, subsequent experiments designed to expose the particle nature of light surprised the physics community by entirely failing to do so. Not for some time did the situation clarify and unambiguous evidence for it appear.

In the first half of this chapter we will recount this story—proceeding cautiously, for the pitfalls of hasty conclusions have turned out to be many and well-camouflaged. In the second half we will turn to recent interference experiments involving photons, which dramatize yet again the strange nature of the quantum.

2.1 Do Photons Exist?

Detection and the Quantum of Light If we think of light as a wave, then when it falls on photographic film we might liken it to an ocean wave hitting the beach. Nothing prevents an ocean wave from hitting the sand simultaneously along its full extent. By analogy, one might expect light falling on film to expose it uniformly along its entire wavefront. But this is not what happens. When examined carefully, one finds that individual grains of silver halide have been blackened, one at a time.

We find a similar situation with more modern detection systems such as photomultipliers, avalanche photodiodes, and the like. These detectors respond to a continuous light source not in a continuous manner, but by "clicking." Light falling on the cathode of a photomultiplier gives rise to ejected electrons; each electron so produced is multiplied by being accelerated from the photocathode through a series of secondary electrodes. Colliding with each electrode in turn, each primary electron produces secondaries that go on to cascade down the dynode chain. The final result is a great number of electrons where initially there was only one. These electrons are then routed through a conventional amplifier and displayed, appearing as a brief electronic pulse. Thus the "click."

Thus, whenever detected, the originally diffused light acts as if it were contracted to the smallest dimensions, arriving in a single place at a single moment in time. All this might argue for a particle picture of light. Isaac Newton's first definition of light rays fits these modern features: "By the Rays of Light I understand its least Parts and those as well Successive in the same Lines, and Contemporary in several Lines." Ever since the American chemist G.N. Lewis named them in 1926, it has seemed natural to identify these "least parts" with photons. Newton's conception seems a prescient anticipation of the quantum theory.

But is this really a good picture of light, or only an artifact of the tools we have used to investigate it? Discrete detection events do not necessarily imply discrete impact events. Looking out a window on a crisp day in late fall, one sees the painted leaves of a maple shower to earth following a gust of wind. Single leaves fall, one by one—but how shall we imagine the wind that caused them to fall? Is the wind a hail of bullets that picks off leaves the way bullets pick off tin cans? Or should we think of the wind as a continuous, undulating fluid that rocks the leaves until their stems snap? Similarly, when light falling on a photocathode causes a shower of electrons, has a hail of light-particles hit the surface? Or have the electrons been rocked by a light-wave, until the force that binds them to atoms snaps, and a single free photoelectron starts its trek down the dynode chain?

Photoelectric Effect In 1922, Albert Einstein received the Nobel Prize—not for his relativity theory, but for his interpretation of the photoelectric effect as being due to particle-like photons striking the surfaces of metals and ejecting electrons. Textbooks regularly repeat Einstein's arguments as proof that light possesses a particle nature. And yet, ironically, it has been cogently argued that Einstein's conclusions were not fully justified. Planck surmised as much, and so was far more cautious in his claims, although Einstein urged Planck on to a particle conception of light. But in 1969, Jaynes and Lamb and Scully[1] showed that one can account for the photoelectric effect without recourse to the concept of the photon at all. We will concentrate on Lamb and Scully's analysis.

In some form, the photoelectric effect stands behind all types of light detection. In it, light illuminates a surface and electrons are emitted. Four features of the phenomenon need to be explained by any theory (Figure 2–1):

a. Electrons are emitted even at times very shortly after the onset of illumination.
b. The photocurrent rises linearly with the light intensity.
c. The current to the cathode decreases with increasing retarding potential, becoming zero at the "stopping" potential, V_0.
d. The stopping potential V_0 is linearly proportional to the frequency of the incident light and shows a definite threshold frequency ν_0.

In Einstein's account, a photon of energy $E = h\nu$ strikes the surface. Part of its energy goes into overcoming the binding of the electron in the atom; this sets the threshold frequency in (d) above. Since even a single photon can ionize an atom, there need be no delay between the onset of the light and the ejection of a free electron, thus accounting for (a). An amount of energy ϕ, the so-called work function, is used to liberate the electron, with the remaining photon energy appearing as electron kinetic energy E. This is summarized by the relationship

$$h\nu = E + \phi \tag{2.1}$$

Since the kinetic energy E can be related to eV_0,the product of the electron charge and the stopping potential, Equation (2.1) shows why the stopping potential is proportional to frequency. And finally, the intensity of light is modeled by Einstein as a measure of the flux of photons, which would account for the linear relationship between intensity and photocurrent.

Thus all four aspects of the photoelectric effect are neatly accounted for by Einstein's theory. But Lamb and Scully showed that this theory, while feasible, is not the only possible one. They were able to find an entirely different theory of the photoelectric effect, one that did not invoke the concept of the particle nature of light at all. Their conclusion was that the photoelectric effect does not constitute proof of the existence of photons.

The theory of Lamb and Scully treated atoms quantum-mechanically, but regarded light as being a purely classical electromagnetic wave with no particle properties. In such a "semiclassical" theory, the atom was quantized in the usual way into energy levels according to the Schrödinger

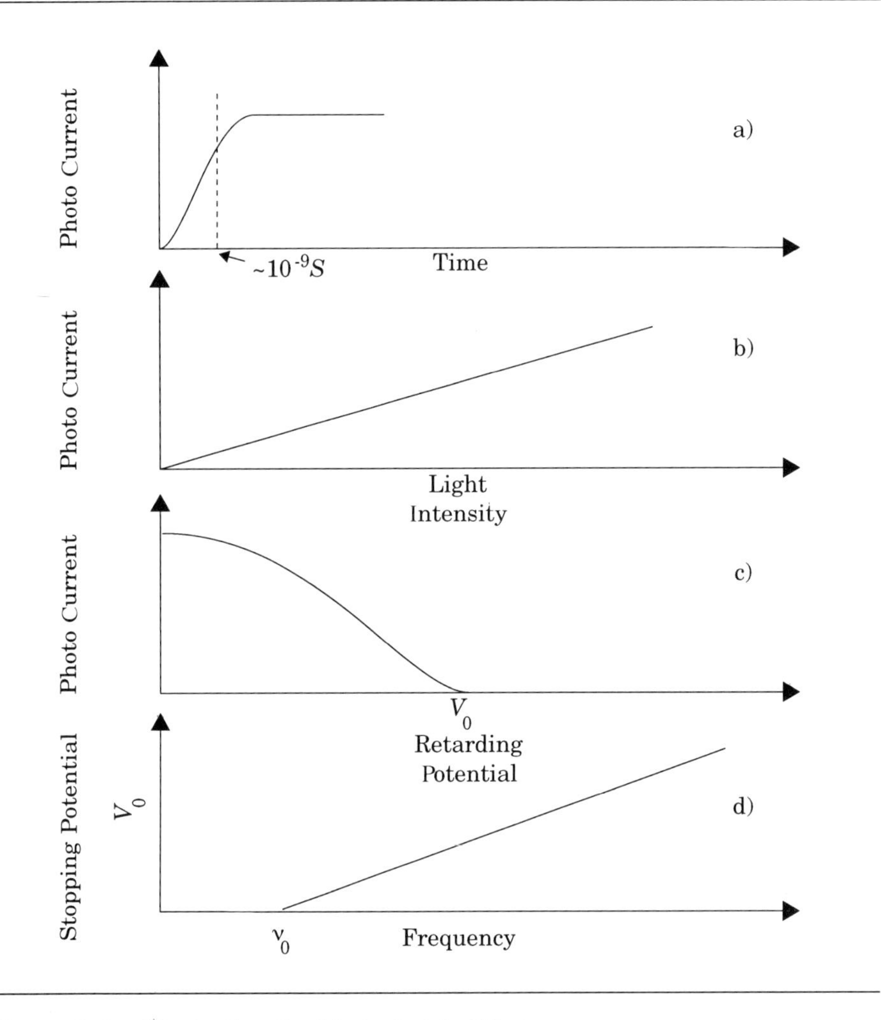

Figure 2–1 *Illustrating the Photoelectric Effect.*

equation. These energy levels were simplified to a ground state g and a series of free-electron states k that formed a continuum (see Figure 2–2). The atom interacted with a classical time-varying electromagnetic field, which they wrote as a single-frequency sinusoidal wave (monochromatic light),

$$E = E_0 \cos \omega t \tag{2.2}$$

This electromagnetic wave was treated as a perturbation, whose interaction potential with the atom was given in the dipole approximation by

$$V(t) = -eE\, x(t) \tag{2.3}$$

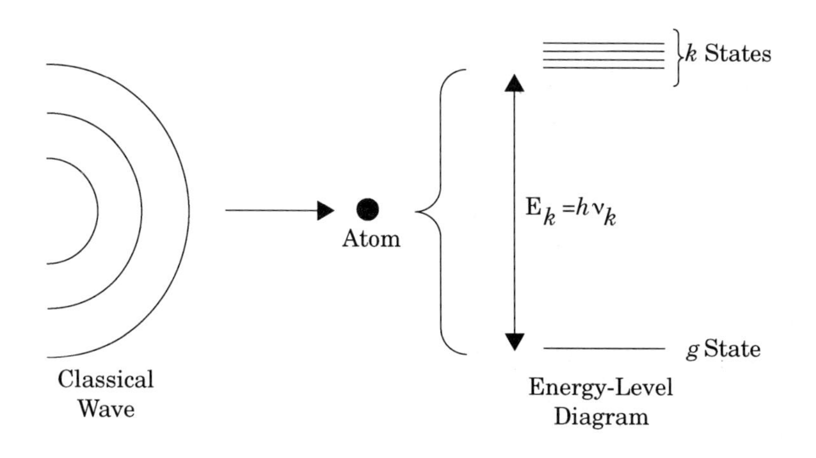

Figure 2–2 *Simplified Energy-Level Diagram* of an atom interacting with a classical wave, in the analysis of Lamb and Scully.[1]

We recognize $-eE$ as the force on the electron that causes its ejection; $V(t)$ is the time-dependent potential associated with that force.

Using standard methods of time-dependent perturbation theory in quantum mechanics, Lamb and Scully found the following expression for the probability that the perturbing field causes a transition from the ground state g to an excited state k—i.e., that the incident light ionizes the atom and liberates the electron:

$$P_k(t) = \frac{4\left|X_{kg}\frac{eE_0}{2\hbar}\right|^2 \sin^2\left[\left(\frac{E_k}{\hbar} - \omega\right)\left(\frac{t}{2}\right)\right]}{\left(\frac{E_k}{\hbar} - \omega\right)^2} \tag{2.4}$$

Here X_{kg} is the matrix element of x between the two states and E_k is the energy of the kth state measured relative to that of the ground state.

This result represents the resonance condition for excitation; excitation only occurs when the incoming frequency ω closely matches that required by the energy-level separation, $\omega_k = E_k/\hbar$. As can be seen, the denominator in Equation (2.4) becomes zero for this value; until the light frequency reaches ω_k, no electron will be ejected, while above that frequency electrons will appear. In this way one can account for the threshold phenomenon, which is just the work function of the metal used. Equation (2.1), therefore, can be thought of as a natural consequence of the resonance condition for excitation by an electromagnetic wave, rather than a reflection of microscopic energy conservation for light, as proposed by Einstein.

The second aspect of the photoelectric effect, that the photocurrent is proportional to the light intensity, is similarly accounted for. The intensity of the light is proportional to E_0^2. But from Equation (2.4), the probability of electron emission is just proportional to E_0^2.

The first property of the photoelectric effect, that electrons are emitted immediately after the onset of illumination, is treated as follows. Equation (2.4) represents the probability for a transition to *one* of the continuum levels k. But the probability of emission of a photoelectron is the probability of a transition to *any* such level, which is the sum of Equation (2.4) over all k. Lamb and Scully did this sum, and showed that the transition probability was proportional to the time. This implied that the transition rate was constant, so that even at short times electrons would be emitted.

Thus all aspects of the photoelectric effect were accounted for without resort to Einstein's Nobel Prize-winning argument. Moreover, the random, unpredictable character of individual quantum-mechanical events was properly preserved, but in this model, was due not to the quantum nature of light, but to that of matter. Many of the other so-called "proofs" of the quantum nature of light are equally suspect; the semiclassical treatment of the Compton effect,[2] for example, is quite successful.

Anticoincidences What, then, are the firm grounds for believing in photons? How might we design an experiment that could give evidence for the particle nature of light? A clue is contained in the very meaning of the term "particle." By its nature, such an object occupies a definite location in space. It is either "here" or "there," but never both. A wave, in contrast, spreads over an extended region. We are therefore led to design an experiment that asks whether light can be in two different places at the same time. The method is to place two detectors at widely separated locations, illuminate them both with the same light source, and *ask whether they click at the same instant. Within the particle picture of light, they should not.*

The experimental apparatus required for such an experiment is consummately simple: a light source, a half-silvered mirror and two detectors (Figure 2–3). Light falls on the half-silvered mirror, which acts as a beam splitter. If the incident light intensity is I, then behind the mirror the detectors each register an intensity $I/2$. While on average this is always true, we can investigate the situation more closely by monitoring the temporal response of the two detectors to the light incident upon them.

Each detector responds with "clicks." As we have seen, this does not necessarily imply that the light itself is quantized, but rather merely that the detectors' response to light is to click. We correlate these clicks by connecting them to a coincidence counter, which records a count only if both detectors click at the same moment. The proposed experimental test is to send light to the half-silvered mirror and measure the number of coincidence counts relative to the number of individual counts of the detectors.

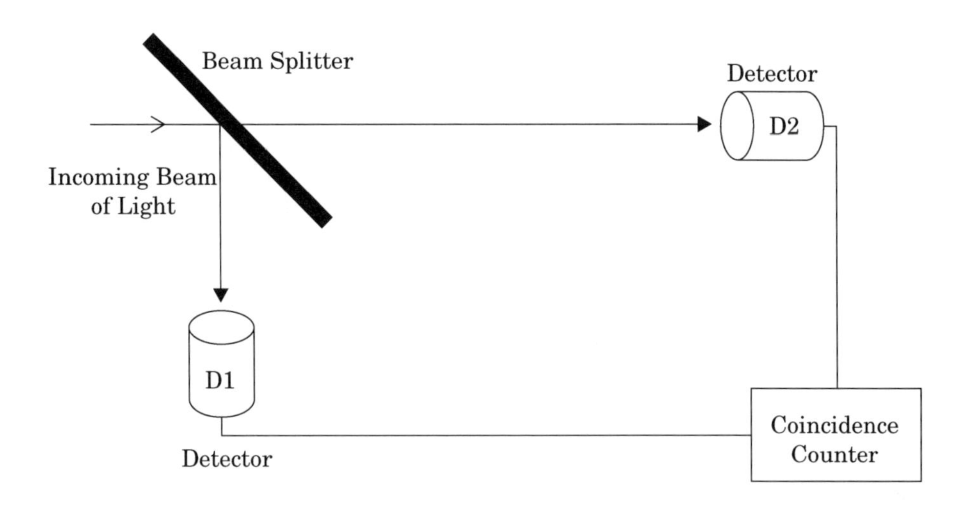

Figure 2–3 *Anticoincidence Experiment* to demonstrate the particle nature of light. If light is composed of photons, the two detectors should never click at the same time.

The results of such an experiment are conveniently analyzed in terms of the so-called anticorrelation parameter A:

$$A \equiv \frac{P_c}{P_1 P_2} \tag{2.5}$$

where P_1 is the experimentally measured probability of detector 1 responding, P_2 the same for detector 2, and P_c the probability of coincidence. The quantity A has several properties that make it a particularly useful diagnostic in this situation. On the one hand, if light is composed of photons, the two detectors should never respond together, making P_c zero so that A should be zero. If, on the other hand, light has no particle-like properties, the detectors should be perfectly capable of clicking together, and A can be nonzero. Indeed, if the detectors turn out to click randomly and independently of one another, we can easily show that A will equal one. The proof is to note that, in such a situation, coincidences will arise purely randomly, by the fortuitous clicking together of the two detectors, and that the probability of two random events occurring together is simply the product of their individual probabilities:

$$\begin{pmatrix}\text{Probability}\\ \text{both click}\end{pmatrix} = \begin{pmatrix}\text{Probability}\\ \text{one clicks}\end{pmatrix}\begin{pmatrix}\text{Probability}\\ \text{the other clicks}\end{pmatrix} \tag{2.6}$$

Thus $P_c = P_1 P_2$, from which we get $A = 1$. Finally, a measured value of A greater than unity would show the two detectors to be clicking together more often than purely random behavior would allow—a "clustering" tendency of the clicks.

In an actual experiment the anticorrelation parameter is measured as follows. The experiment lasts for a time T, and it counts the total number of clicks N_1 and N_2 of the two detectors and the number N_c of coincidence counts in this time interval. By "coincidences" in this context we mean that the time between clicks of the two detectors was less than Δt, the time resolution of the experiment. We can think of the run as consisting of $(T/\Delta t)$ opportunities for each detector to respond, and the same number of opportunities for coincidences. The experimentally measured probability is then the number of events divided by the number of opportunities:

$$P_{1 \text{ or } 2} = \frac{N_{1 \text{ or } 2}}{\left(\dfrac{T}{\Delta t}\right)} \tag{2.7}$$

Thus the anticorrelation parameter is given in terms of experimentally measured quantities by

$$A = \frac{N_c}{N_1 N_2}\left(\frac{T}{\Delta t}\right) \tag{2.8}$$

We turn now to the first attempt at a realization of this experiment and its unexpected results.*

The Hanbury-Brown and Twiss Experiment In 1956 the first careful investigations of photon coincidences were performed by Hanbury-Brown and Twiss.[3] They undertook the apparently simple task of showing that, for dim light sources, single photons arriving on a beam splitter are not split, and therefore lead to anticorrelation ($A = 0$) when detected. The wave theory, by contrast, would predict that no matter what the intensity of light arriving on the beam splitter, it is halved in both directions, so that random coincidences would be expected ($A = 1$).

In their experiment, the 435.8-nm light from an emission line of a mercury arc was isolated by a system of filters and sent to a half-silvered mirror. Downstream were two photomultipliers connected to a coincidence

---

* Even if light is composed of photons, coincidences can always arise by chance if two photons happen to arrive at the same moment. The probability of this happening decreases with the intensity of the light. All experiments must then operate at very low light levels in order to reduce this probability to negligible values.

counter. From atomic physics, Hanbury-Brown and Twiss possessed an explicit picture of the mercury light source. Individual mercury atoms collided with electrons; the impacts excited the atoms to various states, including a state that rapidly decayed to the ground state, emitting a photon of wavelength 435.8 nm. This cycle happened millions of times a second to produce the light that traveled to the detectors. In front of each detector was a narrowband 435.8-nm interference filter. This filter insured that only photons of the correct wavelength entered the photomultiplier tubes: a photon that somehow "split" at the beam splitter, half its energy going one way and half the other, would have the wrong wavelength and be rejected.

If photons were indivisible, Hanbury-Brown and Twiss expected no coincidences, and the anticorrelation parameter A would be zero. But this was not what they found! Indeed, they found precisely the opposite result: a strongly enhanced coincident signal. Their measured value of the anticorrelation parameter turned out to be $A = 2$. Whenever a click occurred at one phototube, they found a higher than random probability that a click had simultaneously occurred at the other.

The result of the Hanbury-Brown and Twiss experiment was astonishing. Not only did it fail to demonstrate the existence of photons and the indivisibility of weak light, it actually showed that light seemed to travel through space "bunched up": one can divide the bunch in half, but the two half-bunches arrive at the photodetectors at the same time. These results startled the physics community and launched an entirely new discipline, the explicit study of the quantum nature of light.

How is this astonishing experiment to be understood? Clearly, it provides no evidence at all for the particle nature of light. Does it argue rather for a classical understanding of light? Let us explore this possibility. We therefore drop the concept of photons and think of the light beam simply as a wave carrying energy. Begin with a completely classical picture, in which the detectors also are thought of classically: they are devices for capturing and storing this energy until enough has been accumulated to power a click. Within such a framework, each detector will then "fill" at the same rate, and therefore click at the same rate. Hanbury-Brown and Twiss's results have this property. Can all their results be understood in these terms?

If the two detectors begin with zero stored energy, they will require the same amount of time to fill and therefore both emit their first clicks at the same instant, yielding a coincidence. They will then empty, commence re-filling, and emit their second clicks as coincidences. Clearly, within this framework, *every* event is a coincidence: $N_c = N_1 = N_2$, yielding an anticorrelation parameter $A = 1/P_1$. Since $P_1 \ll 1$ in the Hanbury-Brown and Twiss experiment, this would give an enormous anticorrelation parameter. But this is not in accord with their measurements.

The expected anticorrelation parameter in such a theory can be reduced by imagining the following scenario. Perhaps Hanbury-Brown and Twiss's experiment began with their two detectors partially, but unequally, filled. In this case one would click and then the other. But this modification will not work, for it predicts that, rather than every event being a coincidence, none is: the expected anticorrelation parameter is not too big, but too small. Similarly, other ways might be imagined in which the classical account might be adjusted to fit the data, but none turns out to be successful. No purely classical explanation for Hanbury-Brown and Twiss's result has ever been found.

We turn then to a *semi*-classical attempt to understand their result—and this is an attempt that will turn out to be wholly successful. Such a way of thinking describes the light in purely classical terms, i.e., as consisting solely of waves and having no particle properties. The detectors, however, are treated quantum-mechanically: they are regarded as systems possessing several energy levels, and the process of detection is regarded as a transition from the ground state to the positive-energy continuum state.

This is precisely the problem treated by Lamb and Scully as described earlier (see "Photoelectric Effect"). Recall their result: the probability that such a transition will occur in a time interval Δt is proportional to Δt and to the intensity of the light beam I. We write the proportionality constants for the two detectors as α_1 and α_2. Thus

$$\begin{aligned} P_1 &= \alpha_1 I\,\Delta t \\ P_2 &= \alpha_2 I\,\Delta t \end{aligned} \tag{2.9}$$

Similarly, the probability of exciting two atoms in the two detectors involves the α's, Δt squared and I squared:

$$P_c = \alpha_1 \alpha_2 I^2 (\Delta t)^2 \tag{2.10}$$

We therefore find the anticorrelation parameter to be

$$A = \frac{\alpha_1 \alpha_2 I^2 (\Delta t)^2}{(\alpha_1 I\,\Delta t)(\alpha_2 I\,\Delta t)} = 1 \tag{2.11}$$

which is *not* in accord with the results of Hanbury-Brown and Twiss.

But Equation (2.11) is valid only if the beam intensity I is constant in time. Hanbury-Brown and Twiss's light source produced light whose instantaneous intensity rapidly fluctuated about an average. This is true of many light sources. Light bulbs and flames, for instance, whose light is produced by a superposition of individual emissions from a multitude of atoms, have this property. For such sources we replace Equations (2.9) and (2.10) by

$$\begin{aligned} P_1 &= \alpha_1 \langle I \rangle \, \Delta t \\ P_2 &= \alpha_2 \langle I \rangle \, \Delta t \\ P_c &= \alpha_1 \alpha_2 \langle I^2 \rangle (\Delta t)^2 \end{aligned} \tag{2.12}$$

where the brackets denote averages: $\langle I \rangle$ is the average intensity over many instantaneous measurements, and $\langle I^2 \rangle$ is the average of the intensity squared.

Using Equation (2.12) in the definition of the anticorrelation parameter A (Equation (2.5)), we obtain

$$A = \frac{\alpha_1 \alpha_2 \langle I^2 \rangle (\Delta t)^2}{(\alpha_1 \langle I \rangle \, \Delta t)(\alpha_2 \langle I \rangle \, \Delta t)}$$

$$A = \frac{\langle I^2 \rangle}{\langle I \rangle^2} \tag{2.13}$$

This result shows that the expected anticorrelation parameter within the semi-classical theory is simply the average of I squared as compared to the square of the average of I. But *we can easily prove that this must always be greater than unity*. To see how this is done, begin with the simple case of a beam whose intensity fluctuates between only two values, I_1 and I_2. Defining x to be the ratio I_2/I_1, the averages are

$$\begin{aligned} \langle I^2 \rangle &= \tfrac{1}{2}(I_1^2 + I_2^2) = \frac{I_1^2}{2}(1 + x^2) \\ \langle I \rangle^2 &= [\tfrac{1}{2}(I_1 + I_2)]^2 = I_1^2 \left(\frac{1 + x}{2} \right)^2 \end{aligned} \tag{2.14}$$

But the first of these quantities is always greater than the second,

$$\frac{1 + x^2}{2} > \left(\frac{1 + x}{2} \right)^2 \tag{2.15}$$

since this can be rewritten

$$2(1 + x^2) > (1 + x)^2 \tag{2.16}$$

which can be rearranged to read

$$(1 - x)^2 > 0 \tag{2.17}$$

which is always true, since the square of every real number is positive. This result can be extended to a beam whose intensity fluctuates between any number of values by using the so-called Cauchy-Schwartz inequality,

$$\langle I^2 \rangle \geq \langle I \rangle^2 \tag{2.18}$$

We have therefore shown that, according to the semi-classical theory, the anticorrelation parameter for a fluctuating source must always be greater than unity. Although this argument does not explain why Hanbury-Brown and Twiss obtained $A = 2$, it is at least in accord with their result. In fact, a more detailed semi-classical analysis can be developed that yields $A = 2$.

The conclusion is that light from sources such as light bulbs and flames can be understood on the basis of a purely classical theory of light coupled with a quantum theory of atoms, and that it provides no evidence whatever that light is composed of particles. With the invention of the laser, the Hanbury-Brown and Twiss experiment was repeated, but now with the mercury arc replaced by a laser.[4] The light emitted from a laser running high above its threshold turned out to show a different anticorrelation parameter from the mercury arc, but still not what one would expect from a source of particles: the anticorrelation parameter A was found to equal one. Recall that the semi-classical picture predicts $A = 1$ for a source constant in time (Equation (2.11)), which agrees with the description of laser light as a stable classical electromagnetic wave with negligible intensity fluctuations. Physicists still lacked direct evidence for light as comprised of indivisible quanta.

Photons at Last Do these experiments pose a problem for quantum mechanics? Does their failure to show anticorrelations cast doubt on this theory, which, after all, regards light as possessing particle properties? Recent work has shown that, while not supporting the photon picture, at least they do not invalidate it. The resolution of the apparent paradox rests on the concept of an eigenstate.

Recall that, within quantum theory, to every observable there corresponds an operator, and that certain wave functions are eigenstates of this operator. These eigenstates possess well-defined values of the observable in question. The familiar hydrogen-atom wave functions, for instance, are eigenstates of the energy operator. If an ensemble of hydrogen atoms is prepared in one of these states—the ground state, say—every succeeding measurement of energy is sure to yield the same answer, the energy of the ground state.

But these are not eigenstates of other operators. If we were to measure, not the energy, but the linear momentum of electrons in a succession of atoms, all in the ground state, we would find each measurement yielding a different result. While the electron's energy possesses a well-defined value, its momentum does not. Within the formalism of quantum theory, this can be seen by noting that the eigenstate of linear momentum is the familiar plane wave e^{ikx} for which the corresponding momentum is k. The ground-state hydrogen-atom wave function can be written as a sum of many such functions, each with a different value of k. This sum, the Fourier expansion of the ground state, contains an infinite number of terms, corresponding to the fact that successive measurements of the linear momentum can yield any result at all.

Similarly, experiments that attempt to show that light is composed of photons will only succeed if the light they study is composed of a well-defined number of photons—namely, one of them. The light must be in an eigenstate of the operator corresponding to photon number. Recent work has shown that the light sources used in early experiments did not have this property. Rather, the light was in a quantum state that was a linear superposition of many different eigenstates of the photon number operator.

The difficulty with these experiments therefore lay in the light sources they had elected to use. Anticorrelations are only expected if the source produces light in an eigenstate of the photon number operator. How to design such a source? This has only recently been achieved, beginning with an important experiment by Clauser in 1974, and nowhere more elegantly than in the 1986 work of Grangier, Roger and Aspect.[5]

Using well-established molecular-beam techniques, Grangier, Roger and Aspect produced a well-collimated stream of calcium atoms, and raised them to an excited state by means of two-photon laser excitation. The light upon which they conducted their anticorrelation experiment was produced by the decay of these atoms back down to the ground state. As in the Hanbury-Brown and Twiss experiment, millions of decay photons were produced each second. These mingled with the laser photons and general background light. How, from this seething chaos, was the single-photon eigenstate to arise? Grangier and colleagues needed a means of isolating individual events. They needed some form of signal, alerting them to the fact that an atom had just decayed.

The means they hit upon was to raise their Ca atoms to a state that decayed by emitting two photons rather than one. The first of these photons was their signal. The second was the photon upon which they conducted their anticorrelation experiment.

Calcium atoms were excited to a high-lying *s*-state that quickly decayed to the ground state, via an intermediate *p*-state, by giving off two photons of different frequency in rapid sequence (Figure 2–4). The first of these photons was allowed to fall directly on a photomultiplier PMT_1, while the other struck a beam splitter as before (Figure 2–5). The first photon was a "trigger" photon that alerted the other detectors, PMT_r and PMT_t, to expect the second photon. The detection electronics was gated open for a brief time following the arrival of the first photon.

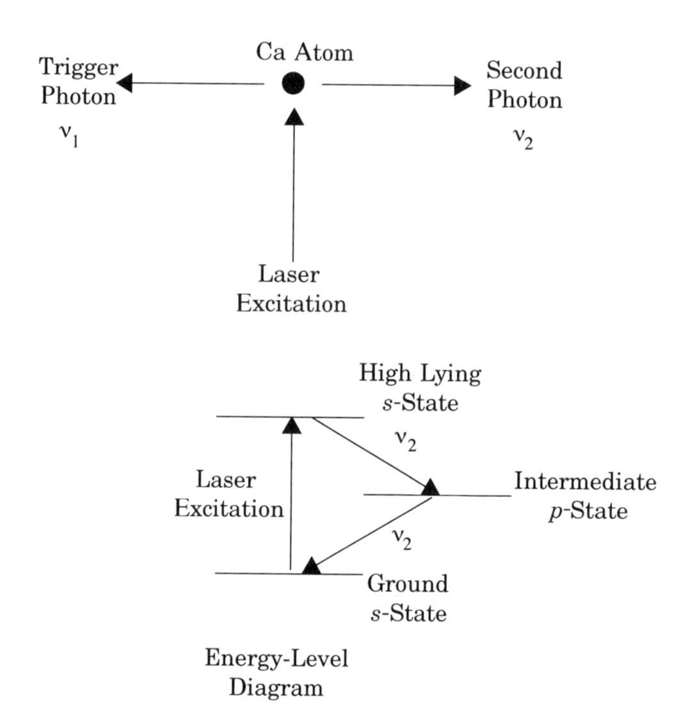

Figure 2–4 *Single-Photon Source* used in the successful anticoincidence experiment of Grangier et al.[5] A calcium atom is illuminated by a laser and makes a transition to a high-lying *s*-state. It decays, first to an intermediate *p*-state with the emission of the trigger photon ν_1, and then to the ground *s*-state with the emission of the second photon ν_2: this is the photon upon which the anticoincidence experiment is conducted.

With this special arrangement, Grangier et al. could reject the random arrival of light at PMT_r and PMT_t, and only detect the single photons sought.

They measured the anticorrelation parameter for this experimental arrangement, and extrapolated the results to low intensity to eliminate limitations due to instrumental resolution. They obtained $A = 0$: perfect anticorrelation. Photons had been detected at last.

Remarks It is ironic that Albert Einstein, arguably the greatest physicist since Newton, received the Nobel Prize for work that subsequently turned out to be flawed. And it is doubly ironic that this work, which was instrumental in placing before us the concept of wave-particle duality, turned out to be correct even though flawed.

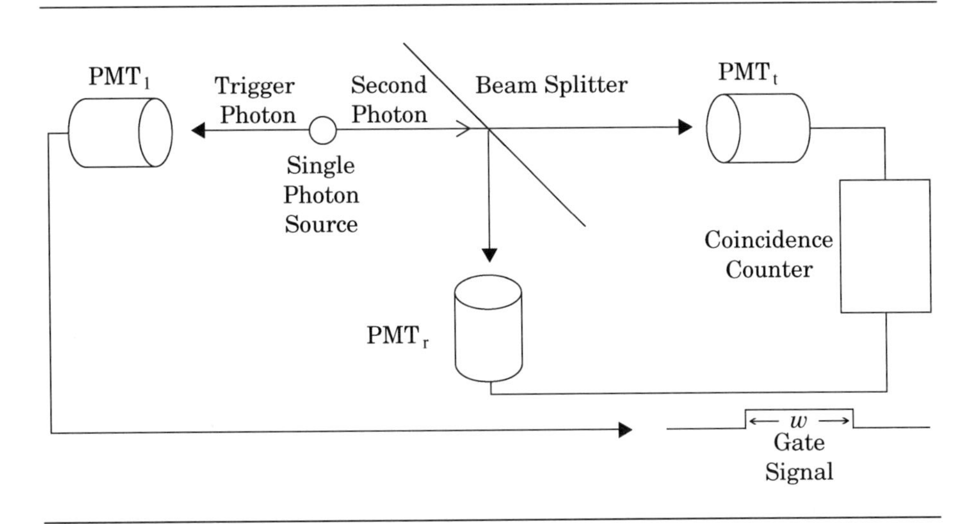

Figure 2–5 *Anticoincidence Experiment of Aspect and Co-workers.*[5] The trigger photon from the single-photon source is detected: this alerts the two detectors PMT_t and PMT_r to expect a photon sometime during the brief "gate period" w.

Many people tend to think of photons as being the constituents of light, in the same sense that atoms are the constituents of matter. But this view is erroneous. While a brick contains a definite number of atoms, the same cannot always be said for light. Most forms of light—sunlight, for example, or light from electric bulbs—are not composed of one photon, or ten photons, or any particular number of photons at all. Indeed, as we have seen, these forms of light can be entirely accounted for on the basis of classical ideas combined with a quantum treatment of the detection process. The central lesson of the story we have recounted in this section is that the concept of the photon is far more subtle than had been previously thought.

2.2 Wave–Particle Duality for Single Photons

With the experiment of Grangier, Roger and Aspect,[5] we have clear evidence at last for the existence of photons. Grangier, Roger and Aspect then set out on a new experiment. Having shown that, at a beam splitter, individual particles from their source were either reflected or transmitted, going one way or the other but never both, they then allowed these same photons to pass through an interferometer.

Their apparatus, known as a Mach–Zehnder interferometer, is diagrammed in Figure 2–6. Light enters through a half-silvered mirror. Instead of proceeding directly to a pair of detectors, the two beams reflect

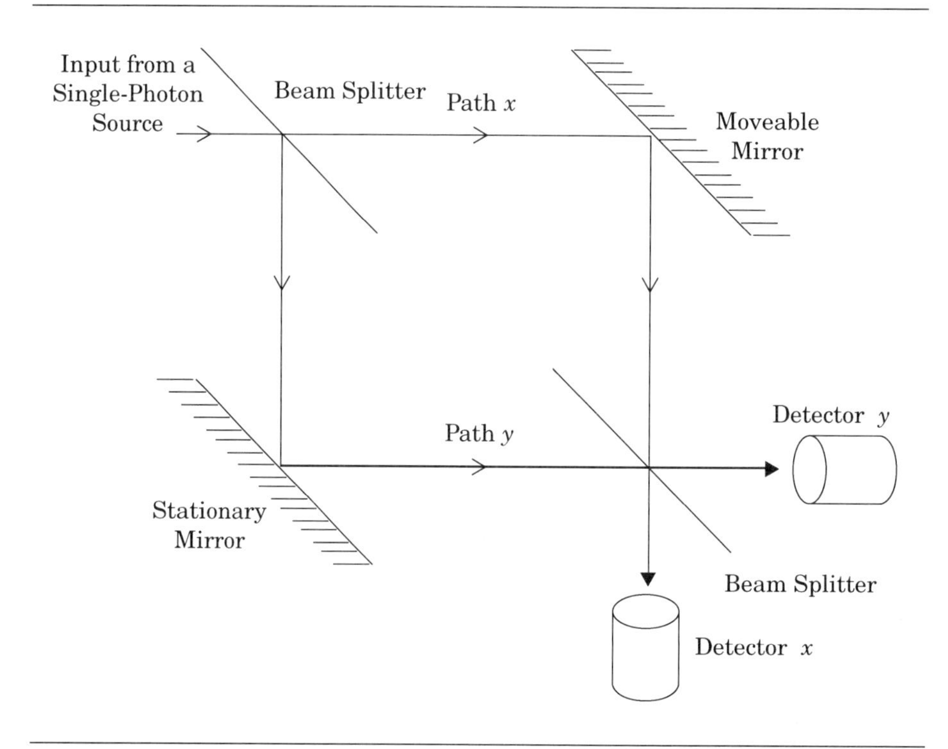

Figure 2–6 *Interference Experiment for Single Photons* of Aspect and coworkers.[5] Light from a single-photon source enters a so-called Mach–Zehnder interferometer and is observed by the detectors. As the position of the moveable mirror is changed, the phase difference between the two paths varies and an interference pattern results.

from mirrors and recombine on a second beam splitter. Thus there are two paths from the input to the output, and interference can occur. Were light purely a wave, it would divide at the first beam splitter and recombine at the second, with some phase shift between them that determines the amplitude in the two output beams. If the interference is constructive for one output direction, then all the light emerges in that direction and none in the other. The phase difference between the two paths can easily be adjusted by moving one of the mirrors slightly.

But would this occur for individual photons? Grangier, Roger and Aspect used their identical Ca cascade light source, and the same triggering scheme to tag the single photon as it entered the apparatus. If interference were to be observed, then the standard interpretation of quantum mechanics would have us think of each particle as splitting at the first beam splitter and traveling both arms of the interferometer. But from their anticorrelation experiment described above, we know that their source produces

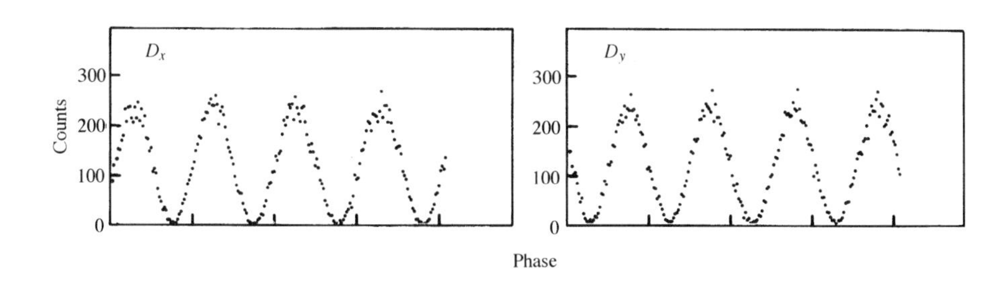

Figure 2–7 *Interference of Single Photons* (the experimental results of Aspect and co-workers). The number of counts in the two detectors of Figure 2–6 are plotted as a function of the phase difference between the two paths. The photon, which before chose one path, now takes both. SOURCE: Modified with permission from P. Grangier, G. Roger and A. Aspect, "Experimental evidence for a photon anticorrelation effect on a beamsplitter," *Europhys. Lett.*, vol. 1, p. 173. Copyright 1986 Les Editions de Physique.

something that never splits at a beam splitter, but rather always goes one way or another. We would therefore not expect interference.

Data from their experiment is shown in Figure 2–7. It clearly shows an interference pattern as the path length traveled by light in one arm of the interferometer is increased relative to the other. The signature is unmistakable. The photon, which before chose one path, now takes both.*

Delayed Choice We confront again the harsh realities of the quantum. The essence of quantum mechanics is held between these two experiments of Grangier et al. Taken individually, neither is particularly problematic; taken together, our understanding grinds to a halt.

The experiments can be summed up by saying that light appears as a wave in certain circumstances and a particle in others. Similarly, the burden of the previous chapter is that precisely the same is true of electrons, neutrons, and atoms. Wave–particle duality forces upon us the necessity of a radical revision in our thinking.

Just how radical need this revision be? Is there any way to grasp these phenomena while keeping common sense intact? One possibility exists that would account for the phenomena we have discussed so far. According to this point of view, the light is not really behaving in an incomprehensible manner after all. Rather, as it leaves the source, the light "senses" the experimental apparatus and adjusts its nature accordingly. If it senses an experiment capable of demonstrating interference, it becomes a wave.

* Recall, however, the crucial role played by the locality assumption in this conclusion.

But if it senses one capable of demonstrating anticoincidences, it becomes a particle. We might refer to such a point of view as a "conspiracy theory" of light.

Whether one attempts to formulate a detailed theory incorporating these ideas, or leaves them in the loose form expressed above, is a matter of taste. The "sensing," for example, could involve some process by means of which the first photons through the apparatus set up conditions that cause the others to behave as waves or particles as required. At any rate, it is clear that this point of view, while obviously requiring a severe revision of our ideas, is nevertheless not so radical as others that could be imagined. But is it correct?

In 1978 the physicist John Wheeler[6] proposed a means of testing it: the so-called delayed-choice experiment. This experiment has recently been performed. Its result implies that no revision of this sort can be sufficient: the conspiracy theory's attempt to soften the crisis in understanding posed by the wave–particle duality is doomed to failure. Moreover, the delayed-choice experiment dramatizes the puzzling nature of light still further, making yet clearer the radical demands placed on our imagination by the phenomena of the quantum world.

Wheeler's delayed-choice experiment is capable of detecting *either* particles (anticoincidences) *or* waves (interference). But the experiment is designed so that the choice of which aspect to observe is delayed until *after* the photon has "decided" what it will be. The physical arrangement is much like that of the Mach–Zehnder interference experiment, except that the second beam splitter can be inserted or removed at any time (Figure 2–8).

Imagine a single photon entering the interferometer via the first beam splitter BS_1. In the absence of the second beam splitter BS_2, the detectors D_x and D_y ascertain which route the light quantum has traveled. If it traveled by path x, the photon shows up in detector D_x; if it traveled by path y, it shows up in detector D_y. Without BS_2 the experiment is essentially the anticorrelation experiment performed by Grangier, Roger and Aspect.

But with BS_2 inserted, it becomes their interference experiment. We irreversibly lose all information as to which path has been taken, and a proper interferometer exists. Under this circumstance, the two detectors show interference. Wheeler's addition is to delay the choice of whether or not to insert the second beam splitter until well after the photon has entered the interferometer. Thus, the experimental configuration is ambiguous until the last moment.

According to the conspiracy theory, this last-minute insertion or removal of the second beam splitter should have the effect of "fooling" the light. Imagine, for instance, that as the experiment begins, BS_2 is absent. The conspiracy theory would hold that this causes each photon to act as a particle, and take either path x or y. Furthermore, it will continue to do so until well past the first beam splitter. The subsequent insertion of BS_2 will not alter this fact, and even though BS_2 is present by the time

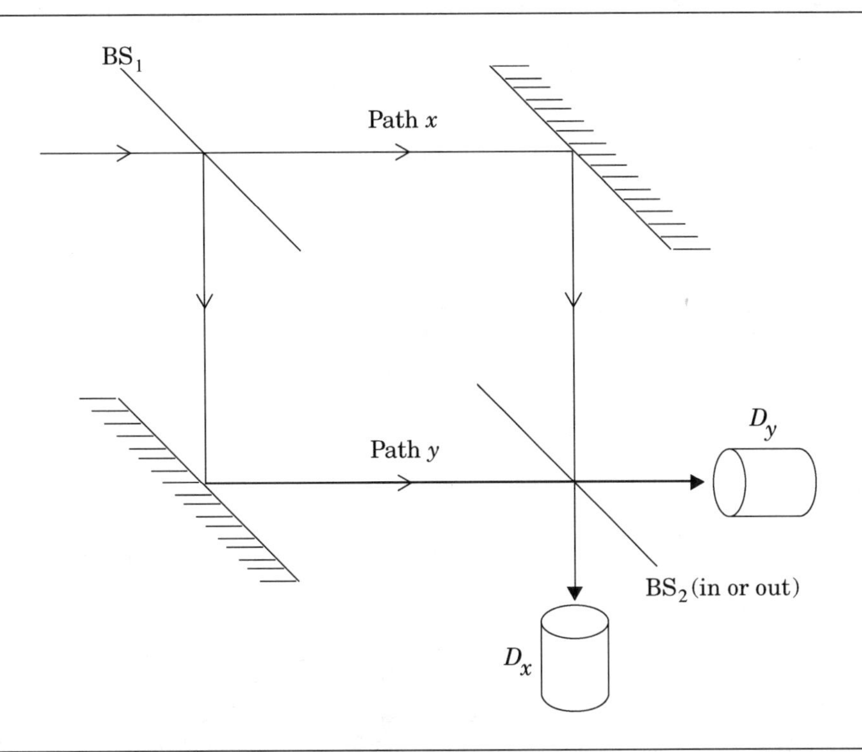

Figure 2–8 *Delayed-Choice Experiment.* The second beam splitter in the Mach–Zehnder interferometer can be inserted or removed at will—*after* the photon has passed through the first beam splitter and "made its choice of whether to behave as a particle or a wave." According to the so-called conspiracy theory, this should have the effect of "tricking" the light into behaving in the wrong fashion.

the light reaches it, interference cannot possibly be observed. The converse is true of the opposite configuration: *if the conspiracy theory is correct, the delayed choice experiment in both cases will force the light into behaving in the wrong fashion.*

But does it? What does experiment reveal? At the Max Planck Institute for Quantum Optics outside Munich, Hellmuth, Walther, Zajonc and Schleich[7] have successfully executed a version of this experiment. For technical reasons, it proved impossible to physically remove BS_2 in the required short interval of time. However, it was possible to rapidly remove and insert the equivalent of a mirror into one of the two paths, say path x (Figure 2–9). This was done by using an electronic Pockel cell which, when a voltage is applied, within 5 ns rotates the plane of polarization of light. A Glans prism then reflects away light whose polarization has been altered, but transmits unrotated light. Thus, when a voltage is applied to the Pockel

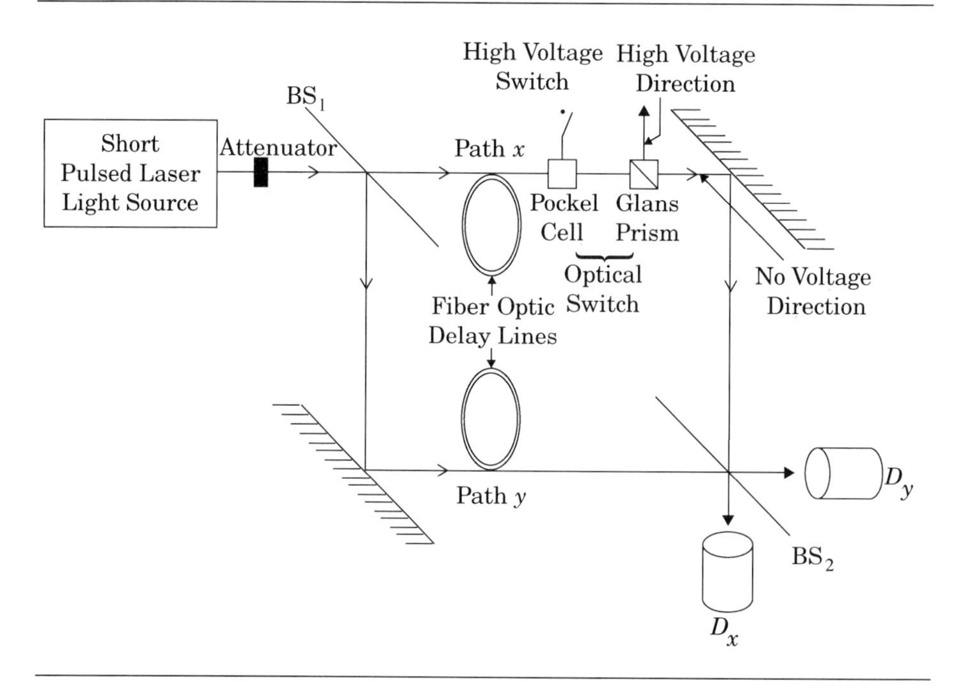

Figure 2–9 *Design of the Delayed-Choice Experiment* employed by Walther and co-workers.[7]

cell, the mirror is effectively in place, and the only light reaching BS_2 came from a single path, path *y*: the interference element of the configuration is lost. Conversely, with the voltage not applied, the mirror is effectively absent: BS_2 receives light from both paths *x* and *y*, and interference is possible.

The experiment used linearly polarized, short pulses of laser light, less than a billionth of a second in duration, with on average one photon in each. The pulse was generated by a mode-locked laser, and provided the exact timing required to do the experiment. The travel time of the photon through the interferometer was extended to about 30 ns by use of 10-m-long fiber-optic delay lines in both arms of the interferometer, which gave time for the Pockel cell to operate. In this way the Munich group devised a high-speed version, containing all the strangeness of Wheeler's experiment.

The results were that no matter when BS_2 was inserted, an interference pattern was observed. Conversely, if the experiment was begun with BS_2 in place, and it was subsequently removed, interference was never observed. These results are exactly what quantum mechanics predicts, and they are contrary to the conspiracy theory. The photon can go from traveling one

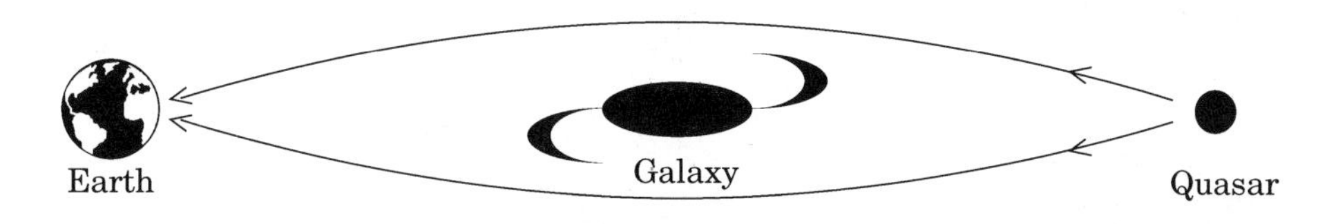

Figure 2–10 *Hypothetical Extreme Delayed-Choice Experiment.* Light from a gravitationally lensed quasar is passed through a delayed-choice apparatus. In such a situation, we are tempted to say that billions of years of history can be altered by our choice of whether to insert or remove the second beam splitter.

path to both paths at any time in its history. Light is never fooled: even when the experimental apparatus is changed "after the light has made its choice," the light still makes the right choice.

What does this tell us? To appreciate the significance of the delayed-choice experiment, Wheeler suggests the following thought experiment (Figure 2–10). A number of so-called "double quasars" are known: apparently identical quasars lying unusually close to one another in the sky. These are, in fact, two separate images of the same distant object, their light focused toward us along two separate paths by a gravitational lens produced by an intervening galaxy or cluster of galaxies. Wheeler emphasizes that, since there exist two possible trajectories by which a photon can make its way from the quasar to us, interference can arise. Only one more step is needed: the insertion of a beam splitter at the meeting point of the two trajectories. Without the beam splitter, an observer would see two images of the quasar; with it, one finds interference.

Quasars, however, are up to billions of light years away, and we can delay our choice of whether or not to insert the beam splitter until the last moment. The conceptual consequences of such a delayed choice are now dramatic. With the beam splitter in place, the photon has been traveling for billions of years via both paths; changing our mind and leaving it out, the photon has been going one way or the other. But what possible difference can our insertion make in the billion-year past history of the light? Our action in this present moment seems to have consequences that stretch back into the cosmic past.*

The delayed-choice experiment shows how flawed the simple wave–particle description is. Once light is in an interferometer, we simply cannot think of it as either a wave or a particle. Nor will melding the two descriptions into some strange hybrid work. All these attempts are

* This formulation of "altering the past" is flawed. As we will see throughout this book, and particularly in the final chapter, it is wrong to think about a real physical situation prior to the observation of that situation. In Chapter 8 we give a more careful interpretation of the implications of the delayed-choice experiment.

inadequate. What is called for is not a composite picture of light, stitched together out of bits taken from various classical theories. Rather we are being asked for a new concept, a new point of view that will be fundamentally different from those developed from the world of classical physics. And furthermore, as we have seen in Chapter 1, the same comments apply to matter.

Comments Once again, we would like to emphasize that a quantum interference calculation can be made for the delayed-choice case, as it was for electron interference, and no disagreement with experiment is found. Quantum theory, therefore, is completely unperturbed by these results. By contrast, we are unsettled for the simple reason that it seems impossible to understand the experiments when taken together. Once again, quantum mechanics avoids the difficulty by refusing to provide a picture of what happens in the delayed-choice experiment. It says nothing at all about splitting at a beam splitter, a photon "choosing" one path or both. All such descriptions are troublesome holdovers from a classical world conception. Quantum theory merely provides us with probabilities of various detection eventualities for the experiment under study.

Yet the theory does something more. The quantum-mechanical calculation of interference always makes use of the superposition principle. The theory always involves the sum of two or more terms that are then squared (as, for instance, in Equation (1.15)). With this principle, something altogether unique enters into physics. Even a single "indivisible" particle can be put into a superposition state, and in this state, it no longer has a location. In a detector, photons, electrons and the like always appear as simple unitary objects—but outside the detector, the very same objects are capable of developing into a highly complex, extended form that appears to sample all aspects of the interferometer.

Wheeler has vividly described the quantum as a "great smoky dragon," simultaneously existing in every nook and cranny of the interferometer, which suddenly bends forward to bite the detector. Perhaps this is as good a description as we can find at present.

These are some of the implications of quantum-mechanical superposition. The objects and structure of quantum theory suggest a deep reformation of our conception of what the world is and how it is put together. The full scope of that transformation is the subject matter of this book. We will always stay close to actual experiments, never venturing too far into speculation. But even so, the magnitude of the change demanded is enormous, with each experiment adding another level of surprise and subtlety to the description.

Chapter 3

The Uncertainty Principle

For all the world's uncertainties, we are confident of its fundamental lawfulness. Mail arrives as if by magic, and we are certain that each letter travels a real path from a sender to its destination. We may know nothing of the postal system that performs this task, but we are sure that here, as everywhere, a sensible, causal sequence stands behind it all.

In particular, a single letter cannot have two points of origin. Even without a return address we are confident that, with a little effort, we can trace a given letter back to its sender. If this makes sense to you, consider the following experiment, performed by Pfleegor and Mandel in 1967.[1]

3.1 The Pfleefor–Mandel Experiment

Two Lasers, One Photon The light from two lasers making a very small angle with each other was incident upon a screen (Figure 3–1). The experimental arrangement was such that individual photons could be detected by sensitive photomultipliers arranged along the screen. Pfleegor and Mandel searched for an interference pattern in the distribution of clicks of the photomultipliers.

In general, two independent light sources are phase-incoherent to one another, and no interference can arise. Two independent lasers, however, do maintain relative coherence over short periods of time. If an experiment is performed lasting no more than this time, known as the "coherence time," interference will be observed. In the Pfleegor–Mandel experiment the coherence time was roughly 20 μs. Repetitive measurements were made, each lasting no longer than this time, and the many individual results were compiled and analyzed. Excellent evidence for interference was obtained.

The wave picture of light can easily account for this result: the wave train from one laser is interfering with that from the other. But

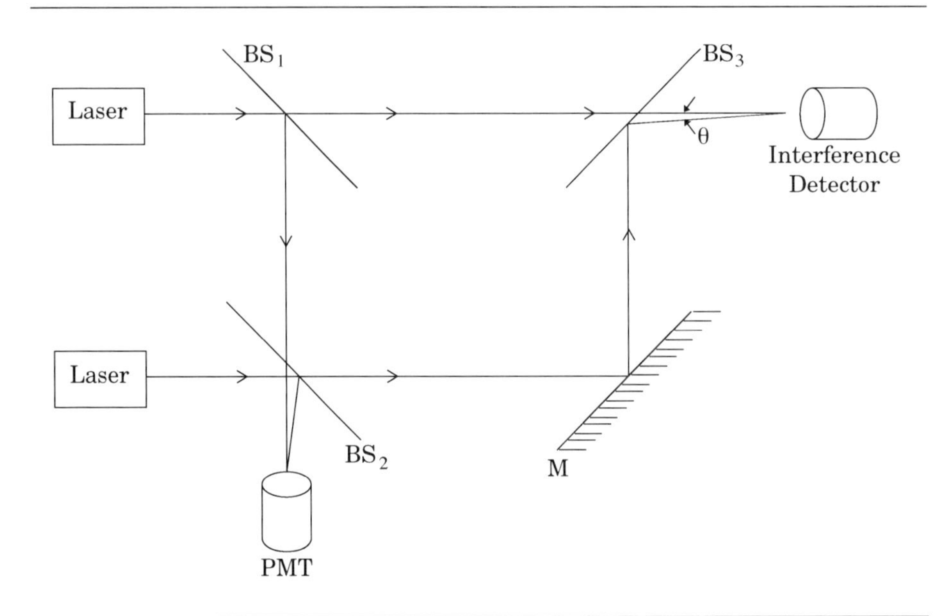

Figure 3–1 *A Single Letter Mailed from Two Locations.* Schematic diagram of the Pfleegor–Mandel experiment.[1] Mirror M and beam splitter BS_3 direct the beams from two lasers onto an interference detector, at which they form an angle θ with each other. Beam splitters BS_1 and BS_2 direct portions of the laser beams to a photomultiplier, which monitors the difference in their frequencies. When these frequencies are nearly identical, the detector is gated open to search for interference.

Pfleegor and Mandel now added a new twist to their experiment. They attenuated the intensity of their light source enormously until, with high probability, *only one photon at a time was present in their experimental apparatus.* They found weak but unmistakable interference fringes in this case as well.

Thinking in terms of light quanta, it is natural to suppose that photons from one laser can interfere with photons from the other. But in this experiment, only one laser at a time was producing photons! P.A.M. Dirac, one of the creators of quantum mechanics, has written that "...each photon interferes only with itself. Interference between different photons never occurs."[2] It is relatively easy to see how Dirac's statement applies to the experiments recounted in the previous chapter, in which we discussed interference phenomena involving a single photon traveling along two paths. But in the present experiment, two separate sources are emitting the light. In what possible sense is a photon interfering with itself in this case? Dirac's dictum would seem to require that *the single quantum is being "co-produced" in the two different lasers.*

We will now proceed to argue that this is precisely the case. Quantum theory possesses no means of determining which source each photon came from. Furthermore, this inability turns out to arise for fundamental reasons, rather than being merely a matter of poor experimental design: no conceivable experiment will ever be capable of making this distinction. The conclusion is that quantum theory does not even carry within it the notion of each photon's being produced in a particular laser.

The demonstration will make use of the famous Heisenberg uncertainty principle, to which we now turn. In the following section we will return to the Pfleegor–Mandel experiment.

The Heisenberg Uncertainty Principle Often, when we measure something, we disturb it. Looking in on a sleeping child at night requires that we open the door and turn on the light, possibly waking the child. Similarly, to measure the position of an atom requires that we scatter light (or something) off it, which obviously will disturb it. All this is pure, classical reasoning. Within classical physics there are two ways to get around the problem. On the one hand, we can always reduce the magnitude of the disturbance as much as we wish—by reducing the intensity of the light, for instance. On the other hand, since any intrusion is governed by the deterministic laws of classical physics, we can correct for it. The game of billiards, for example, depends on the predictability of disturbances. From a final energy and momentum analysis, we can determine the change the cue ball must have caused in the paths of other balls, even without looking at the collisions themselves. We can therefore work back and correct our measurements to any accuracy we like.

So far, nothing remarkable has entered the story. Heisenberg's unique contribution was not to point out that measurement affects the system being measured. Rather, it was to recognize the new fundamental limits to measurement set by the "quantum of action." There are two such limits. First, while according to classical physics we can make the disturbance as small as we wish, according to quantum mechanics, we cannot. The action of light, for instance, is quantized, so that a photon cannot avoid disturbing a particle it strikes. The second limit imposed by quantum mechanics is that this disturbance is uncontrollable and unpredictable. This latter feature reflects the deeply statistical nature of quantum mechanics, to which we will later return. The two new features appearing in Heisenberg's analysis, therefore, are:

1. The disturbance cannot be reduced in magnitude below a fundamental limit, and
2. Correction for the disturbance is impossible.

Heisenberg's famous "uncertainty microscope" illustrates the analysis. It concerns the means whereby one determines the position of a particle by

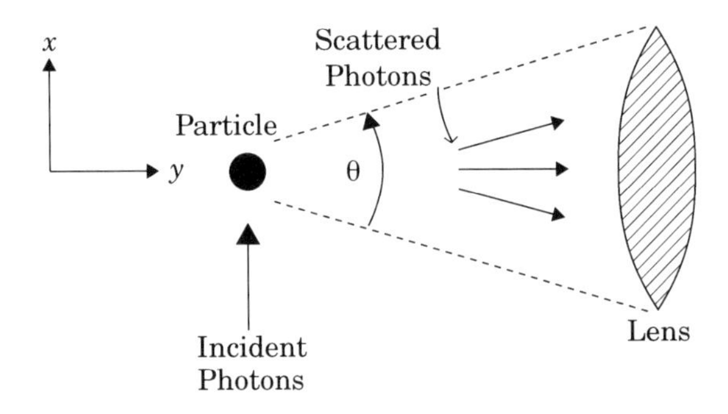

Figure 3–2 *The Heisenberg Uncertainty Microscope.* A particle is observed by illuminating it with light; the scattered light is collected by a lens of angular diameter θ.

illuminating it with light and examining the scattered light. Figure 3–2 diagrams the configuration. An incident light ray is scattered by the particle into a lens, which then focuses the light toward the observer. From classical optics it can be shown that the resolving power of this lens is given by

$$\Delta x = \lambda/\theta \tag{3.1}$$

where λ is the wavelength of the light and θ is the angle subtended by the lens. Equation (3.1) gives the uncertainty Δx in the position of the particle as determined by this observation.

Figure 3–2 illustrates the particular situation in which the incident light is propagating along the x-axis, while the scattered light is propagating more or less horizontally along the y-axis. The component of momentum along the x-axis given to the particle in the scattering process is then roughly equal to the incident momentum p_{light} of the light. But it is not precisely equal to this, for the scattered light is not propagating precisely along the y-axis. As illustrated in Figure 3–2, the scattered light could be propagating at an angle plus or minus $\theta/2$ to the y-axis and still be collected by the lens. The uncertainty in the x-component of the scattered light's momentum is then, for small θ,

$$\Delta p_x = (p_{\text{light}})(\theta/2) \tag{3.2}$$

This equals the corresponding uncertainty in the particle's momentum after the scattering. Combining the above two equations we obtain

$$\Delta x\, \Delta p_x = \lambda p_{\text{light}}/2 \tag{3.3}$$

Until this point, the analysis has been entirely classical. Using the laws of classical wave optics, we have derived an expression for the product of uncertainties $(\Delta x)(\Delta p_x)$. Clearly, a high-resolution experiment will seek to minimize this product, allowing the experimenter to accurately determine both the particle's position and momentum.

From Equation (3.3) it is evident that classically this product can be reduced in two ways: by choosing short-wavelength light or by choosing low-momentum light. The first alternative leads us to select gamma rays. The second alternative leads us to reduce their intensity, since the momentum carried by a classical electromagnetic wave is proportional to its intensity. Thus, by employing light of arbitrarily short wavelength and arbitrarily low intensity, the product of position and momentum uncertainties can be made as small as we like. In classical physics, there is no fundamental lower limit to the product of these uncertainties.

Quantum mechanics changes the situation completely. The previous analysis is valid only until the granularity of light's interaction with matter becomes important. For very low intensities, we must think in terms of the quantized interaction between light and matter—the Compton effect. At the lowest intensity conceivable, scattering is by a single photon, not a small-amplitude electromagnetic wave. According to quantum mechanics, the momentum of this photon is related to its wavelength through de Broglie's relation,

$$p_{\text{light}} = h/\lambda \tag{3.4}$$

Substituting this quantum-mechanical relation into the classical equation, Equation (3.3), leads to the cancellation of λ, and the famous Heisenberg uncertainty relation

$$(\Delta x)(\Delta p_x) = h/2 \tag{3.5}$$

A more formal derivation shows that the actual relationship is:

$$\Delta x\, \Delta p_x \geq \hbar/2 \tag{3.6}$$

Once this level of accuracy is reached, reducing the wavelength or the light intensity no longer helps. Quantum mechanics takes over, and the product of uncertainties can never be reduced below the value given in Equation (3.6).

According to Heisenberg's uncertainty relation, nothing prevents us from measuring the particle's position more and more precisely—but if we do, nature will conspire to make our momentum measurement more and more inaccurate. The same is true if we elect to make our momentum determination exceedingly precise; the accuracy in our determination of the particle's position will be spoiled. It is easy to see physically how this disturbance comes about in the gamma-ray microscope. There are only two ways to make our measurement of position more accurate. One is to use gamma rays of a shorter wavelength. But according to the de Broglie relation (Equation (3.4)), this increases the photon's momentum, and so increases the uncontrollable recoil imparted to the particle under observation. The only other way to refine our position measurement is to increase the lens diameter. But doing this increases our ignorance of the scattered photon's momentum along the x-axis, thus increasing our ignorance of the particle's recoil momentum. Similar comments apply to any effort we might make to reduce the error in the momentum determination. The Heisenberg uncertainty relation (Equation (3.6)) expresses this unbeatable trade-off.*

Uncertainty in the Pfleegor–Mandel Experiment Returning to the Pfleegor–Mandel experiment, we can now recognize the explicit role played by the uncertainty relation in ensuring that no means exists for determining which laser produced a given photon. In Figure 3–3 we diagram the experiment more carefully. We imagine the detectors that record arrivals of the photons are individual atoms arranged along the screen. Each has two internal states: exposed and unexposed, corresponding to its having been struck by a photon and not struck. Atoms located at interference minima will be unexposed; those at interference maxima will be exposed.

In order to observe the interference pattern, we need to observe the detector atoms. We do so by scattering light off them, and we will assume that exposed atoms scatter the light differently from unexposed ones. Conversely, in order to determine which laser each photon came from, we need to observe the recoil of each atom. When a photon is detected, it transfers its momentum to the detecting atom. As illustrated in Figure 3–3, if the photon was produced in laser #1, the detector will recoil in one direction; if the photon was produced in laser #2, the atom will recoil in another direction.

Thus, in order to observe the interference pattern successfully, we need to determine each atom's *position*. Furthermore, we need to do so to high accuracy—to an accuracy greater than the separation between interference maxima and minima. Conversely, to observe the recoil successfully, we need to determine each atom's *momentum* to high accuracy—to an accuracy greater than the difference between p_1 and p_2. But these two measurements

* We emphasized in Chapter 2 that it is wrong to think of photons as "atoms of light." The present analysis emphasizes this point yet again. That light is composed of photons is essential to Heisenberg's argument. But there is no such thing as an "elementary" photon—a photon of the smallest energy. We can always imagine a photon of lower and lower energy. The problem is that, as we do so, we are imagining a photon of a longer and longer wavelength, and photons of large wavelength are capable of resolving the position of a particle only to a poor accuracy.

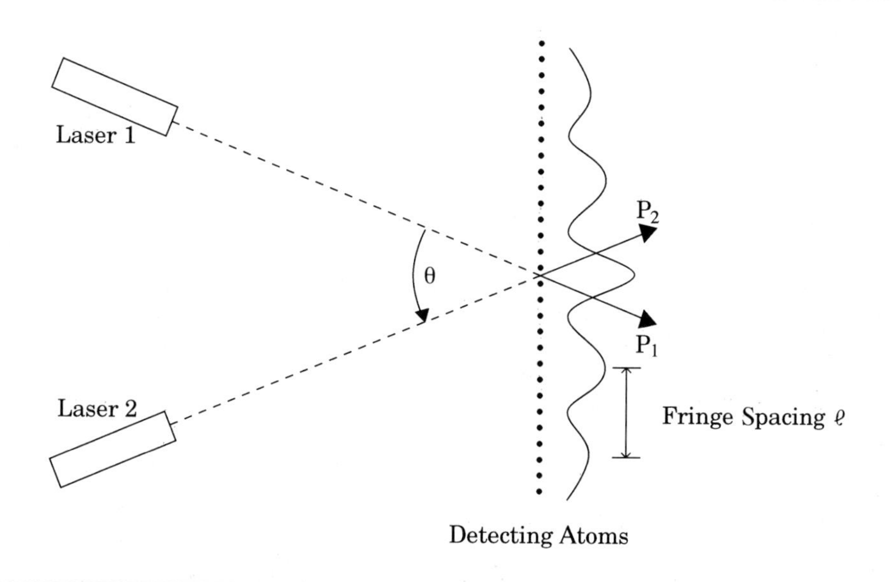

Figure 3–3 *The Pfleegor–Mandel Experiment,* illustrating the role played by the uncertainty principle in its analysis.

are impossible. As we will now show, the required accuracy is greater than that allowed by the uncertainty principle.

In order to detect the fringe spacing, the spatial uncertainty in the measured position of an atom, Δx, must be less than ℓ, the fringe separation. One can easily show that the fringe spacing is given by the ratio of the wavelength to the angle of convergence: $\ell = \lambda/\theta$. Seeing fringes therefore requires us to measure the atom's position to an uncertainty $\Delta x \ll \lambda/\theta$. If this is done, then Heisenberg's uncertainty relation requires the uncertainty in the x-component of the atom's momentum to be

$$\Delta p_x \gg \hbar\theta/2\lambda \tag{3.7}$$

where λ is the wavelength of the photon produced by the lasers. But by the de Broglie relation, $P_{\text{gamma}} = h/\lambda$ is the photon momentum, which equals that transferred to the atom P_{atom}. So Equation (3.7) implies

$$\Delta p_x \gg \theta P_{\text{atom}}/4\pi \tag{3.8}$$

From Figure 3–3, however, the x-component of an atom's recoil momentum from a single photon is

$$P_x = P_{\text{atom}}\theta/2 \tag{3.9}$$

Comparing Equations (3.8) and (3.9) and noting that the inequality in Equation (3.8) is a strong one, we reach our essential conclusion: *the uncertainty in P_x is greater than P_x itself.* Thus, the momentum uncertainty is enough to rule out any possibility of identifying which laser a given photon has come from.

We repeat the point we made earlier: that this inability arises for fundamental reasons, rather than being merely a matter of poor experimental design. The uncertainty principle is completely general, and it ensures that no alternative strategy for simultaneously determining position and momentum will fare any better than the gamma-ray microscope. So long as we retain the interference pattern, no conceivable experiment will ever be capable of determining the origin of a photon. Under such circumstances, quantum mechanics does not even carry within it the notion of each photon's being produced in a particular laser in the Pfleegor–Mandel experiment.

3.2 Reflections on the Uncertainty Principle

Quantum Uncertainty versus Classical Ignorance We may make the above conclusion more vivid by means of the following analogy. Replace the two lasers in the Pfleegor–Mandel experiment by two rifles, and assume that while a shell has been loaded into each, one of them is a blank. The two guns are fired simultaneously, and a single bullet strikes the screen. The experiment is repeated many times, and the distribution of bullet holes along the screen is observed.

The result will be that the pattern is exactly what one expects from classical reasoning: the sum of the patterns for the two guns, each fired alone. In particular, an interference pattern will not be observed. But in the Pfleegor–Mandel experiment, it was.

The distinction between the experiment with rifles and the experiment with photons is the distinction between two entirely different concepts: *classical ignorance* and *quantum uncertainty.* Classical ignorance is the perfectly normal state of being unsure about things. We are in a state of classical ignorance when we do not recall today's date, or when we are unsure of someone's name—or when we do not know from which of two rifles a bullet emerged. But although we may not know these facts, we are sure that the facts exist: today does indeed have a date, people do possess names, and a single bullet can only be fired from a single rifle. Classical ignorance can be expressed as follows: *the world has a well-defined state, but we do not happen to know what it is.*

But *this is not what we mean by quantum uncertainty. In quantum uncertainty, it is no longer the case that the world possesses a definite classical state.* Even particles with a well-defined quantum state do not possess trajectories, and they are perfectly capable of passing through more than one slit at the same time. They are even capable of being co-produced by two lasers. (A crucial question, of course, is whether such a quantum state captures all the physical properties of a system, or whether, alternatively, the quantum description is incomplete. We have already asked this question, and we will take it up in detail in Chapter 5.)

We emphasize that this dichotomy between quantum uncertainty and classical ignorance is no abstract distinction. It has a perfectly clear experimental signature: the appearance and disappearance of an interference pattern in the experimental results. Recall that, as we have seen in Chapters 1 and 2, the appearance of an interference pattern is usually taken to be the signal that a single quantum has traveled along two different paths.

Interpretation of the Uncertainty Principle The uncertainty principle is of fundamental importance for physics, and it will continually resurface throughout the remainder of this book. In our continuing explorations of its significance, two themes will emerge:

(a) Recall that in Chapter 1, we discussed the inability of quantum theory to describe what is going on in the double-slit experiment. We described two attitudes toward this inability. One school of thought, led by Bohr, regarded it as a virtue of quantum mechanics. Another school, most notably exemplified by Einstein, regarded it as a defect. The same is true of the limitations imposed by the uncertainty principle. Throughout his career, Einstein argued that the principle pointed to a profound *incompleteness* in quantum theory. He and others longed to truly know the world, and they sought strategies to circumvent the uncertainty principle in order to complete the partial picture given by quantum theory. While none of their efforts turned out to be successful, they have proved extraordinarily fruitful in deepening our understanding of quantum mechanics. We will return to them often in coming chapters.

(b) Even if we accept the uncertainty principle as unavoidable, two different interpretations of it seem possible. On the one hand, we can imagine that uncertainty arises because the quantum world simply does not have a well-defined state. Alternatively, we might imagine that such a state does indeed exist, but that we are forever prevented from learning about it. The Heisenberg uncertainty microscope might seem to support the second interpretation, involving as it does a disturbance of a previously existing state. However, it is important to note that the formal treatments whereby the uncertainty relation is derived from operator algebra contain no trace of this kind of reasoning. This is an issue we will return to in Chapter 5, on the EPR paradox and Bell's theorem.

The Uncertainty Principle and Causality The Pfleegor–Mandel experiment clearly violates our commonsense notion of causality. Light is normally produced—i.e., caused—by some kind of process in a device. Yet in this experiment an ambiguity arises as to which source emitted the photon, an ambiguity due not to classical ignorance, but to the very nature of the experiment itself. This essential ambiguity means that we are also uncertain about the explanation for physical events. This issue of causality is sufficiently important to merit closer attention.

In 1812 Pierre-Simon de Laplace wrote of an all-seeing "Intelligence" that could know "the positions of all things of which the world consists." Because classical physics embraced the principle of strict determinism, the present state of the world, he argued, would lead through an inexorable chain of cause and effect to its future state. "Nothing would be uncertain for this Intelligence," he wrote. "The past and the future would be present to its eyes."[3]

Standing behind this passage is the classical concept of causality: the notion that the universe rigorously obeys laws, and everything that happens does so for a reason. Classical physics postulates an objectively real universe, possessing objectively real properties evolving in perfect accord with the laws of nature. Measurement is capable, in principle at least, of determining these properties instant by instant to whatever accuracy we wish. No one has ever claimed that it was possible in practice to attain complete information with perfect accuracy through measurement. But no one needed to make this claim; Laplace's argument was one of principle, and the principle was strict determinism. The world was completely knowable, and it evolved according to laws.

The advent of quantum mechanics called determinism into question. Before detailing the issues raised by quantum mechanics, we must further clarify exactly what we mean by causality and determinism as they applied to classical physics.

In the universe according to Laplace, atoms moved through a void, interacting with each other by means of physical forces. At any given moment, nothing prevented his sublime Intelligence from knowing the positions and momenta of each and every particle in the universe. Taking this as an initial state of the universe, and using the laws of physics together with a knowledge of the forces between particles, Laplace's Intelligence could determine both the entire future and past of the universe. With these three pieces of information—initial conditions, forces of interaction and the laws of physics—everything was determined.

But quantum theory demands a reconsideration of this framework, and with it a reworking of our ideas concerning causality and determinism. This arises because Heisenberg's uncertainty principle limits our knowledge of the world. As we have seen, this is not merely a practical limitation, but one tied to the quantum-mechanical nature of interactions and, therefore, is unavoidable and uncorrectable. Thus, even if we possessed a fully deterministic set of physical laws, the initial conditions required for the most mundane calculation would always be uncertain. All prediction or retrodiction would thereby be limited because of this initial uncertainty.

Laplace's Intelligence would try in vain to gain complete knowledge of the present situation, and so would be prevented from knowing past and future.

In 1927, while under the influence of Bohr's thinking, Werner Heisenberg put it this way:

> Using the sharp formulation of the law of causality, "If we know the present exactly, we can predict the future," it is not the conclusion but rather the presupposition that is false. In principle, we can not know the present in full. Therefore, all observation is a selection from a complete domain of possibilities, and a limitation of future possibilities. Since the statistical character of the quantum theory is so tightly bound to the uncertainty of all observation, one could be led to the supposition that hidden behind the sense-perceptible, statistical world there is a "real world" in which causal law is valid. But we would like to say explicitly, such speculations appear to us unfruitful and senseless. Physics should only describe the formal relationship between observations. One can truly characterize the situation in the following way: In as much as all experiments are subject to the laws of quantum mechanics, through quantum mechanics the invalidity of the law of causation is definitively established.[4]

The Uncertainty Principle and Descriptions of Natural Phenomena If we accept Heisenberg's extreme position, then our understanding of physical process changes dramatically. The uncertainty principle prevents us from giving a complete description of the behavior of the world. To illustrate what we mean, we consider an example pertaining to the operation of a nuclear reactor.

A considerable fraction of the electrical power generated today derives from nuclear reactors employing U-235 as fissionable material. In such reactors, uranium nuclei are induced to fission by the absorption of a neutron. Upon fissioning, each nucleus itself releases other neutrons that are absorbed by other nuclei, so maintaining a chain reaction. A difficulty is that the emitted nuclei are of relatively high energy, and the cross section for nuclei to absorb neutrons is relatively small at these energies. Thus such reactors slow the emitted neutrons by means of a so-called moderator, until they reach energies on the order of thermal energies, where their probability of being absorbed and maintaining the chain reaction is relatively large.

The mean energy of each neutron, after it has been slowed to thermal energies by the moderator, is given by $E_{\text{mean}} = (3/2)kT$, where k is Boltzmann's constant and T is the temperature. This works out to about 6.3×10^{-21} J at room temperature. At this energy, the neutron momentum is

$$p_{\text{mean}} = \sqrt{2mE_{\text{mean}}} \tag{3.10}$$

and, by the uncertainty principle, its position cannot be specified more accurately than

$$\Delta x = \frac{\hbar}{2\Delta p_x} = \frac{\hbar}{2p_{\text{mean}}} = 1.1 \times 10^{-11}\,\text{m} \tag{3.11}$$

But if the reactor material is pure U-235, the cross section at these energies for absorption of such a neutron is about $5.5 \times 10^{-26}\,\text{m}^2$. This corresponds to the nucleus acting as if it had a radius given by

$$\begin{aligned} \pi r^2 &= \sigma \\ r &= \sqrt{\frac{\sigma}{\pi}} = 1.3 \times 10^{-13}\,\text{m} \end{aligned} \tag{3.12}$$

We see that the uncertainty in position of the neutron is one hundred times greater than the size of the nucleus it strikes.

This has great relevance for our attempt to comprehend the operation of the reactor. Classically, it is possible to follow in the mind's eye the passage of events within the reactor. We can imagine each individual neutron striking its nucleus, each nucleus fissioning and emitting other neutrons, which themselves move in definite paths through space till, by chance, they strike other nuclei. In this way we can imagine a movie, which shows in detail the actual sequence of events within the reactor.

But according to quantum mechanics, such a movie cannot exist. The uncertainty principle forbids it. Thus we find ourselves entirely unable to visualize the operation of a nuclear reactor. We have already encountered a similar situation before. We emphasized in Chapter 1 that the quantum-mechanical account of electron interference simply evades the problem of describing the particle's passage through two slits at once. Here we encounter the same circumstance, but now in a guise intimately connected with the uncertainty principle. Furthermore, the reader will find this circumstance recurring again and again throughout this book, and often for yet other reasons. This impossibility of visualizing its behavior is, in fact, a general element of the quantum world.

3.3 Some Consequences of the Uncertainty Principle

The uncertainty principle was revolutionary when first proposed, and its importance has only grown with the passage of time. While revolutionizing our conceptual understanding of physics, it also solved certain problems that had, until its discovery, been deeply perplexing. The range and diversity of such applications are quite remarkable.

Atoms So fundamental a property of the physical world as the very existence of atoms is related to the uncertainty principle. It was widely recognized in the early decades of this century that, according to classical physics, atoms should not exist. Rutherford had proposed in 1911 that an atom consisted of a small, dense nucleus about which electrons orbited. Subsequent experiments established the basic validity of this model. The problem was, however, that according to classical electromagnetic theory, these orbiting electrons should continually emit electromagnetic waves, lose energy, and therefore spiral inward into the nucleus. Calculations revealed that the electrons would be expected to hit the nucleus and be absorbed into it in an exceedingly short time.

The modern quantum theory of electromagnetism shows what was wrong with this argument, and it explains why electrons in an atom do not spiral inward in reality. Unfortunately this theory is beyond the scope of this book. On the other hand, it is easy to see that such a spiraling, if it occurred, would be inconsistent with the uncertainty principle. For imagine that it had taken place, and that the atom, as predicted by classical physics, had shrunk to a point. We would then have to say that each electron in the atom was confined to a region of space Δx of quite literally zero size. By the uncertainty principle, then, the electrons' momenta would have to be infinite, which is absurd.

We can extend the argument and attempt to learn something about the characteristic magnitude of atomic energies by using the uncertainty principle in conjunction with the measured sizes of atoms. To say that an atom has radius r is to say that each electron within it is confined to a region of size $\Delta x = 2r$. By the uncertainty principle, its momentum therefore can be no less than $p_{\text{min}} = \hbar/4r$. Its kinetic energy, therefore, can be no less than

$$KE_{\text{min}} = p_{\text{min}}^2/2m = \hbar^2/32mr^2 \tag{3.13}$$

For an atom, a typical size would be a few Bohr radii. If we adopt $r = 10^{-10}$ m (about two Bohr radii), we obtain $KE = 4 \times 10^{-20}$ J, or about 0.2 eV. For comparison, the binding energy of an electron in hydrogen is 13.6 eV.

We can go further and actually use the uncertainty principle to attempt to *predict* the typical size of an atom. Consider an electron at a distance r from a nucleus of charge Ze. The electron, moving in a circle with velocity v, experiences a centripetal acceleration of magnitude $a = v^2/r$. This is provided by the force of electrostatic attraction, which by Coulomb's law is Ze^2/r^2. Newton's second law, $F = ma$, reads then

$$\frac{Ze^2}{r^2} = \frac{mv^2}{r} \tag{3.14}$$

so that the kinetic energy is

$$\tfrac{1}{2}mv^2 = \frac{Ze^2}{2r} \tag{3.15}$$

If we combine this with Equation (3.13), we obtain

$$\frac{Ze^2}{2r} \geq \frac{\hbar^2}{32\,mr^2} \tag{3.16}$$

so that

$$r \geq \frac{\hbar^2}{16\,Ze^2m} = \frac{1}{16\,Z}\ \text{Bohr radii} \tag{3.17}$$

is an estimate of the typical size of an atom. For comparison, the root-mean-square radius of the $1s$ state of hydrogen in reality is 5.48 Bohr radii.

We conclude that the uncertainty principle is very useful in getting a crude idea of the order of magnitudes of atomic properties, but that the specific numerical values obtained by it are not to be trusted.

Nuclei A similar analysis can be carried out of the typical energies associated with nuclear processes. We possess no simple formula, analogous to Coulomb's law, describing the force between neutrons and protons in an atomic nucleus. But we can use the measured size of a nucleus, in conjunction with Equation (3.12). Taking $r = 10^{-15}$ m and m the mass of a nucleon, we find energies on the order of an MeV.

We note in passing that this is a far from academic exercise. The energy we have obtained, which is the typical energy obtainable from nuclear reactions, is some five *million* times greater than our earlier estimate of the typical energy of an electron in an atom, which is the typical energy obtainable from chemical reactions. This is the origin of the terrible destructiveness of nuclear, as opposed to conventional, weapons.

Trajectories The uncertainty principle prevents us from observing the trajectory of an electron as it orbits about the nucleus in an atom. As before, we imagine shining a beam of light on the electron and detecting the scattered photons. Classical optics tells us that the wavelength of the light λ must be far less than the radius of the atom r if we wish to resolve the electron's trajectory. But in this case, the momentum of the photons, $p_{\text{light}} = h/\lambda$, greatly exceeds the momentum of the electron that we get from the uncertainty principle, $p_{\text{electron}} = \hbar/4r$. Thus the electron, as it scatters off the photons, suffers a violent recoil that totally disrupts its motion. We conclude that the attempt to observe the electron's trajectory violently disrupts it. Indeed, it is easy to show that the recoil is actually sufficient to ionize the atom.

A precisely similar argument also forbids us from observing the trajectories of the neutrons and protons within a nucleus. Indeed, the argument can be stated quite generally. Quantum mechanics prevents us from observing the orbit of *any* particle confined to *any* region of space, just so long as its momentum does not greatly exceed the minimum value set by the uncertainty principle. The concept of a trajectory includes two more fundamental concepts: that of position and that of the rate of change of position—the velocity, or p/m. The uncertainty principle connects these two. The precise specification of a trajectory depends upon the simultaneous specification of both position and momentum, and this is forbidden. Thus the very idea of a particle's exact path through space loses a well-defined meaning. Quantum theory radically alters the way we must think about the world, for in classical physics we are, of course, accustomed to thinking of the trajectories of objects through space.

This circumstance has an intimate relationship to the conundrum we posed in Chapter 1, in our discussion of the interference of material particles. In that chapter we emphasized that the phenomenon was completely impossible to comprehend in any normal sense of the word. It is worth pointing out that the phenomenon is so striking precisely *because* we find ourselves unable to conceive of a trajectory that passes through two slits at once. Our difficulty in accounting for the interference of particles arose because we had been unconsciously assuming that the classical concept of trajectory applies to them. The Pfleegor–Mandel experiment emphasizes the problem still further.

3.4 The Energy–Time Uncertainty Relation

The Heisenberg uncertainty relation is but one of many uncertainty relations. We now proceed to discuss a second. Just as there is a trade-off in the accuracies with which position and momentum can be measured, so, too, with energy and time. The uncertainty relation connecting the two is

$$\Delta E \, \Delta t \geq \hbar \tag{3.18}$$

We will discuss three instances of the use of this relationship. As our analysis proceeds, it will become evident that it differs considerably from the first.

Average Properties of Systems We begin by showing that *if the energy of a system is not precisely defined, but rather possesses an uncertainty ΔE, then its average properties will change in a time given by the energy–time uncertainty relation.*

The average value of any observed property of a system is its *expectation value*:

$$\langle O \rangle \equiv \int \psi^* \tilde{O} \psi \, d^3r \tag{3.19}$$

where $\tilde{O}$ is the operator corresponding to the observable and ψ is the wave function. What is this wave function? To say that the energy of a system is well-defined is to say that ψ is an eigenstate of the energy operator (the Hamiltonian). Conversely, if the energy is not well-defined, ψ must be a superposition. Consider the simple case in which the system is in a superposition of two states of energies E_1 and E_2. Recalling that for conservative systems, the time evolution of the wave function is always through the factor $\exp(-iEt/\hbar)$, we see that this superposition will be of the form

$$\psi = a_1\psi_1(x)\, e^{-iE_1t/\hbar} + a_2\psi_2(x)\, e^{-iE_2t/\hbar} \tag{3.20}$$

where $\psi_1(x)$ and $\psi_2(x)$ are the two eigenfunctions and a_1 and a_2 are the coefficients of the two terms in the superposition. It is easy to show that if Equation (3.20) is used in Equation (3.19), $\langle O \rangle$ will fluctuate in time with a period $t = h/(E_1 - E_2)$.

Rather than working out the general case, we will discuss the specific problem of determining the *radius of an atom* when the atom is in the superposition state (3.20). This radius is given by

$$r = \sqrt{\langle r^2 \rangle} \tag{3.21}$$

The expectation value of the radius squared is

$$\langle r^2 \rangle = \int \left[a_1^*\psi_1^*\, e^{+iE_1t/\hbar} + a_2^*\psi_2^*\, e^{+iE_2t/\hbar}\right] r^2 \left[a_1\psi_1\, e^{-iE_1t/\hbar} + a_2\psi_2\, e^{-iE_2t/\hbar}\right] d^3r$$

$$\langle r^2 \rangle = \int a_1^2\psi_1^2 r^2\, d^3r + \int a_2^2\psi_2^2 r^2\, d^3r + \int a_1 a_2^*\psi_2^* r^2 \psi_1\, e^{-i[E_1 - E_2]t/\hbar}\, d^3r$$

$$+ \int a_1^* a_2 \psi_1^* r^2 \psi_2\, e^{+i[E_1 - E_2]t/\hbar}\, d^3r \tag{3.22}$$

The first term in this expression has a simple physical meaning. It is what we would have obtained had the atom been in the eigenstate of energy E_1—and notice that this term is independent of the time. So, too, with the second term. But the third and fourth terms are not independent of the time; each of them varies with time as

$$e^{\pm i(E_2 - E_1)t/\hbar} \tag{3.23}$$

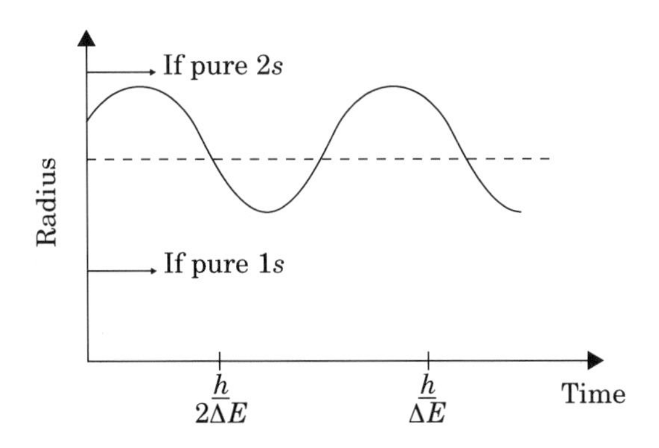

Figure 3–4 *Energy–Time Uncertainty.* If the energy of an atom is uncertain, its size varies over a time given by the energy–time uncertainty relation.

As an illustration, Figure 3–4 graphs $\sqrt{\langle r^2 \rangle}$ for a superposition consisting of a 50–50 mixture of the ground and first excited states (1*s* and 2*s*) of the hydrogen atom. It can be seen that the atom "breathes" in and out, expanding and contracting over a time scale of order $\Delta t = h/\Delta E$.

Although we have derived this result for a particular example, the result is, in fact, quite general. For times short relative to $\Delta t = h/\Delta E$, measured properties of a system will change little. But for times long relative to Δt, they change significantly. Thus, the rate of change of an observable is set by the uncertainty in its energy.

Lifetimes and Line Widths The excited state of an atom decays with time. So, too, does the excited state of a radioactive atomic nucleus. *If the lifetime of such a state is Δt, it can be shown that the energy of the excited state is uncertain by $\Delta E = \hbar/\Delta t$.* Since the frequency of the photon emitted in the decay is $\nu = E/h$, this implies that the spectral line produced by the transition is not perfectly sharp, but rather possesses a finite width. The width is inversely proportional to the lifetime: long lifetimes correspond to narrow widths, short lifetimes to broad widths.

As an example, the 21-cm spectral line of hydrogen has proved to be of great importance in radio astronomy. This line corresponds to a transition in which the spin of the electron goes from being parallel to antiparallel to that of the proton. The lifetime of the excited parallel state is exceedingly long, some 12 million years. As a consequence, the wavelength of the 21-cm spectral line is exceedingly sharply defined: the half-width of the line is 5×10^{-16} Hz. Therefore, minute changes in this wavelength, arising from motions of the source via the Doppler effect, can readily be detected. Radio astronomers regularly use this technique to observe velocities of interstellar hydrogen clouds to a high accuracy.

At the other extreme, certain elementary particles are known, termed resonance particles, whose decays are extraordinarily rapid. As a consequence, the energies of these particles are very uncertain. This implies that their masses do not possess well-defined values, but rather exhibit a certain range

$$\Delta m = \Delta E/c^2 = \hbar/\tau c^2 \tag{3.24}$$

where τ is the lifetime. As an example, the rho meson decays in an astonishingly brief 4.4×10^{-24} s. Its mass–energy, therefore, is uncertain by 150 MeV; this uncertainty amounts to fully 19% of its mass.

Time and Frequency Standards It can be shown that *if a time Δt is required to measure the energy of a system, the result will be uncertain by an amount given by the energy–time uncertainty relation.* This result has important practical applications in optical spectroscopy, particularly atomic clocks and international frequency standards.

Time and frequency standards make use of a very stable, precise energy splitting between two atomic energy levels. Present-day experiments proceed by illuminating an atom with precisely tuned light from a laser. The light's frequency is gradually shifted until the light is absorbed; by measuring the frequency at which this occurs, one can determine the ΔE of the transition.

What sets the limits to the accuracy of such a procedure? If the experiment lasts a time Δt, it will measure the energy separating two states of an atom to within an accuracy ΔE given by the uncertainty relation. But Δt is often limited by so-called "transit-time broadening." Imagine an atom drifting with velocity v through a laser beam of diameter d (see Figure 3–5). It will spend a time $t = d/v$ in the laser beam. This transit time will limit the energy resolution to $\Delta E = \hbar v/d$. Therefore, even if the atomic line width were infinitely narrow, our measurement of it would be limited by the finite transit time and it would be broadened.

Various clever strategies have been developed over the years to increase the transit time, but clearly the best idea would be to work with stationary atoms. Getting an atom to hold still, however, is something of a trick. At room temperature, atoms possess about 0.04 eV of energy, implying an average velocity on the order of a kilometer per second. In an experimental *tour de force*, Steven Chu of Stanford University and collaborators attained unparalleled precision by using laser techniques to decelerate and then trap sodium atoms. Finally, they used a laser pulse to toss the atoms gently upwards in an "atomic fountain."[5] As shown in Figure 3–6, the Na atoms rose and then fell back in the earth's gravitational field, moving extremely slowly. Because the atoms moved so slowly, transit-time broadening was reduced enormously, leading to the world's most precise measurement of the energy difference between two levels: a frequency splitting of 1 771 626 129.2 Hz.

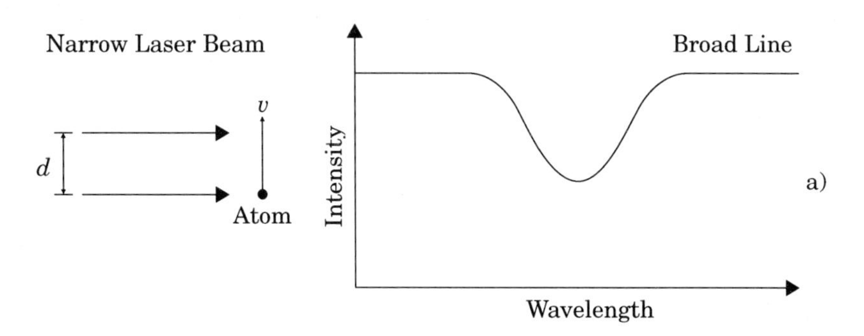

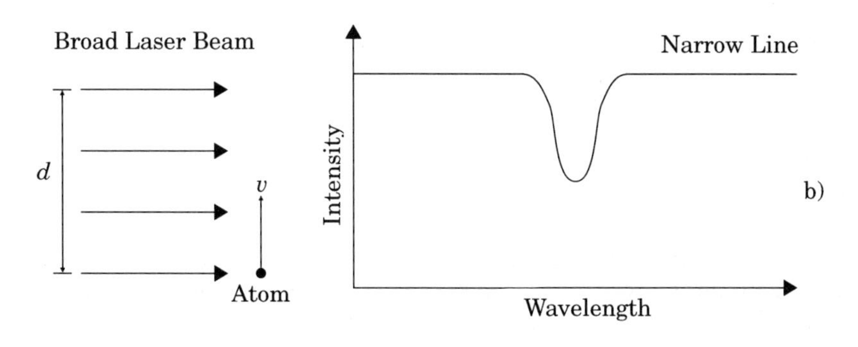

Figure 3–5 *Transit-Time Broadening.* An atom of velocity v drifts through a laser beam of width d. If (a) the beam is narrow, the atom is illuminated by it for a short time and its spectral line will be broad. Conversely, if (b) the beam is wide, the spectral line will be correspondingly narrower.

More on Causality: The Uncertainty Principle and an Ambiguity in Time We have seen that in interference experiments, the uncertainty principle prevents us from learning which slit a quantum passed through. In the Pfleegor–Mandel experiment, it prevents us from learning which laser produced a photon. Similarly, in certain situations the energy–time uncertainty relationship prevents us from finding out whether an effect comes after or before its cause.

Compton scattering is a process in which an x-ray photon scatters from a free electron, with a concomitant shift in the photon's frequency. We may schematically diagram the phenomenon as in Figure 3–7.

Prior to the interaction, we have a photon in the momentum state k and an electron in an initial state i; after the scattering event, the photon is in a

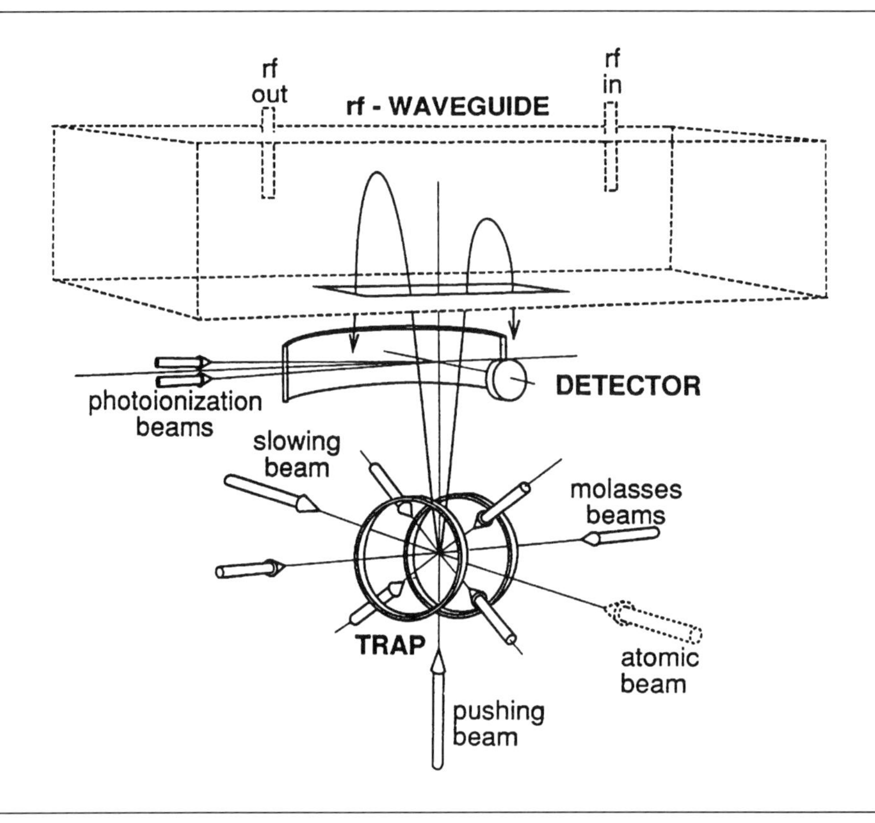

Figure 3–6 *Atomic Fountain.* Atoms are slowed in a trap, and then gently pushed upward into a waveguide where a transition is excited. They then fall back downward, where they are photoionized and then electrostatically focused by a curved metal shield into a detector. SOURCE: Reproduced with permission from M.A. Kasevich, E. Riis, S. Chu and R.G. DeVoe, "Rf spectroscopy in an atomic fountain," *Phys. Rev. Lett.*, vol. 63, p. 612 (1989), published by The American Physical Society.

new momentum state k' and the electron is in state f. When evaluated carefully, it turns out that two distinct Feynman diagrams contribute significantly to Compton scattering; as usual, they must be added and then squared to determine the probability. The first diagram corresponds to a process in which the photon is briefly absorbed by the electron to create a short-lived intermediate state, and then a photon is emitted. Diagrammatically, this can be represented as in Figure 3–8(a).

Nothing is peculiar about this. The photon is in a microscopic ball game in which it is caught, held briefly, and then thrown. The second Feynman diagram, however, cannot be understood so simply [Figure 3–8(b)].

Here the initial and final states are exactly as before, but the intermediate state is quite different. In this case, *first the final photon is*

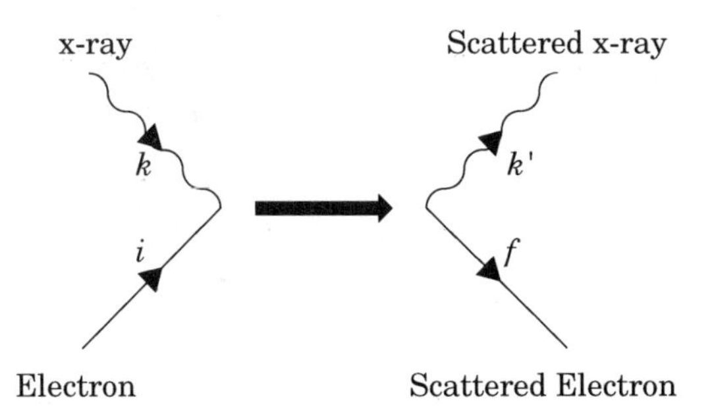

Figure 3–7 *Compton Scattering.* A photon of momentum k scatters against an electron of momentum i, changing the photon's momentum to k' and the electron's momentum to f.

emitted, and only later is the initial photon absorbed. No ball game we know of has the player throw the ball before catching it. If interpreted literally, the process represented by this second diagram says precisely this, and so does violence to our ideas of a well-running, causally ordered universe.

We might ask if we really need the perverse second quantum amplitude? The answer turns out to be a clear "yes." One can calculate the cross section for Compton scattering in two ways: first by using only the straightforward first Feynman diagram of Figure 3–8(a), and second by using both. The result is that the two calculations differ significantly from each other. Furthermore, experiment has clearly shown that the second calculation agrees with the data and the first does not. We conclude that the Feynman diagram of Figure 3–8(b), in which the normal flow of time is scrambled, must be included in the analysis.

It turns out, however, that we can never catch the scattering in its "time-scrambled" state. We now show that to do this would require us to make a measurement in a time shorter than that allowed by the uncertainty principle.

To be concrete, let the incoming photon be an x-ray with an energy of 100 keV. The Compton shift is given by the formula

$$\Delta\lambda = \lambda' - \lambda = \frac{\hbar}{mc}[1 - \cos\theta]$$

or

$$\Delta E = \frac{E^2}{mc^2}[1 - \cos\theta] \tag{3.25}$$

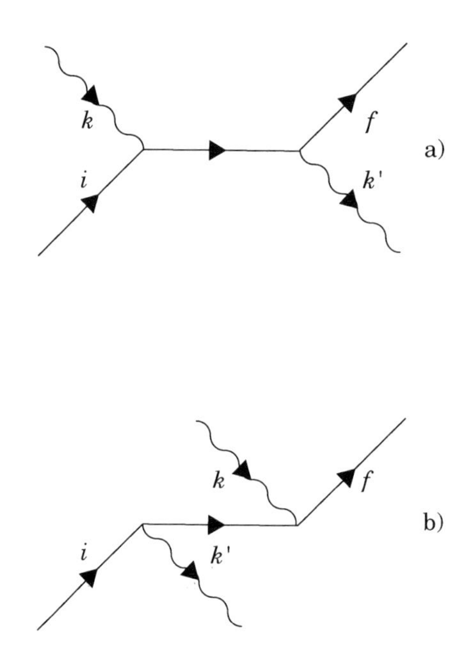

Figure 3–8 *The Two Feynman Diagrams Describing Compton Scattering.* Both (a) and the "time-scrambled" diagram (b) must be included in the calculation.

ΔE has a maximum, for $\theta = \pi$, of 40 keV. Therefore, to be able to distinguish between incoming and outgoing photons, we need an experimental energy resolution of better than 40 keV. By the uncertainty principle, the experiment must therefore last longer than

$$\Delta t = \hbar/40\,\text{keV} = 1.7 \times 10^{-20}\,\text{s} \tag{3.26}$$

If the intermediate state in the two Feynman diagrams lasted for a time shorter than this, the experiment would not be able to distinguish between the two; we would not be able to say whether the emission was before or after the absorption.

While 1.7×10^{-20} s seems a very short time, it is not short enough. The second Feynman diagram [Figure 3–8(b)] violates energy conservation. This is not a problem as long as the violation lasts an exceedingly short time, because the resultant energy uncertainty will then be sufficient to mask the violation. In this case the energy violation is 100 keV, which, from the uncertainty principle, corresponds to a maximum lifetime for the intermediate state of 6.6×10^{-21} s. This is 2.5 times *shorter* than the required duration of the measurement as given by Equation (3.26) above.

Thus, while we can distinguish the incoming from the outgoing x-ray photons by their energy shifts, we cannot tell whether the outgoing photon originated from a normal process or one in which the ordering of cause and effect is reversed. As before, the uncertainty principle has masked what happened. In this case, however, the two possible sequences of events differ in their ordering in time; the one perfectly classical, and the other entirely incomprehensible in classical terms. Although the second process does violence to the concept of causality, its existence is hidden by the uncertainty principle.*

Comments on the Energy–Time Uncertainty Relation These examples clearly differ in their "feel" from Heisenberg's uncertainty microscope. In contrast to it, they provide us with no visualizable mechanisms or disturbances whereby the energy–time uncertainty relation comes about. Moreover, this relation cannot be derived from the formalism of quantum mechanics in the same manner as the position–momentum relation. The position–momentum uncertainty relation can be derived from the commutators of two operators. The energy–time relation cannot be so derived, however, for in quantum mechanics time is a parameter, not an operator. Nevertheless, in its practical applications, this new principle can be used in much the same way as the more familiar one.

3.5 Squeezed Light and the Detection of Gravitational Radiation

Up to this point, our discussion has primarily focused on relatively well-known consequences of the uncertainty principle. In recent research, however, the principle has emerged in new and unexpected ways. We now turn to a description of some of this current work. We begin with a topic from astrophysics: present-day attempts to detect gravitational radiation.

Gravitational radiation, predicted by the General Theory of Relativity, is an extraordinarily elusive form of radiation. In spite of intense efforts by many strong research groups over decades, its direct detection remains beyond our reach at the time of this writing. Detectors have improved enormously in recent years. Until now, the limitations on their operation have been classical in origin: thermal noise, acoustic vibrations, and the like. One by one, these limitations are being overcome by such strategies as cooling the detectors to near absolute zero, or by levitating them in

---

* A caveat: One needs to be very careful about interpreting Feynman diagrams too literally. While these diagrams taken together make up the quantum calculation, it is much less clear that each individual diagram always has a sensible meaning.

magnetic fields. But so minuscule are the effects of gravitational radiation, that in order to detect it, experiments will ultimately run up against the limits set by the uncertainty principle. And in contrast to the former, these limits will never be overcome, for they are set by fundamental physical principles. In recent years, however, methods have been proposed for performing measurements that neatly evade what one might suppose the quantum limits to be.

Notable among these methods are squeezed states and quantum non-demolition measurements. We turn here to the subject of squeezed light, deferring until the next section non-demolition techniques. First we will briefly discuss gravitational radiation, and then the squeezed states of the simple harmonic oscillator, before finally passing on to squeezed light.

Gravitational Radiation Gravitational radiation bears a strong resemblance to electromagnetic radiation. Electromagnetic waves are produced by accelerating charges; gravitational waves are produced by accelerating masses. Conversely, an electromagnetic wave is detected by monitoring its effect on charges—charges in, for instance, an antenna. The passage of an electromagnetic wave sets the charges in the antenna in motion, and the resulting flow constitutes an electric current that is amplified and detected. Similarly, the passage of a gravitational wave sets mass into motion.

The most significant difference between the two forms of radiation lies in their strengths. In the laboratory, electromagnetic radiation is incomparably more intense than gravitational radiation. Electrons, for instance, possess both charge and mass, so that they emit both forms of radiation when accelerated. But the electromagnetic radiation carries something of the order of 10^{43} times more power than the gravitational radiation.

This gravitational wave power turns out to depend on the square of the mass of the emitter. So if the emitter is very massive, the gravitational emission will be much more intense. This implies that gravitational radiation will be significant in the astronomical context, in which the emitters are massive objects such as stars. For instance, when a star reaches the end of its nuclear-burning lifetime and collapses inward to form a black hole, something like 10^{46} J of gravitational energy can be produced.

The detection of even such a strong burst of gravitational radiation is, nevertheless, extraordinarily difficult. Indeed, the effort to detect gravitational radiation is one of the most ambitious projects underway in astrophysics today.

Gravitational wave detectors are of two types. The early detectors were metal bars, with masses ranging up to tens of tons, which would be set into vibration by a passing gravitational wave. The motion, however, was extraordinarily minute. The amplitude of the vibration set up in a bar detector by a burst of gravitational radiation from a nearby collapsing star, for instance, is a mere 10^{-21} m. This is a hundred-billionth the size of a single atom! A second strategy involves optical interferometry.[6] LIGO, the proposed Laser Interferometer Gravitational-wave Observatory, will be a Michelson interferometer with each mirror replaced by a 4-km-long Fabry–Perot optical cavity. Figure 3–9 gives a schematic view. Laser

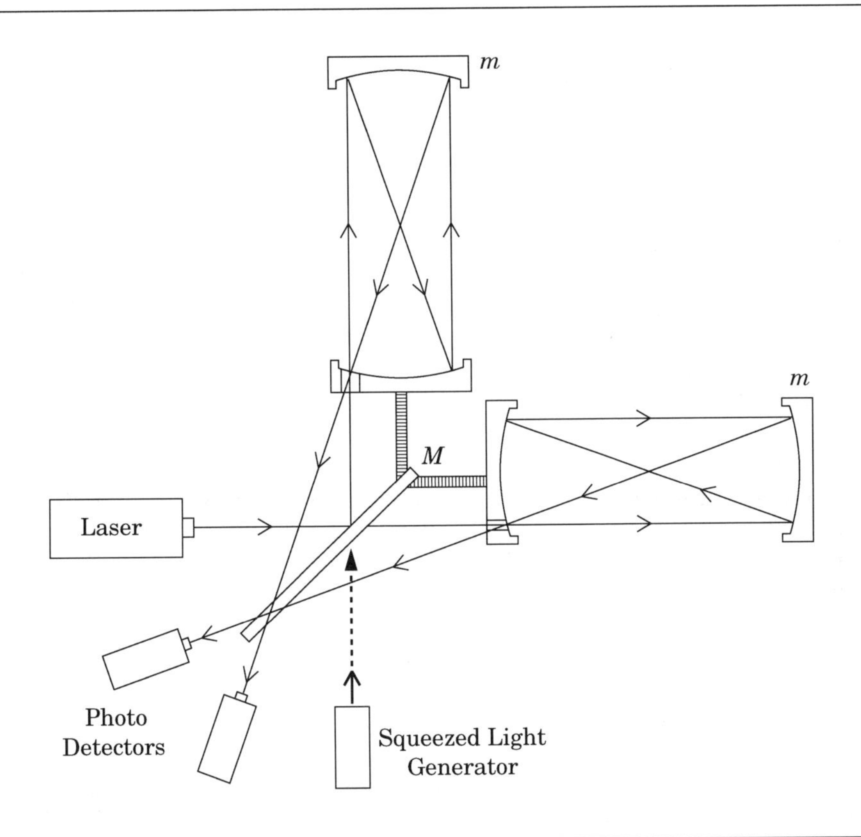

Figure 3–9 *LIGO, the Proposed Laser Interferometer Gravitational-wave Observatory.* Laser light is split at a beam splitter and enters the two arms of the interferometer. There it bounces back and forth a number of times, ultimately exiting and being recombined at the beam splitter and directed to photodetectors. The end mirrors are attached to large masses m, and the beam splitter and inner mirrors are attached to even larger masses M. A passing gravitational wave causes these masses to oscillate, thus changing the relative phases of the two arms. Squeezed light, which is injected into the interferometer via a second entry port, has been proposed as a method for improving the operation of the interferometer.

interferometric techniques will be used to detect differences in the lengths of the two cavities, induced by gravitational waves.

In order to observe such vibrations, one needs to measure the position of one of the ends of the detector. The uncertainty principle restricts the accuracy with which this can be done. Note in this regard that the Heisenberg uncertainty relation is an inequality: the product of uncertainties in position and momentum must be greater than or equal to $\hbar/2$. States for which the equality holds, that is: $\Delta x \, \Delta p = \hbar/2$, are called "minimum-uncertainty states": these are clearly the states one wishes to work with.

Note also that the uncertainty relation places no constraints whatsoever on the individual uncertainties, but only on their product. To detect gravitational radiation, we would be willing to sacrifice knowledge of one observable for more accurate knowledge of its complement. This is perfectly permissible from the standpoint of the uncertainty principle; the problem is rather to successfully produce a state with required properties. Squeezed states are a means of accomplishing this. (For a general introduction to squeezed states, see Henry and Glotzer.[7])

Squeezed States of the Simple Harmonic Oscillator In 1981, Carleton Caves showed[8] that, if squeezed light were used rather than light in a more normal state, the operation of an instrument such as LIGO could be greatly improved. In preparation for our study of squeezed light, we begin with a study of the squeezed states of the simple harmonic oscillator in quantum mechanics.

Consider first the properties of the energy eigenstates of the simple harmonic oscillator. Demonstration of these properties can be found in any standard textbook.

Just as the hydrogen atom possesses an infinite number of discrete eigenstates, labeled by a set of quantum numbers, so too with the simple harmonic oscillator. In one dimension it has an infinite series of equally spaced energy levels, of energy

$$E = (n + \tfrac{1}{2})\hbar\omega \tag{3.27}$$

Here ω is the natural frequency of the oscillator and n is the quantum number of the state. The ground state corresponds to $n = 0$, the first excited state is $n = 1$, and so forth. Figure 3–10 graphs the three lowest eigenstates.

To discuss the widths of these states, we think in terms of the so-called variances, defined to be the squares of the uncertainties:

$$\begin{aligned} \mathrm{var}(x) &\equiv (\Delta x)^2 = \langle x^2 \rangle - \langle x \rangle^2 \\ \mathrm{var}(p) &\equiv (\Delta p)^2 = \langle p^2 \rangle - \langle p \rangle^2 \end{aligned} \tag{3.28}$$

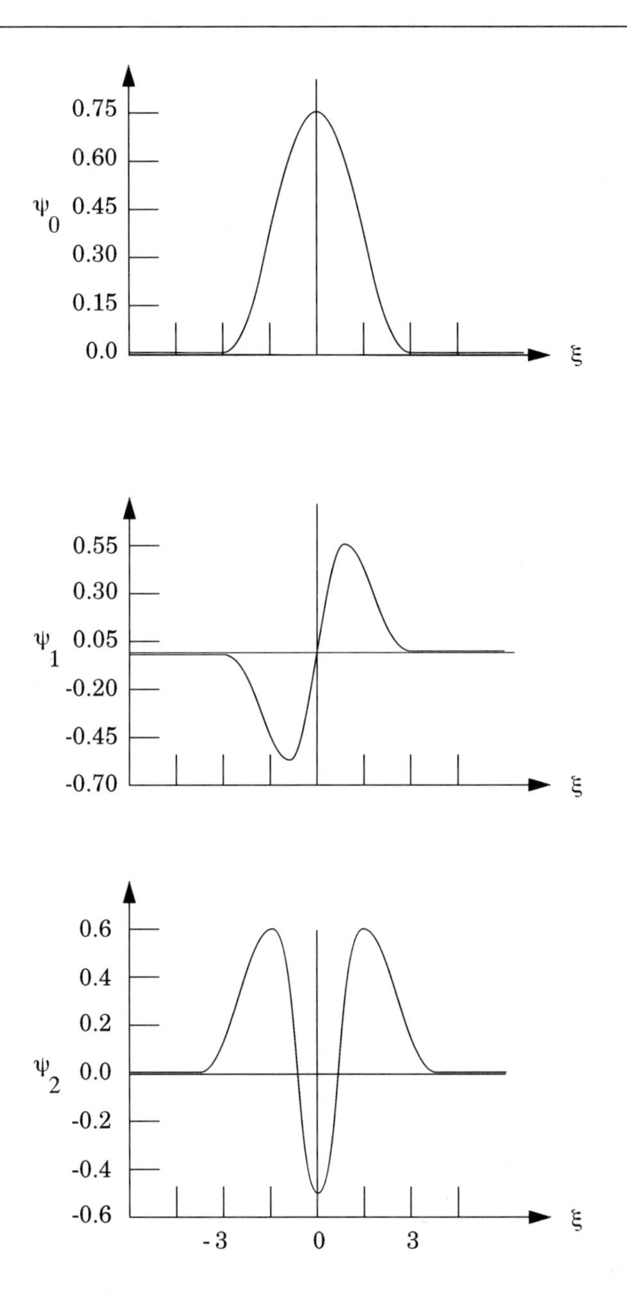

Figure 3–10 *Simple Harmonic Oscillator Wave Functions* corresponding to the ground and first two excited states. The dimensionless coordinate ξ is related to x through $\xi = \sqrt{m\omega/\hbar}\,x$ where m is the mass of the oscillator and ω its natural frequency.

These variances are made unnecessarily complicated by the fact that x and p have different units. So to make things simple, let us define new dimensionless variables $\hat{x}$ and $\hat{p}$:

$$\hat{x} \equiv x\sqrt{\frac{m\omega}{\hbar}} \qquad \hat{p} \equiv \frac{p}{\sqrt{m\omega\hbar}} \tag{3.29}$$

where m is the mass of the oscillator. It can be shown that for the eigenstates, the variances of $\hat{x}$ and $\hat{p}$ are:

$$\text{var}(\hat{x}) = \text{var}(\hat{p}) = n + \tfrac{1}{2} \tag{3.30}$$

Notice that the variances are equal; the energy eigenstates do *not* allow us to sacrifice knowledge of one variable for the sake of gaining greater accuracy in our knowledge of the other.

In terms of $\hat{x}$ and $\hat{p}$, the uncertainty principle states that

$$\text{var}(\hat{x})\ \text{var}(\hat{p}) \geq (\tfrac{1}{2})^2 \tag{3.31}$$

From Equation (3.30), the product of the variances is

$$\text{var}(\hat{x})\ \text{var}(\hat{p}) = (n + \tfrac{1}{2})^2 \tag{3.32}$$

Notice that this product obeys the uncertainty principle, as it must. Notice also that the product increases from a minimum for $n = 0$ to ever greater values for the excited states ($n > 0$). Only the ground state is a minimum uncertainty state.

Squeezed states are constructed as linear superpositions of these energy eigenstates, and the coefficients of the superposition are ingeniously chosen to give the states the required properties. In contrast to the energy eigenstates, which are constant in time, the squeezed states are functions of time. The squeezed states oscillate back and forth in the potential well at exactly the oscillator frequency. Furthermore, as they do so, they "breathe" in and out, growing first broader, and then narrower. The special character of squeezed states that makes them interesting for our purposes is that *when they are narrow, they are narrower than the energy eigenstates.*

In Figure 3–11 we present a sketch of a representative squeezed-state wave function. The origin of time, $t = 0$, is chosen to be the moment at which the peak of the wave function is farthest to the right in its motion. Furthermore, at this moment it is also narrowest. As time passes, the wave packet starts moving left. After $\frac{1}{4}$ of a cycle, it has moved to the center of its motion—and by this point the wave function has expanded to

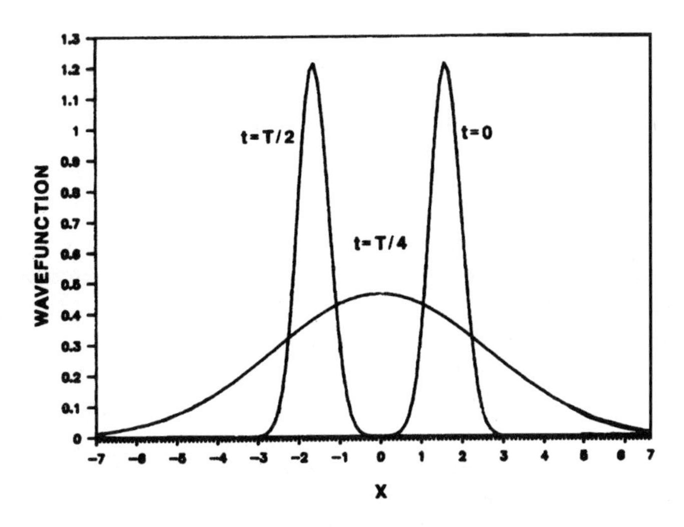

Figure 3–11 *A Squeezed State* of the simple harmonic oscillator, constructed from its energy eigenstates. SOURCE: Reproduced with permission from Richard Henry and Sharon Glotzer, "A squeezed state primer," *Amer. J. Phys.*, vol. 56 (4), p. 318 (1988).

its maximum width. During the next $\frac{1}{4}$ cycle the peak moves to the left-hand limit of its motion, by which point it has again collapsed to its smallest width. The remainder of the motion simply repeats this pattern; twice each cycle, the wave function collapses to a narrow, sharply defined peak.*

Contrast this behavior with that of a free particle. If a particle is measured to have a position x with an accuracy Δx, this is normally represented in quantum mechanics by constructing a Gaussian wavepacket centered at x with a width Δx. It is well known that the width of such a wavepacket *increases* monotonically with time. The variance is given by the formula

$$\operatorname{var} x(t) = [\Delta x(t)]^2 = [\Delta x(0)]^2 \left[1 + \frac{\hbar^2 t^2}{4m^2[\Delta x(0)]^4}\right] \tag{3.33}$$

Mathematically, the spreading arises because the wavepacket is a superposition of plane waves—a Fourier sum, each term of which has a different time evolution.

While the width of a wave packet for a free particle must continually increase in time, the width of the squeezed state of the simple harmonic

* The state we have described reaches its narrowest width at the endpoints of its motion. States can also be constructed that reach their narrowest width at the center of the motion.

oscillator initially increases *but then decreases* in time. For the squeezed state, the variances are

$$\begin{aligned} \text{var}(\hat{x}) &= A - B\cos(2\omega t) \\ \text{var}(\hat{p}) &= A + B\cos(2\omega t) \end{aligned} \tag{3.34}$$

where A and B are constants. These variances are plotted as a function of time in Figure 3–12. Notice in this figure that the variances of both $\hat{x}$ and $\hat{p}$ periodically increase and decrease, and at their smallest they are smaller than that of the energy eigenstates. Notice also that the squeezed states do not somehow violate the uncertainty principle, for when the variance of $\hat{x}$ is small, that of $\hat{p}$ is big, as the principle requires. Figure 3–12 also explains the origin of the term "squeezed" to describe these states: the uncertainty in one variable is "squeezed" out of it and into that of the complementary variable.

Let us place a simple harmonic oscillator into a squeezed state, and observe it not continuously but "stroboscopically"—that is, only at times: $t = 0$, $P/2$, P, $3P/2, \ldots$, where P is the period of oscillation. If we do so, we will find the position to be very sharply defined at every measurement. Clearly, were we able to place a gravitational wave detector into such a

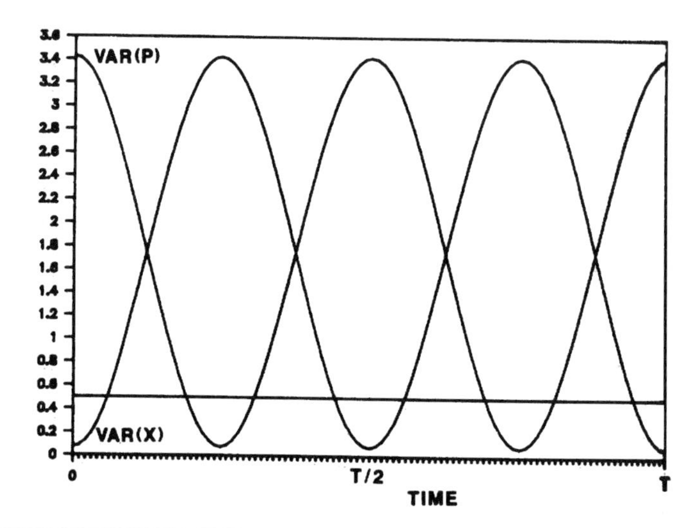

Figure 3–12 *Variances of the Squeezed State* illustrated in Figure 3–11. The horizontal line indicating a value of 1/2 is the lowest variance allowed by the normal eigenstates. Note that variance of the squeezed states can drop below this. SOURCE: Reproduced with permision from Richard Henry and Sharon Glotzer, "A squeezed state primer," *Amer. J. Phys.*, vol. 56 (4), p. 318 (1988).

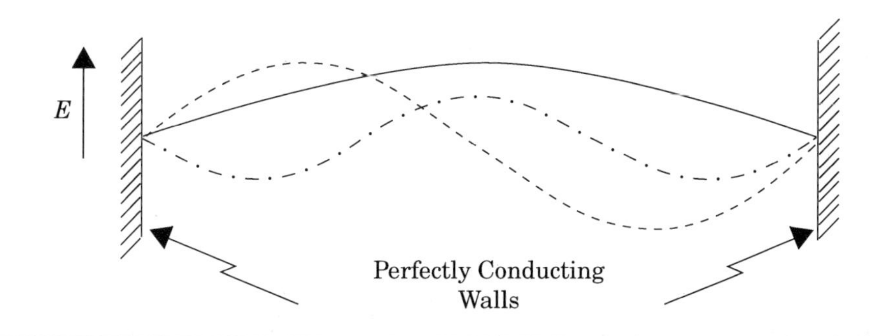

Figure 3–13 *Normal Modes of Vibration of a Field in a Cavity.* Only certain wavelengths are allowed. The longest allowed wavelength is indicated by a solid line, the second longest is indicated by a dashed line, and the third longest is indicated by a dot-dashed line.

state, limitations on its operation due to the uncertainty principle could be lessened. The task of doing so, however, appears to be impossible with current technology. The situation with light, however, is different. It is far easier to place electromagnetic radiation in a cavity into a squeezed state; indeed, at the time of this writing, several groups have already done so. In addition, the special statistics associated with squeezed light make it a promising candidate in LIGO.

Squeezed States of Light The electromagnetic field in a cavity is subject to certain boundary conditions at the cavity walls. For example, at a perfectly conducting wall, the electric field must be zero. Thus, as illustrated in Figure 3–13, the wavelength of the oscillation of the electric field can have only certain values. Each of these allowed values is a possible mode of vibration of the field.

The quantum theory of radiation treats these modes as simple harmonic oscillators, and it quantizes them. So the discussion we have given above for the *mechanical* simple harmonic oscillators is, in many ways, analogous to the discussion given by quantum electrodynamics of the *abstract* oscillators describing the possible states of light. For instance, each mode of the electromagnetic field of a cavity possesses a series of energy eigenstates and eigenvalues identical with those of the mechanical harmonic oscillator. Similarly, squeezed (and other) states can be built up as superpositions of these eigenstates.

In Figure 3–14 we sketch the amplitude of the electric field as a function of time for a squeezed state of light. The solid line in this figure represents the expectation value of E. It is a simple sine wave. The grey area represents the uncertainty in this value—the square root of the

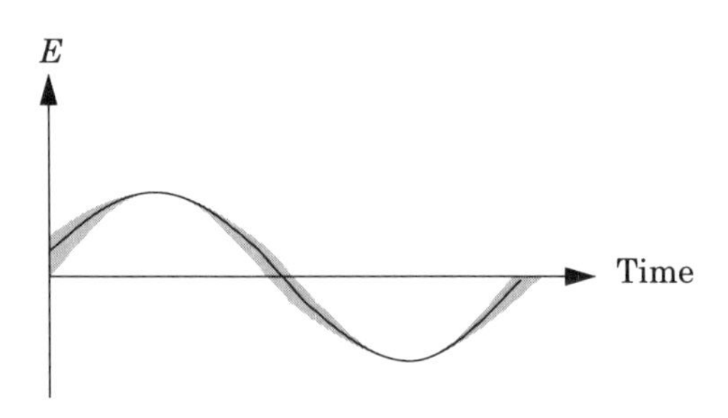

Figure 3–14 *A Squeezed State of Light* in a cavity. The electric field is plotted as a function of time. Its variance grows and then shrinks periodically. Note the strong resemblance between this variance and those of Figures 3–11 and 3–12.

variance of E. Notice the fluctuations in this uncertainty. When E is greatest, the uncertainty in its value is smallest, and when E is zero, its uncertainty is largest. This bears a strong resemblance to Figure 3–11 describing the motion of the squeezed-state wave function for the mechanical oscillator; when its wave function reached its greatest excursion, its width was smallest; when it passed through the origin, its uncertainty was bigger.

The race to squeeze light culminated in 1985 with the successful experiment of Slusher and Yurke[9] at AT&T Bell Labs. Within two years, squeezing had gone from a few percent to 60%. The various techniques that have been used to produce squeezed light generally follow a common strategy: phase-sensitive amplification and attenuation. Imagine a child swinging on a playground swing. It can pump the swing by standing and crouching, but whether this leads to an increase or a decrease in the swing's amplitude depends on the phase relationship between the instantaneous position of the swing and the child's pumping action. In like manner, optical squeezing makes use of the phase relationship between two optical signals. Two optical waves are mixed within a nonlinear medium—typically a crystal or an atomic vapor—inside a cavity. The output wave is very sensitive to the relative phase between the two inputs. Conditions can be arranged such that one input is maximally amplified, while the other is maximally attenuated. This amplification or attenuation can affect not only the signal, but also its noise—the uncertainty in the signal.

As we have mentioned, Caves has shown that if squeezed light is used in LIGO, its operation can be improved. The dominant classical sources of noise in LIGO are seismic and thermal, but the quantum nature of light also leads to photon shot noise. We therefore turn to a discussion of photon counting statistics.

Recall that each mode of an electromagnetic field can be in any of an infinite set of energy eigenstates labeled by "n," the degree of excitation of the associated abstract oscillator. Quantum electrodynamics treats "n" as the *number of photons* present in that mode. For example, if a particular mode is raised to its first excited state $n = 1$, there is one photon present of that mode's frequency. Similarly, if the mode is in its ground state $n = 0$, there are no photons present.

A mode whose state is an energy eigenstate is therefore one characterized by a definite number of photons; it is an eigenstate of the photon number operator we discussed in Chapter 2. States that are superpositions, on the other hand, do not have well-defined numbers of photons. The squeezed states are instances of such states. Suppose a radiation field were to be prepared in just the state sketched in Figure 3–14. As we mentioned, such squeezed states are constructed as linear superpositions of energy eigenstates; in Figure 3–15 we give the coefficients of that particular superposition. As we can see, that wave function is built up primarily from the first ten or so energy eigenstates, with small admixtures of higher levels. The probabilities, then, of finding "n" photons would be given by the squares of the superposition coefficients shown in that figure. For this state, we can speak of the *mean number of photons*—that is, the expectation value of "n"—and we can speak of *fluctuations about this mean*, characterized by the width of the distribution—the uncertainty in "n."

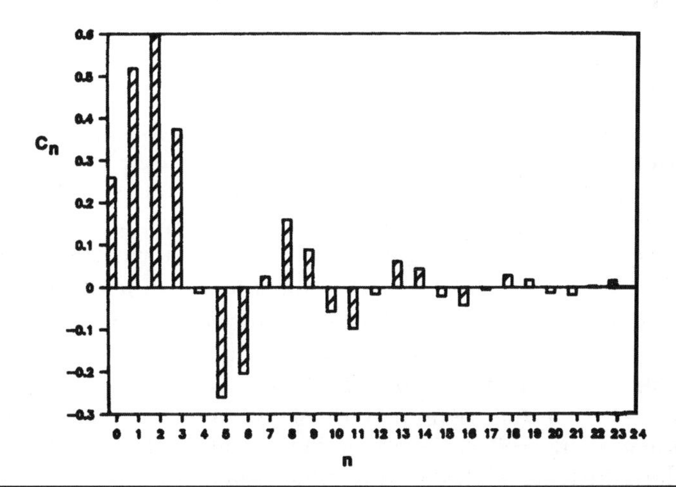

Figure 3-15 *Coefficients of the Superposition Yielding the Squeezed State* illustrated in Figure 3–14. C_n is the coefficient of the nth term. SOURCE: Reproduced with permission from Richard Henry and Sharon Glotzer, "A squeezed state primer," *Amer. J. Phys.*, vol. 56 (4), p. 318 (1988).

There exist certain states for which histograms such as Figure 3–15 are Poissonian. Radiation emitted by a laser is an example. Poisson statistics, of course, are characteristic of purely random events. Thus a photon detector exposed to laser light responds purely randomly. We emphasize, however, that lasers do not produce squeezed light. Histograms for squeezed light have the remarkable property that their widths are less than Poissonian: *The counting rates of detectors exposed to squeezed light are more regular than those exposed to light whose photons arrive randomly.* This fact has important consequences for the transmission of information along a light beam: the information is degraded by fluctuations in photon counting rates, so that transmission along a beam of squeezed light is more error-free than along normal light beams.

Caves's analysis of the quantum limits on the accuracy of LIGO identified two factors, both related to the photon nature of light. First, as the light beams were reflected by the mirrors, they exerted a certain radiation pressure on these mirrors; and since the photons in the beams arrived at the mirrors irregularly, this radiation pressure fluctuated in time. Second, the detectors monitoring the interference pattern counted photons, and these photons were arriving irregularly. Thus, in any series of measurements, even if the interference pattern had not changed, the detectors would give differing results.

Caves asked how these two effects could be minimized. The first would be minimized by reducing the intensity of the light beams, thus reducing the radiation pressure. Unfortunately, however, this increased the second effect, for as a random variable (such as the number of photons counted) grows smaller, its relative error grows larger. If one sought the best balance between these two competing effects, one found a result known as the standard quantum limit. Unfortunately, however, this limit was only reached for very large laser intensities—intensities so great that the brilliant beams of light would be expected to rapidly degrade the mirrors of the interferometer.

The essence of Caves's analysis was to exploit the fact that the photons of squeezed light exhibit a certain order. He showed that one could approach the standard quantum limit more easily if squeezed light, rather than more normal light, were used in the interferometer. Specifically, if the beam splitter in Figure 3–9 were exposed to the squeezed vacuum (the $n = 0$ state) along the indicated dotted path, this light interfered with the laser light reaching the beam splitter along the normal path in such a way that the standard quantum limit would be reached at far lower laser intensities.

At the time of this writing, LIGO represents the best chance we have for observing gravitational radiation. The "first generation" LIGO detectors being planned today will not exploit squeezed light. But, if all goes well, succeeding generations will.

We close this section with a brief comment on the nature of squeezed light. Recall that the $n = 0$ state represents the ground state of light: zero photons. But this state possesses a definite uncertainty. Thus, even in the absence of light, detectors will occasionally register photons. But the uncertainty of a squeezed state is less than that of other states. Squeezed light, therefore, can be accompanied by fewer fluctuations than pitch blackness: it is darker than the state that classical thinking would identify as perfect darkness.

3.6 Quantum Non-Demolition Measurements

Consider a gravitational wave incident upon a detector. The wave sets the detector to vibrating; we must observe this vibration. That means we must measure the position of one end of the detector and notice that this position has changed. So two or more position measurements must be made. We are attempting to determine the trajectory of the detector's end. As we have seen above, the uncertainty principle restricts our ability to do this. The study of quantum non-demolition (QND) measurements extends that analysis to include a new feature: *back-action.*

Suppose we measure the position of one end of the detector to an accuracy Δx. Then by the uncertainty principle, its momentum is uncertain by $\Delta p = \hbar/2\,\Delta x$, and its velocity is uncertain by $\Delta v = \hbar/2m\,\Delta x$. Even if we think the end of the detector is at rest, we do not know this with absolute certainty. Because of quantum limitations, it could be in motion with a velocity up to Δv without our being able to notice the fact.

Wait a time t and then perform the second measurement. In this time, even if no gravitational wave has passed by, the end of the bar will have moved. It will have moved an unknown distance due to this unknown velocity. So, if the initial measurement of the position was accurate to $\Delta x(0)$, the uncertainty induced by this measurement on the second one will be:*

$$\begin{aligned}\Delta x(t) &= \Delta x(0) + (\Delta v)t \\ &= \Delta x(0) + \hbar t/(2m\,\Delta x(0))\end{aligned} \tag{3.35}$$

Let us put some realistic numbers into this analysis. A typical detector might have a mass of ten tons. Since the frequency of a gravitational wave burst from a collapsing star is on the order of 1000 Hz, we must monitor the position of the end of the bar one thousand times per second or so to observe the oscillation. Thus, the time interval between the first and second measurements must be 0.001 s or less. If the accuracy of the initial

---

* We are assuming for simplicity here that the end of the detector is free to move, with no external forces acting on it. Thus v is constant during the time interval t. A detailed analysis shows that this is, in fact, not a bad approximation.

measurement was $\Delta x(0) = 10^{-21}$ m, we obtain the uncertainty in the second measurement $\Delta x(t) = 6.7 \times 10^{-20}$ m. But this accuracy is so poor that it becomes impossible to observe the effects of a passing gravitational wave! Thus, when the second measurement is performed, we are sure to obtain a result different from that of the first, but we will have no way of knowing whether this was because a gravitational wave passed by, or merely because of effects introduced by the uncertainty principle through back-action.

What is the best we can do? From Equation (3.35) we see that Δx reaches its minimum value for some intermediate value of $\Delta x(0)$, which we can find by differentiating Equation (3.35) and setting the result to zero:

$$0 = 1 - \frac{\hbar t}{2m[\Delta x(0)]^2} \tag{3.36}$$

Solving, we obtain the optimum accuracy:

$$\Delta x(0) = \sqrt{\frac{\hbar t}{2m}} \tag{3.37}$$

for which

$$\Delta x(t) = 2\sqrt{\frac{\hbar t}{2m}} = 4.5 \times 10^{-21}\ \text{m} \tag{3.38}$$

This is known as the *standard quantum limit.* Notice that it is still too great to allow for the successful detection of gravitational radiation. Thus back-action demolishes the possibility of performing position measurements of sufficient accuracy to detect gravitational waves. One might have thought that to observe the tiny oscillations induced in the detector by the passing wave, all we need do is measure the position of one of the detector ends to great accuracy. But this initial, highly accurate position measurement induces a correspondingly large and unknown velocity to the detector, thereby spoiling the accuracy of the second measurement. We say that the measurement of position is a *quantum-demolition measurement.*

The strategy behind *quantum non-demolition (QND) measurements* is to find a means of avoiding back-action.[10] A simple example is the measurement of momentum. Let us repeat the above analysis, but assume that rather than measuring the position of one end of the detector, we measure its momentum. If the initial measurement has an accuracy $\Delta p(0)$, this induces an uncertainty in position $\Delta x(0) = \hbar/2\,\Delta p(0)$. But this uncertainty in position has no effect on the second momentum measurement! Because momentum is conserved, Equation (3.35) is now replaced by

$$\Delta p(t) = \Delta p(0) \tag{3.39}$$

Notice that this equation, in contrast to Equation (3.35), contains no back-action term; nothing prevents us from performing a series of measurements of the momentum as accurately as we may wish. Of course, via the uncertainty principle, this induces a large uncertainty in position, but the fact is of no importance. Nothing now prevents us from detecting the change in velocity of one end of the detector induced by the passing gravitational wave. Momentum is a quantum non-demolition variable, and so evades back-action.

Unfortunately, the measurement of momentum presents far greater technical challenges than that of position. There is no likelihood in the near future of performing these measurements with sufficient accuracy to detect gravitational radiation. Rather, the strategy now being explored is to find other QND variables that are easier to measure. Various practical QND detection schemes have been advanced, and in a few cases partially realized using laser light interaction with either solid-state or atomic non-linear media. In 1995, Grangier and co-workers succeeded in performing repeated back-action–evading measurements of the kind required for continuous monitoring of a QND variable.[11] These successes have demonstrated that QND measurements are possible, although they are still far from finding application in gravitational wave experiments.

Chapter 4

Complementarity

In the previous three chapters we have explored a wide variety of topics. Although we have not pointed out the fact, a common element has been present through this variety. We might call it a persistent "doubleness" in quantum mechanics. *Whereas in classical physics there is a unity, in quantum mechanics this unity is replaced by a duality.* Bohr, the first to identify this curious feature, termed it *complementarity.*

Complementarity has many facets. Sometimes it pertains to *the picture of a physical situation that we attempt to build up in our minds.* In discussing the experiment of Tonomura et al., recounted in Chapter 1 on matter waves, we emphasized that it was quite impossible to understand how electrons could pass through two slits at once to produce an interference pattern. The same, of course, is true of neutrons, atoms and photons. While classical physics allows us to have a unified picture of a phenomenon, here we are forced to simultaneously hold in our minds two mutually inconsistent descriptions: "particle" and "wave." Bohr would say that the particle-nature of the object is complementary to its wave-nature.

In other situations, complementarity refers to *what quantum mechanics allows us to know.* In Chapter 3 on the uncertainty principle, we saw that any two observables whose operators do not commute obey an uncertainty relation. Thus one may measure either the position or the momentum of a particle; either the energy or the time. The squeezed states we recounted in that chapter are explicit instances in which one chooses which variable to know with accuracy at the expense of the other. Whereas in classical physics we can arrive at a complete description of a state by measuring both members of a pair of variables, in quantum theory we can measure only one. Two attitudes to this fact can be adopted. In the first we admit that our *knowledge* is constrained to be partial. In the second we go further and say that they do not both simultaneously *exist.* In either interpretation,

Bohr would say that position is complementary to momentum and energy is complementary to time.

Finally, complementarity refers to what an experiment can reveal. Recall our discussion in Chapter 2 of the delayed-choice experiment. In that experiment, the second beam splitter BS_2 could be inserted or removed at will (see Figure 2–8 of that chapter). On the one hand, if it was removed we could determine which route the photon had traveled (if D_x recorded the photon, it must have traveled by path x; if D_y, then path y). On the other hand, if the beam splitter was inserted, all information about the path traveled was lost, and an interference pattern was observed. Here the complementarity is between *our knowledge of which path the quantum took and the possibility of observing an interference pattern.* Note that no version of the experiment allows us both: which-path information and interference are complementary.

In Chapter 2 we commented

> ... how flawed the simple wave–particle description is. Once light [or a material particle] is in an interferometer, we simply cannot think of it as either a wave or a particle. Nor will melding the two descriptions into some strange hybrid work. All these attempts are inadequate. What is called for is not a composite picture of light, stitched together out of bits taken from various classical theories. Rather we are being asked for a new concept, a new point of view that will be fundamentally different from those developed from the world of classical physics.

Bohr felt that complementarity provided this new point of view.

4.1 Bohr's Discovery of Complementarity

From all reports, Niels Bohr's gentle but absolutely tenacious character was much in evidence during Schrödinger's visit to Copenhagen in early November of 1926. Already at the train station, the two were at it. Their debate concerning the interpretation of quantum physics was carried on without pause at Bohr's institute and in Bohr's home, where Schrödinger stayed from early morning to late at night. Both argued mightily for their respective viewpoints, neither making the least concession.

Bohr's thinking about quantum mechanics crossed a watershed between the fall of 1926 and the spring of 1927. During these months, Bohr hosted both Schrödinger and Heisenberg at his institute in Copenhagen. In the months preceding those conversations, Heisenberg and Schrödinger had independently succeeded in formulating quantum mechanics rigorously, the youthful Heisenberg in the language of matrix mechanics and Schrödinger, only two years Bohr's junior, in terms of his wave mechanics. Bohr felt that, for the first time, all the pieces of the quantum puzzle were in hand. He wanted these two at his institute to sort it out and reach a definitive understanding.

Schrödinger, a cultivated man and deep thinker, had his own opinions about the subject. Bohr, who was legendary for his indefatigable, soft-spoken, but dominating intellectual manner, was relentless. Heisenberg remarked that

> Bohr, who was otherwise most considerate and amiable in his dealings with people, now appeared to me almost as an unrelenting fanatic, who was not prepared to make a single concession to his discussion partner or to tolerate the slightest obscurity. It will hardly be possible to convey the intensity of passion with which the discussions were concluded on both sides, or the deep-rooted convictions which one could perceive equally with Bohr and with Schrödinger in every spoken sentence.[1]

Within a couple of days, Schrödinger collapsed under the strain and took to bed with a feverish cold. Mrs. Bohr nursed him with tea and cakes, yet her husband could still not relent but "sat on the bedside and spoke earnestly to Schrödinger: 'But surely you must realize that . . .' "[2]

They could not agree. Schrödinger sought for realism even in the quantum world, seeking for some clear picture of submicroscopic phenomena; Bohr de-emphasized the search for reality, and rather held to the descriptive language of classical physics and the phenomena themselves as evidenced through experiment, contradictory though they might be. They parted with admiration for each other, but unmoved from their differing views. In the months following Schrödinger's visit, Heisenberg took Schrödinger's place as sparring partner. Together they continued to grapple for solid ground beneath the elusive theory of quantum mechanics, with little success.

The paradoxical nature of quantum theory was fully evident to Bohr from the early days of its creation, and by 1926 he was completely committed to resolving what he regarded to be a paradox inherent in the dual nature of quantum phenomena. Bohr lamented that "even the mathematical scheme does not help. I want first to understand how nature actually avoids contradictions . . ."[3] The approach of Heisenberg was to hold closely to the mathematics of quantum theory and to forgo using the traditional language of physics. By contrast, Bohr insisted on seeking a way *within the ideas and language of classical physics* to resolve the dilemma posed by this duality. He had already expressed himself often in this regard. For example, in 1923 he insisted that, "Every description of natural processes must be based on ideas which have been introduced and defined by the classical theory."[4] This was a view he would continue to defend throughout his life. Four years later, in 1927, he wrote, "Our interpretation of the experimental material rests essentially upon the classical concepts."[5] And to Einstein in a letter from the same year,

> It has of course long been recognized how intimately the difficulties of the quantum theory are connected with the concepts,

> or rather with the words that are used in the customary description of nature, and which always have their origin in the classical theories ...[6]

Bohr's insistence on restricting the framework for understanding quantum mechanics to classical concepts was not to Heisenberg's liking. And so the discussions between the two raged on, to such a degree that by Christmas they were both exhausted and tense. In February, Bohr set off to Norway for a ski holiday, leaving Heisenberg on his own. Within days of Bohr's departure, Heisenberg discovered the uncertainty relationships that today bear his name, and which we have examined in the previous chapter. Together with wave–particle duality, the uncertainty relationships set the stage for Bohr's articulation of what he took to be a solution of the puzzle of quantum mechanics.

Como, 1927 To mark the centenary of the death of Alessandro Volta, a major conference was arranged at which many of the great scientists of the day gathered in Como, Italy. Bohr took it as the opportunity to express himself concerning the philosophical foundations of the quantum theory. The duality evident in wave–particle experiments and the uncertainty relationships was elevated by Bohr in his lecture to the level of a principle he termed *complementarity*:

> ... [the quantum of action] forces us to adopt a new mode of description designated as complementarity in the sense that any given application of classical concepts precludes the simultaneous use of other classical concepts which in a different connection are equally necessary for the elucidation of the phenomena.[7]

This was as close as Bohr came to defining what he meant by complementarity. It baldly states that quantum phenomena require the use of two mutually exclusive concepts for their elucidation, in contrast to classical physics, which allows us to meld the two together to form a unity.

Bohr emphasized the need for complementary pictures, such as wave and particle, to interpret experimental results; or complementary information, such as of position or momentum, to specify the state of a system. Wave versus particle may appear on the surface to be contradictory, but Bohr declared that,

> In fact, here again we are not dealing with contradictory but with complementary pictures of the phenomena, which only together offer a natural generalization of the classical mode of description.[8]

Thus, Bohr argued that the classical concepts of wave and particle *together* offer us the possibility of understanding quantum phenomena: no single classical idea can embrace the results of quantum experiments, but the use of two complementary classical concepts can.

Bohr was convinced that we must always dress our understanding in concepts and language drawn from the world we directly perceive—the world of classical physics. But as we investigate a level that is beyond the senses, as with quantum phenomena, we are forced to meld opposites in a perverse union. Like some figure from a medieval bestiary, or the Egyptian images of their gods as half-human and half-beast, wave–particle duality joins complementary concepts in order to encompass the full range of laboratory experience.

"Exclusivity" is an important element here. Complementarity maintains that wave and particle are *mutually exclusive concepts*. When a particular experiment shows one, the other is absent. They never appear together. As an example, return to the delayed-choice experiments recounted in Chapter 2. There was no way to run both an anticorrelation (particle) experiment and an interference (wave) experiment at the same time. We can choose to perform one or the other experiment as late as we wish, but we must choose. Both classical models are required for elucidation of the phenomena, and they are never evoked simultaneously. Similarly, knowledge of both the position and momentum of a particle is required in order to fully describe its motion. But the two can never be known simultaneously, for an accurate measurement of position excludes the possibility of accurately measuring the momentum.

The principle of complementarity states that we can never know everything about the world; indeed, we can only know half of everything. Imagine writing down the set of all true statements about a given physical situation. According to classical ideas, these statements could be written down in one big list; this list would constitute a complete description of the situation. But according to Bohr, we are required to write them on two half-lists. Furthermore, we must enter them in such a manner that to each entry on one half-list, there corresponds an entry on the other. The particle-nature of the electron goes on one half-list, its wave-nature on the other; the position of a particle on one half-list, its momentum on the other; knowledge of the path a quantum took on one, the possibility of interference on the other. Bohr's principle of complementarity insists that we can choose either one half-list or the other—but never both.

4.2 Einstein's Attack on Complementarity

Einstein's dissatisfaction with quantum mechanics extended to the principle of complementarity. The condition of "mutual exclusivity" is the central axis around which complementarity turns. Is it possible to get around this condition somehow? In meetings with Bohr, Einstein constantly sought a means to do so. Physicists continue to debate the issues he raised down to the present day.[9]

The Solvay Meetings: Complementarity between Which-Path Information and Interference Bohr's Como lecture on the philosophical foundations of quantum mechanics, and his enunciation of the principle of complementarity, did not arouse in all his listeners the response he hoped for. Following Bohr's talk, the eminent physicist Eugene Wigner remarked to Leon Rosenfeld, "This lecture will not induce any one of us to change his own opinion about quantum mechanics."[10] One month later, however, the memorable fifth Solvay meeting of 1927 took place in Brussels. It was a stellar gathering, including Planck, Einstein, Bohr, de Broglie, Dirac, Ehrenfest, Heisenberg, Pauli, Schrödinger, Born and Lorentz. Ehrenfest left the meeting with the distinct impression that Bohr "towered over everybody. At first not understood at all ... then step by step defeating everybody."[11] Bohr's defense of the uncertainty principle and complementarity against the daily probing of Einstein, and the subsequent confrontation between Bohr and Einstein at the next Solvay meeting three years later, are legendary events in the chronicles of modern physics.

Otto Stern has given a first-hand description of the informal discussions at the 1927 Solvay meeting. Each day

> Einstein came down to breakfast and expressed his misgivings about the new quantum theory, every time [he] had invented some beautiful experiment from which one saw that [the theory] did not work ... Pauli and Heisenberg, who were there, did not pay much attention, "Ah well, it will be all right, it will be all right." Bohr, on the other hand, reflected on it with care and in the evening, at dinner, we were all together and he cleared up the matter in detail.[12]

One of Einstein's morning misgivings concerned two-slit interference. He proposed a modification of the conventional double-slit experiment so as to allow us to deduce which slit the particle passed through, while at the same time allowing the interference pattern to persist. If this could be done, of course, it would be a direct contradiction of the principle of complementarity.

Figure 4–1 sketches Einstein's proposed modification. In it, the screen containing the two slits is not fixed, but rather is mounted on rollers and is free to move. Note that if a particle arrives at point P, it must have received an upward kick as it passed through the screen. Therefore, the screen must have received a downward kick. Note also that, had the particle passed through slit 1, it would have received a *bigger* kick than had it passed through slit 2. Einstein's proposal was simply to observe the motion of the slits after the particle had traversed them. Depending on how rapidly they were moving, one could deduce which slit the particle had traversed. Thus

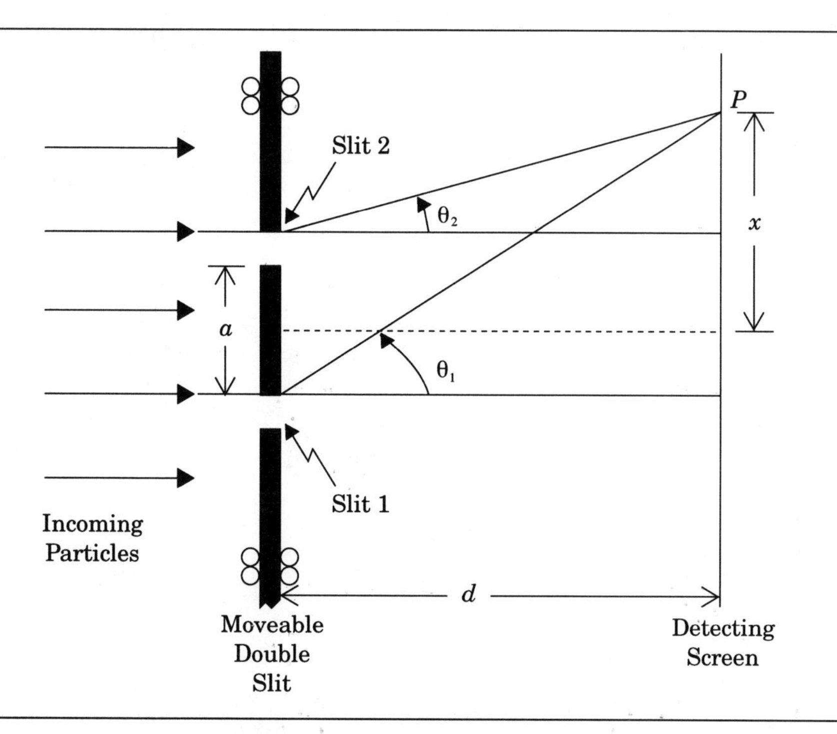

Figure 4–1 *Einstein's First Attack on Complementarity.* The two slits of the classic double-slit experiment are free to move. By measuring their recoil, Einstein argued, we can find out which path the particle took.

Einstein showed that "which-path" (particle) information could be obtained in the experiment together with interference.

The flaw Bohr found in this argument connected the position uncertainty of the slits with the uncertainty in the momentum given to the particle. Had the particle passed through slit 1, the momentum given to the screen containing the slits would have been

$$P_{\text{screen}}(1) = P_{\text{particle}} \sin\theta_1 \approx P_{\text{particle}}\theta_1 \tag{4.1}$$

(for small θ_1), and similarly had it passed through slit 2. The difference in slit momenta

$$P_{\text{screen}}(1) - P_{\text{screen}}(2) \approx P_{\text{particle}}(\theta_1 - \theta_2) \tag{4.2}$$

then tells us which slit the particle traversed. Bohr argued that, in order to determine which slit the particle had traversed, the momentum of the screen containing the slits would have to be measured to an accuracy greater than this difference:

$$\Delta P_{\text{screen}} < P_{\text{particle}}(\theta_1 - \theta_2) \tag{4.3}$$

Therefore, by the uncertainty principle, the position of the slits would be uncertain by

$$\Delta x_{\text{screen}} > \frac{h}{P_{\text{particle}}(\theta_1 - \theta_2)} \tag{4.4}$$

The geometry illustrated in Figure 4–1 allows us to write

$$\frac{x + \frac{a}{2}}{d} = \tan\theta_1 \approx \theta_1 \tag{4.5}$$

$$\frac{x - \frac{a}{2}}{d} = \tan\theta_2 \approx \theta_2 \tag{4.6}$$

which, when combined with Equation (4.4) yields

$$\Delta x_{\text{screen}} > \frac{h}{P_{\text{particle}}\left(\frac{a}{d}\right)} = \frac{d\lambda}{a} \tag{4.7}$$

where, in the last step, we have used the de Broglie relation connecting the particle's momentum and wavelength. *But the distance between interference maxima is just $d\lambda/a$.* Thus, the position uncertainty of the slits is just sufficient to wipe out the interference pattern! Mounting the slits on rollers, which is essential to measure the recoil momentum of the slits and so get "which-path" information, leads to an uncertainty in the slit positions of just the amount needed to wash out the interference fringes and save the principle of complementarity.

Bohr successfully defended his view of quantum mechanics against all comers at the 1927 Solvay meeting. Heisenberg was convinced. Shortly afterwards, the German version of Bohr's Como lecture appeared; concerning it, he wrote to Schrödinger in May of 1928, with real satisfaction, "I am afraid to have greatly bored you with these many words. You must ascribe this to my enthusiasm. After years of struggle in the dark I feel perhaps particularly strongly the fulfillment of old hopes brought to us by your and others' new discoveries."[13] Bohr and Heisenberg may have felt fulfillment, but their feelings were not shared by all. Einstein left Brussels unswayed, writing to Schrödinger that "The soothing philosophy—or religion?—of Heisenberg–Bohr is so cleverly concocted that for the present it offers the believers a soft resting pillow from which they are not easily chased away. Let us therefore let them rest. ... This religion does damned little for me."[14] Schrödinger agreed, saying that "Bohr wants to 'complement away' all difficulties."[15]

Complementarity in the Energy-Time Uncertainty Relation Three years later, the sixth Solvay meeting took place. Einstein arrived in Brussels armed with yet another argument, this time against the complementarity involved in the energy–time uncertainty relation. His proposed thought experiment[16] and Bohr's ultimate refutation of it are classic, and they are worth recounting.

Imagine, said Einstein, a perfectly reflecting box in which a certain amount of light is trapped. The presence of the light contributes to the weight of the box, via the equation $E = mc^2$. For example, if one million photons from the visible part of the spectrum are trapped in the box, their additional mass would be about 10^{-30} kg, which is roughly the mass of an electron.

The box is equipped with a shutter connected to a clock. At a specific time, known as accurately as we wish, the shutter opens briefly and lets a single photon escape. We can measure the weight of the box at our leisure to arbitrary accuracy, which implies that we can obtain an exact measure of the energy of the emitted photon and, by means of the clock, the moment of its production. This is in direct contradiction to the energy–time uncertainty relationship: $(\Delta E)(\Delta t) > \hbar$.

The measurement of energy and time are, according to Bohr, always complementary acts. The simultaneous measurement to arbitrary accuracy of the energy and time-of-emission of a photon should be impossible. Yet Einstein had apparently conceived of an experiment that could, in principle, do just that! Leon Rosenfeld, who was present at the conference, recalled that when Einstein presented his thought-experiment,

> It was quite a shock for Bohr—he did not see the solution at once. During the whole evening he was extremely unhappy, going from one to the other, trying to persuade them that it couldn't be true, that it would be the end of physics if Einstein were right; but he couldn't produce any refutation. I shall never forget the sight of the two antagonists leaving (the Foundation Universitaire), Einstein a tall majestic figure, walking quietly, with a somewhat ironic smile, and Bohr trotting near him, very excited.... The next morning came Bohr's triumph.[17]

Bohr's panic vanished when he recognized that the clock used to time the emission was, through the equivalence principle of general relativity, sensitive to its position in the earth's gravitational field. Here is how Bohr refuted Einstein through a brilliant application of Einstein's own theory.

Figure 4–2 shows Bohr's rendition of Einstein's experimental apparatus. By adjusting the mass suspended from the bottom of the box, the pointer

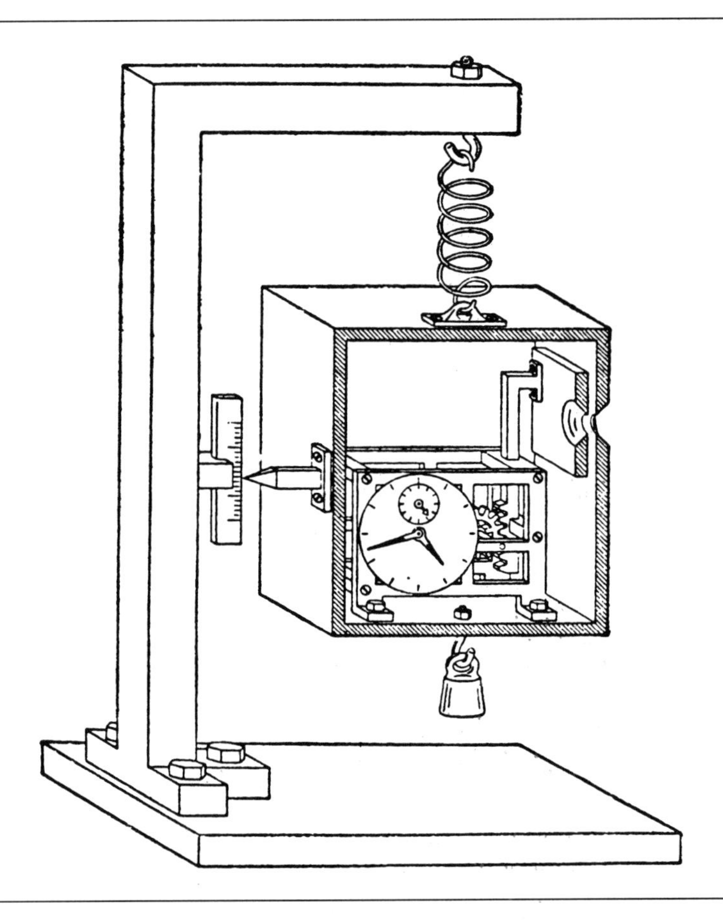

Figure 4–2 *Einstein's Second Attack on Complementarity.* The box contains light; at a predetermined time, known as accurately as we wish, the mechanism opens the shutter and allows a single photon to escape. We then measure the new mass of the box and so, according to Einstein, determine the escaped photon's energy to arbitrary accuracy. SOURCE: Reprinted by permission of Open Court Trade & Academic Books, a division of Carus Publishing Company, Peru, IL, from *Albert Einstein: Philosopher–Scientist*, P.A. Schilpp (ed.) (Evanston, IL: Library of Living Philosophers, 1949), p. 227.

position, or spring extension, z can be adjusted. The force of gravity acting on the box is mg, which is counterbalanced by the upward force from the spring kz. To measure the mass (or energy) of the departed photon, we increase the suspended mass so as to re-zero the pointer. The amount by which we must increase the mass equals the mass of the emitted photon.

Of course this procedure entails a measurement of the position of the box (to verify that the pointer still points to zero). Thus, since Heisenberg's momentum–position uncertainty relation holds, the best we can hope for in momentum uncertainty is $(\Delta P_z) = \hbar/2\,\Delta z$, where Δz is the accuracy with which we have re-zeroed the pointer. Bohr's first crucial insight was that this momentum uncertainty translates into an uncertainty in the measured mass of the box. To see this we need to recall the concept of impulse from classical physics. Impulse is the integral of an applied force over the time of its application, and it equals the change in momentum produced by that force. The momentum uncertainty ΔP_z implies that the box's momentum could be nonzero by this amount without the experimenter noticing. Just such a nonzero momentum would be caused by an error Δm in the mass we added to the box. Such a mass imbalance would produce a force imbalance $(\Delta m)g$ in the earth's gravitational field. This force acts over the duration of the measurement* T to produce an impulse $(\Delta m)gT$. Using Einstein's mass-energy relation, we obtain

$$\Delta E = (\Delta P_z)c^2/gT \tag{4.8}$$

Thus the uncertainty in the box's momentum translates into an uncertainty in photon energy. Combining this with the uncertainty relation between position and momentum, we find

$$\Delta E = (c^2/gT)(\hbar/2\,\Delta z) \tag{4.9}$$

This provided Bohr with half of the energy–time uncertainty relationship he sought. The measurement of time occurs through the agency of the clock. It is not immediately clear how the measurement of time can be uncertain, but here Einstein's own theory of relativity came to Bohr's rescue (an ironic turn of events). General relativity had showed that the rate at which a clock ticks depends upon its position in a gravitational field. If this position were uncertain by an amount Δz, then relativity states that any time interval T measured by the clock is uncertain by

$$(\Delta T)/T = g(\Delta z)/c^2 \tag{4.10}$$

---

* That a certain time is required to perform the mass measurement can be seen as follows. If the pointer is at zero, an error in the mass added to the box causes the pointer to start moving toward its new equilibrium position. Suppose the time required for it to get there is T. Then for times short compared to T, we can treat the force acting on the box as essentially constant, and the above connection between impulse and change in momentum is valid. Conversely, for times long compared to T, the box is essentially at rest at its new equilibrium position. Thus the time T required to perform the mass measurement is the time for the pointer to reach its new equilibrium position.

Solving Equation (4.10) for Δz and combining the result with Equation (4.9) gives

$$\Delta E \, \Delta T = \hbar/2 \tag{4.11}$$

which is the uncertainty relation.

4.3 The New Paradigm: Information

Bohr's analysis of Einstein's two thought experiments demonstrated by exactly what mechanism complementarity was enforced: both discussions relied on the uncertainty principle. But in recent years, a new way of thinking about complementarity has evolved, one that says nothing about disturbances or mechanisms or uncertainty relations. Rather, this new view speaks only of information. The information approach is a powerful means of analyzing experiments involving complementarity.[18]

Quantum Beats Raise an atom to an excited state. The state decays with time, following the well-known exponential law of decay, as illustrated in Figure 4–3. Precisely the same phenomenon is observed in the decay of any other sort of excited state of a system; for example, the decay of a radioactive atomic nucleus. But beginning in the mid-60s, experimenters discovered in certain cases a rapid modulation of this normal exponential decay.[19] Such modulations have been named *quantum beats*.

As an example, Hellmuth, Walther, Zajonc and Schleich[20] performed an experiment in which a beam of barium atoms entered into a weak magnetic field. This field split the upper $^1P_1$-state of the barium into three Zeeman sublevels, separated by the Larmor precession frequency ω_L. These sublevels were excited by a 1.5-ps pulse of broadband laser light at 553 nm, linearly

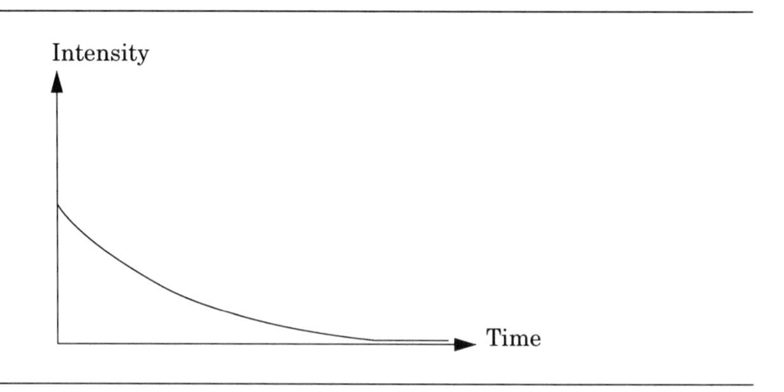

Figure 4–3 *Exponential Decay* of an excited state.

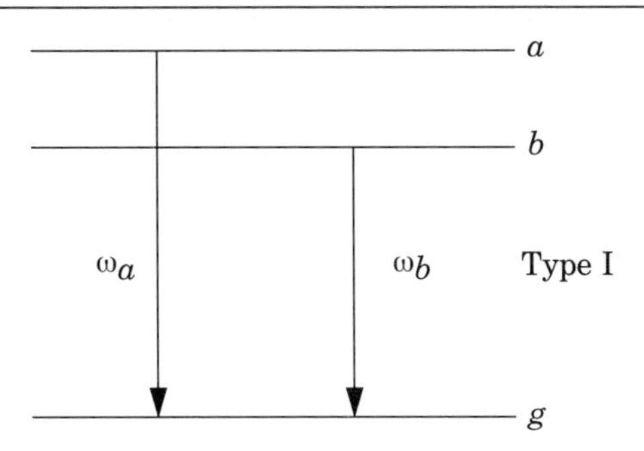

Figure 4–4 *Energy Level Diagram of an Atom whose Upper State Is Split.* Such an atom, if the upper states are excited, will exhibit quantum beats as it decays.

polarized perpendicular to the magnetic field direction. Because of the selection rules governing atomic transitions, the pulse excited only two of the Zeeman sublevels, those with magnetic quantum numbers $m = -1$ and $m = +1$. These two upper states, together with the ground state, are illustrated in Figure 4–4.

Ten thousand times a second, a pulse of laser light illuminated the atomic beam of barium. Even though the barium was highly dilute, each pulse excited many atoms. But the detector was designed to accept one and only one photon for each laser pulse. Thus the recorded signal was due to a series of individual events, in which one photon in each laser pulse excited one atom, which in turn decayed by giving off one photon into the detector. This arrangement came very close to an ideal experiment, in which we work with one atom and one photon at a time.

Data illustrating the decay observed in this experiment is shown in Figure 4–5. In this figure we can clearly see the normal exponential decay. But superimposed on this curve, we also see a clear modulation of the light intensity.

The phenomenon is reminiscent of acoustic beats. If we strike two nearly identical tuning forks that have natural frequencies of vibration f and f', we will hear, in addition to their fundamental tone, a so-called "beat note." We hear it as a slow modulation of the sound intensity, at a frequency equal to $f - f'$. The effect exhibited in Figure 4–5 is similar, and so has been named quantum beats. (The analogy, in fact, is quite close, since the sound from the tuning forks will decrease in time after being struck, as does the light from the atoms.)

Acoustic beats never occur when sound of only one pitch is present. At least two differing frequencies are required for the phenomenon to arise. Similarly, quantum beats only arise when the light emitted by the decaying atom is of two differing frequencies. This cannot happen when a single excited state decays; rather, we must always excite two upper levels, each one of which emits a light wave.

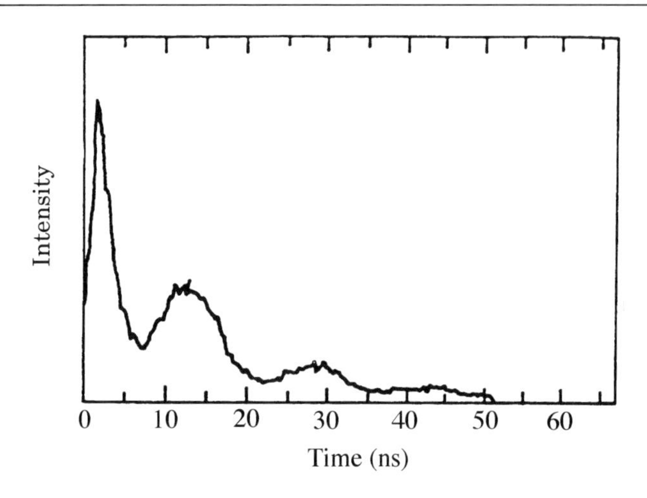

Figure 4–5 *Quantum Beats* observed in the decay of an atom whose upper state is split. SOURCE: Reproduced with permission from T. Hellmuth, H. Walther, A. Zajonc and W. Schleich, "Delayed-choice experiments in quantum interference," *Phys. Rev. A*, vol. 35, p. 2532 (1987), published by The American Physical Society.

It is not hard to guess an explanation for quantum beats. By analogy with acoustic beats, we can imagine that since the light from the atom is of two differing frequencies, they will combine together in precisely the same way as do sound waves to produce the beats. Remarkably, however, it has been experimentally discovered that such an analysis will not do. To see this, consider now a second type of energy-level diagram, one with an "inverted" structure, shown in Figure 4–6. Here it is the ground state,

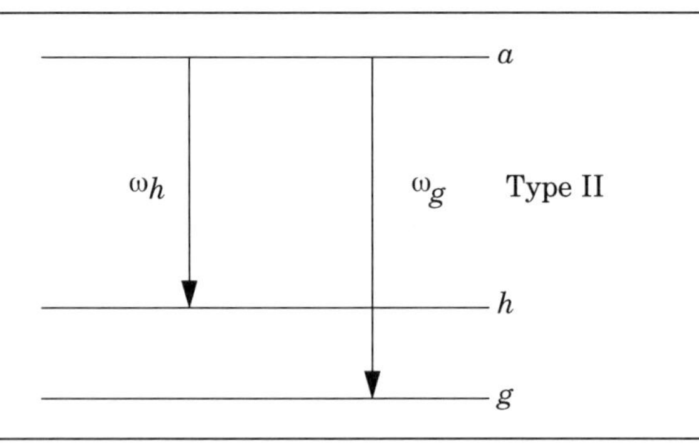

Figure 4–6 *Energy Level Diagram of an Atom Whose Lower State Is Split.* Such an atom, if the upper state is excited, will *not* exhibit beats as it decays.

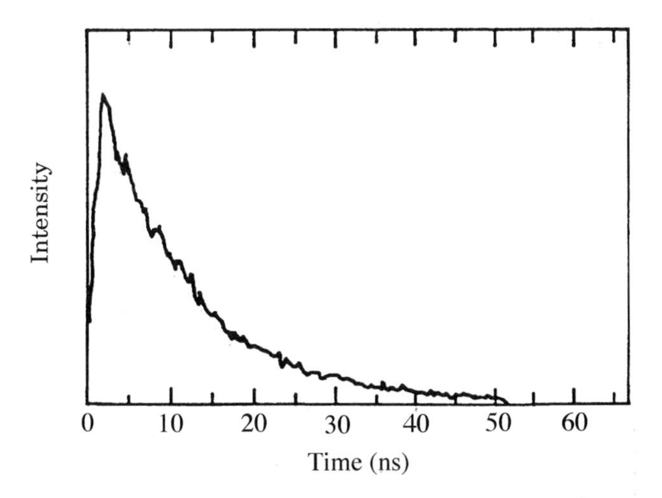

Figure 4–7 *No Quantum Beats* are observed in the decay of the atom whose lower state is split. SOURCE: Reproduced with permission from T. Hellmuth, H. Walther, A. Zajonc and W. Schleich, "Delayed-choice experiments in quantum interference," *Phys. Rev. A*, vol. 35, p. 2532 (1987), published by The American Physical Society.

rather than the excited state, that is split into two sublevels. Clearly, if such an atom is raised to its excited state, light of two different frequencies will be emitted. We would thus expect to see beats. But in fact, we do not! Rather, the normal purely exponential decay is observed, as shown in Figure 4–7.

It is clear, therefore, that quantum beats differ from classical beats in an essential way. It will develop that they arise by means of a quantum-mechanical interference process. Furthermore, in our analysis we will find that a good way to approach them will be via the information-theoretic approach.

Theory of Quantum Beats: Complementarity Let us attempt to formulate a theory of quantum beats. Our first attempt will be semi-classical,* in which the atoms are treated quantum-mechanically but the light will be taken to obey the laws of classical electrodynamics. This attempt will turn out to be only partially successful, which will lead us to turn to a purely quantum treatment and a consideration of complementarity. In the next section we will turn to the role of information.

* Technically, since we will take expectation values as applying to single atoms as opposed to ensembles, the treatment is called "neoclassical."

Following conventional usage, we call atoms whose energy-level diagram is illustrated in Figure 4–4 type I, and those with the inverted diagrams of Figure 4–6, type II. Type I atoms exhibit beats; type II's do not. Begin with type I atoms. The two excited states a and b in Figure 4–4 are Zeeman sublevels, in which the atom is exposed to a magnetic field. Detailed calculations reveal that such a field induces an electric dipole moment in the excited states. Furthermore, this dipole is time-varying: the individual dipoles rotate at the Larmor frequency about the field lines. And according to classical electrodynamics, electromagnetic radiation is produced by just such time-varying dipoles: the radiation intensity is proportional to the dipole moment squared.

Let us use this as a clue in our attempt to formulate our theory. We will use quantum mechanics to calculate the expectation value of the dipole moment; then we will square it to find the emitted light intensity. To find the expectation value, we need to know the wave function of the atom. It is

$$\psi(t) = A(t)\, e^{-i\omega_a t}\psi_a + B(t)\, e^{-i\omega_b t}\psi_b + G(t)\psi_g\, e^{-i\omega_g t} \tag{4.12}$$

where the factors $A(t)$ and $B(t)$ are the usual exponential terms describing the decays of the excited states; similarly, $G(t)$ describes the "filling up" of the ground state. The expectation value of the dipole moment is

$$\langle O \rangle = \int \psi^*(er)\psi\, d^3r \tag{4.13}$$

where e is the charge of the electron. The calculation is somewhat involved; the final result turns out to be

$$\begin{aligned} I\alpha|\langle O \rangle|^2\alpha&\left|\int \psi^*(t) r \psi(t)\, d^3r\right|^2 \\ &= \left|A^*(t)G(t)\int \psi_a^* r\psi_g\, d^3r\right|^2 + \left|B^*(t)G(t)\int \psi_b^* r\psi_g\, d^3r\right|^2 \\ &\quad + 2\mathrm{Re}\left\{A^*(t)B(t)|G(t)|^2 \int \psi_a^* r\psi_g\, d^3r \int \psi_g^* r\psi_b\, d^3r\, e^{i(\omega_a - \omega_b)t}\right\} \end{aligned} \tag{4.14}$$

The first term in this expression describes the decay from state a to g and the second describes the decay from state b to g. These terms exhibit the normal exponential behavior. But the last term involves the factor

$$e^{i(\omega_a - \omega_b)t} = e^{i[(E_a - E_b)/\hbar]t} \tag{4.15}$$

which oscillates in time with frequency $(E_a - E_b)/\hbar$. *This is the quantum beat.*

Note the strong analogy with two-slit interference here. In our treatment of Chapter 1, we saw a similar mathematical structure: one term describing a wave from one slit, a second describing a wave from the other, and finally an interference term involving their product (see Equation (1.15)). Theoretically, therefore, beats are due to the interference between amplitudes describing the two decay paths: a to g and b to g.

So far our treatment has successfully reproduced the beat phenomenon. Nevertheless, it is insufficient. To see this, turn now to a treatment of decays in a type II atom, one with an "inverted" level structure, as shown in Figure 4–6. Precisely the same analysis can be performed: as before, oscillating electric dipoles are created, now between a and h and between a and g. If one carries through the identical calculation, one finds that these should interfere to produce a beat. However, recall that if the experiment is actually performed, no beat is seen.

Why not? What is wrong with the above analysis? To answer this question, we turn now to a consideration of complementarity as it applies to quantum beats.

We pointed out above the mathematical similarity between beats and interference. Recall that the principle of complementarity maintains that *either* one may observe interference *or* one may determine which path a quantum followed. Is there a way we might adapt this principle to the case of quantum beats? To obtain interference, it is essential that the trajectory of the quantum be ambiguous. Note in this regard that for a type I atom, *the history of the atom after it is struck by the laser pulse is indeed ambiguous.* The initial and final state of the atom is g—but there are two distinct ways it has of making the circuit. It can absorb a laser photon into state a, and decay by emitting a photon ω_a, or it can absorb a laser photon into state b and decay by emitting a photon ω_b. The absorbed and emitted photons would possess different frequencies and polarizations; however, care is taken in the experimental setup to ensure that both frequencies and polarizations are present in the input laser pulse, and also that the detector is insensitive to all distinguishing characteristics of the two decay channels. Thus the two decay modes are indistinguishable.

But they are not indistinguishable for a type II atom. For such an atom, it *is* possible to determine the train of events following the laser pulse. A pulse of laser light may excite the upper state a, but the decay is now to two distinct lower states, g and h. This implies that, some time after the decay photon has been detected, it would be possible to go back to the type II atom and determine what the final state actually was, either g or h. But according to the principle of complementarity, for interference we require that this be impossible.

We can frame the complementarity principle as it applies to interference in general terms:

> If it is, in principle, possible to distinguish by which path the quantum has traveled from source to detector, then no interference will occur.

As it applies to quantum beats, the principle of complementarity reads

> If it is, in principle, possible to distinguish by which history the atom has gone from initial to final state, then no beats will occur.

Two remarks should be made. First, we need not actually perform a measurement that gives path information. It is sufficient that such an experiment is *possible*; if it is, interference phenomena will be absent. Second, in the above statement no mention is made of the uncertainty principle, nor of any other mechanism of enforcement of complementarity. All we need examine is the distinguishability of paths. This "information" alone is sufficient to predict the experimental outcomes.

Orthogonality and the Role of Information in Quantum Beats The presence of *information* in the atom as to its past history is enough to block the appearance of interference. So far, our treatment of information has been completely nonmathematical. While at one level this is perfectly sufficient, we might well ask if the information description can be captured in a more exacting theoretical language. To see how this is possible, we must give up the picture of radiating dipoles, and move from a semiclassical treatment to one that includes the quantum physics of the radiation field. While the full development of quantum electrodynamics is beyond the scope of this book, we can appropriate certain conceptual aspects into our treatment in a simple way.

We include the state of the radiation field by adding to the wave function for the atom a notation indicating the number of photons of each kind that are present. For a type I atom immediately following excitation, no photons are present, and the state is that given by Equation (4.12) with $t = 0$. At a later time, however, the total wave function must include terms describing the emitted photons. These will be of the form

$$C_1(t)\psi_g\phi_a + C_2(t)\psi_g\phi_b \tag{4.16}$$

where ϕ_a and ϕ_b are the photon parts of the wave function. We may read C_1 as the probability amplitude that the decay to the ground state g occurred with the emission of a photon of frequency ω_a. The second term describes emission of a photon with frequency ω_b.

Note that the final-state wave function is a superposition state. Because the detector cannot distinguish the two types of photons, the two decay paths are completely indistinguishable and both must be kept in the calculation. Once again, interference arises because of cross-terms which, after some simplification, now take the form

$$C_1^*(t)C_2(t)\,e^{i(\omega_a - \omega_b)t}\int \psi_g^*\psi_g\,d^3r \tag{4.17}$$

Note here the term

$$e^{i(\omega_a - \omega_b)t} \tag{4.18}$$

describing the sinusoidal variation of the emitted intensity; this is the quantum beat. Note also that in Equation (4.17), the integral over the ground-state wave function is equal to unity. We have shown it explicitly only to compare with the calculation to follow for type II atoms.

The analysis of quantum beats from type II atoms proceeds in the same way, with one crucial difference. There are two final states: g and h. This implies that the expression comparable to Equation (4.16) is

$$C_1(t)\psi_g\phi_a + C_2(t)\psi_h\phi_b \tag{4.19}$$

and the interference cross-term responsible for quantum beats is

$$C_1^*(t)C_2(t)\,e^{i(\omega_g - \omega_h)t}\int \psi_g^*\psi_h\,d^3r \tag{4.20}$$

The crucial difference lies in the integral. We now show that *it is equal to zero, implying that for type II atoms there are no beats.*

It is a principle of quantum mechanics that the state of a system can always be expressed as the sum of terms involving its basis states, and that these basis states form a complete, orthogonal set. For example, consider the well-known hydrogen-atom energy eigenfunctions $\phi_{n\ell m}$, where n, ℓ, and m are the hydrogen-atom quantum numbers. When we say that these eigenfunctions form a complete set, we mean that even if a hydrogen atom happens to be in a state that is not an eigenstate of the energy, its state can always be written as the sum of terms involving these eigenfunctions. And when we say that these eigenfunctions are orthogonal, we mean that a term such as

$$\int |\phi_{n\ell m}|^2\,d^3r \tag{4.21}$$

is nonzero, but a term such as

$$\int \phi_{n\ell m}^*\phi_{n'\ell'm'}\,d^3r \qquad n' \neq n, \quad \ell' \neq \ell, \quad m' \neq m \tag{4.22}$$

is always zero. But the integral appearing in Equation (4.20) is simply a shorthand version of that in (4.22) and therefore is zero. In contrast to the semi-classical calculation, this one predicts the beats to be absent.

The orthogonality of the two possible final states of the atom reflects the residual information left in the system after the decay. As long as such information exists somewhere in the atom–photon system, an orthogonality will arise that suppresses the beats.

In the above example, the residual information was in the atomic ground-state sublevels, but it can also exist in the radiation field. To see this, return to the case of type I atoms, which exhibit beats. But now modify the detector so it can distinguish between ω_a and ω_b photons. In this case, the orthogonality will occur, not between atomic wave functions, but between the photon wave functions. Once again, the beats are suppressed. Figure 4–7, taken from the quantum beat experiments of Hellmuth, Walther, Zajonc and Schleich,[20] illustrates the effect. In this experiment, the detector was made sensitive to photon polarization. Since the two photons ω_a and ω_b have different polarizations, this allowed the experiment to determine the history of the atom. The beats were absent; if information about the decay mode existed anywhere, no interference was observed.* (This experiment was also operated in the delayed-choice mode, in which the decision as to whether the detector would be sensitive to polarization was delayed until after the photon had been emitted. Once again, the paradoxical result was obtained that the decision appeared to have "altered the past history of the photon.")

Partial Information Until this point we have only considered situations in which we either had information or we did not—black or white. Sometimes things are not so clear; we may possess partial information. How does this affect interference?

Wootters and Zurek[21] have returned to Einstein's modification of the classic double-slit interference experiment, and analyzed it from the standpoint of partial information. Recall his thought experiment (Figure 4–1). The slits are free to move; after the particle has passed through, we measure the slits' momentum. As illustrated in Figure 4–1, if the slits are moving downward, the particle must have passed through slit 2.

How can one think of this experiment from the standpoint of partial information? Wootters and Zurek noted that the above conclusion is not, in fact, entirely certain. The same motion of the slits would also be observed had the particle passed through the wrong slit—*if* the initial slit momentum had been large and downward. What are the chances that this had been the case? They considered a model in which the screen containing the slits was held in place by a spring, and so was represented by the wave function of the simple harmonic oscillator. They evaluated the probability of the initial slit momentum being large enough to yield such an erroneous conclusion, and so obtained an expression for the *probability that we had*

---

* Again, notice that no uncertainty argument has been used to account for the loss of interference; information and the associated orthogonality of wave functions suffice. We repeat that debate continues as to whether there is a hidden mechanism that enforces complementarity in quantum beats.

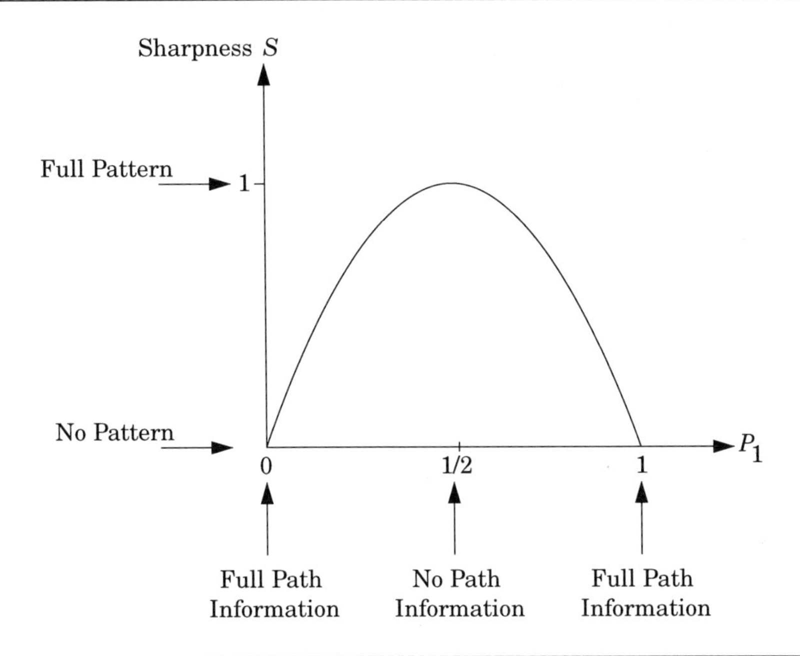

Figure 4–8 *Partial Information and Interference.* The horizontal axis plots the amount of information we have concerning the particle's path; the vertical axis indicates the sharpness of the resulting interference pattern.[21]

obtained path information. Using the same wave function, they also calculated the resulting pattern of arrivals at the final screen. It turned out to be a *partially smeared-out interference pattern.*

In Figure 4–8 we schematically sketch their result. Consider first the x-axis. Along it, P_1 is the probability that the particle passed through slit 1. When this is equal to unity, we know with certainty which path the particle took: it passed through slit 1. Similarly, when P_1 is equal to zero we also have perfect path information: the particle definitely passed through the other slit. Conversely, if P_1 is equal to $\frac{1}{2}$, the particle is equally likely to have taken either route, and we have no path information whatsoever.

The vertical axis in Figure 4–8 measures the sharpness of the interference pattern: $S = 1$ corresponds to a perfect pattern and $S = 0$ to no pattern at all. Complementarity insists that $S = 0$ when $P_1 = 0$ or 1. Figure 4–8 has this property. But it also fills in all the intermediate values. A surprising result is that the curve turns out to be quite broad: one can obtain a moderately good interference pattern while obtaining a fairly large amount of path information.

From the many experimental studies of complementarity with partial information, we draw on the results of Wang, Zou and Mandel.[22] They

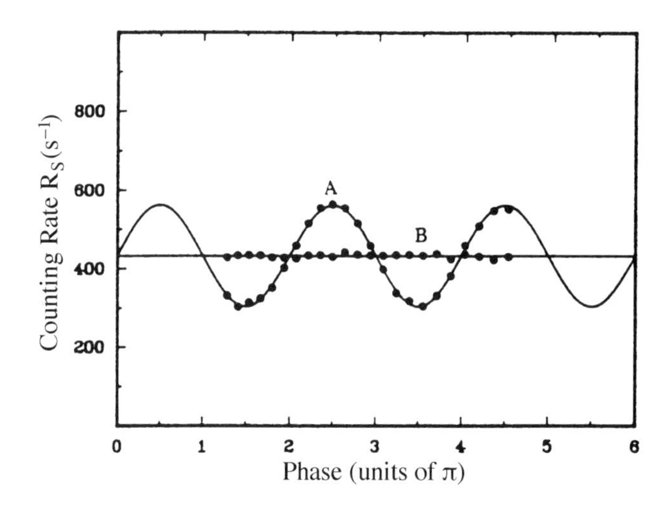

Figure 4-9 *Interference Patterns* observed with no (curve *A*) and full (curve *B*) path information by Mandel and co-workers. SOURCE: Reproduced with permission from L.J. Wang, X.Y. Zou and L. Mandel, "Induced coherence and indistinguishability in optical interference," *Phys. Rev. A*, vol. 44, p. 4614 (1991), published by The American Physical Society.

performed a series of beautiful optical interference experiments in which, by varying the transmissivity of a filter, it was possible to continuously vary the amount of path information available. In Figure 4–9 their results are shown for two extreme cases. In curve *A* there was no path information; a perfect interference pattern was obtained. Conversely, in curve *B* there was full path information; no interference pattern was obtained. Finally, in Figure 4–10 we indicate their results for the sharpness *S* of the interference pattern as a function of path information. We see a continuous variation between these two extremes.

In their discussion of their experimental results, Wang and co-workers noted that in their analysis they made no use of a large uncontrollable disturbance acting on the system, in the spirit of the Heisenberg gamma-ray microscope. The disappearance of the interference pattern was simply a consequence of the fact that the two possible photon paths had become distinguishable. Was there an enforcing mechanism associated with their variable filter that somehow disrupted, via an uncertainty mechanism, these experiments? If so, it is not obvious. Nor is it needed; information is enough.

Wang et al. went on to point out that their experiment did not actually determine the paths taken by the photons. This was unnecessary. It was sufficient that they could, in principle, have made such a measurement. As

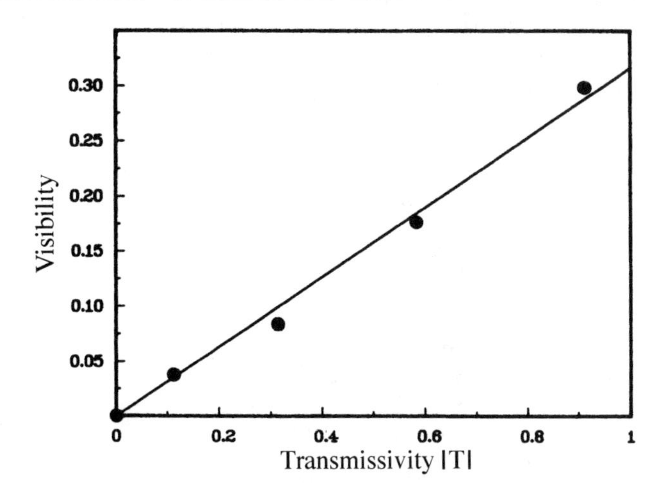

Figure 4–10 *Sharpness of the Interference Pattern as a Function of Path Information* observed by Mandel and co-workers. SOURCE: Reproduced with permission from L.J. Wang, X.Y. Zou and L. Mandel, "Induced coherence and indistinguishability in optical interference," *Phys. Rev. A*, vol. 44, p. 4614 (1991), published by The American Physical Society.

before, the mere possibility of path information is sufficient to wipe out interference effects. Even if the information is only potentially available, and even if it is only partially available, the interference pattern will reflect the fact.

4.4 Concluding Remarks

Complementarity has many faces. At the opening of this chapter we indicated three; to these, recent work has added a fourth, one related to information.

Differing views can be held as to the significance of complementarity. For example, we can argue that it implies that quantum mechanics is incapable of providing us with a full description of reality. This, of course, was Einstein's view: if one accepts the traditional meaning of understanding, quantum theory forbids us from attaining it.

It is important to emphasize, however, that implicit in this position is an unstated assumption: the assumption that *there is such a thing as an objective reality whose state we are trying to discover.* On the face of it, this assumption seems so obviously true that it seems silly to question it. However, as we will discuss in the next two chapters, it has been called into question by certain experiments.

Bohr took a differing view of the significance of the principle of complementarity. He held that the principle should not be regarded as expressing the incompleteness of quantum theory, but rather that it was an important insight into the very nature of knowledge. It expressed a philosophical limitation on what we can know. He wrote:

> Complementarity denotes the logical relation, of quite a new type, between concepts which are mutually exclusive, and which therefore cannot be considered at the same time—that would lead to logical mistakes—but which nevertheless must both be used in order to give a complete description of the situation.[23]

Note in this passage Bohr's recurring use of the word "logical"; he speaks of complementarity as a philosophical principle, rather than a physical one.

We must confess to being unable to understand *why* Bohr took this point of view. While valuing his principle for the light it throws on the perversity of the quantum world, we do not agree with him that it resolves the unrest caused by modern experiments in quantum mechanics. Rather, we believe that the complementarity principle forcefully illustrates the scope of the dilemma they pose. If, as Einstein expressed it, Bohr hoped complementarity would prove a soft pillow to lull scientific thinking to sleep, Bohr failed. The challenges to thinking have only intensified and broadened.

Chapter 5

The EPR Paradox and Bell's Theorem

Progress concerning the foundations of quantum mechanics took a dramatic turn with the publication of two extraordinary theorems by John Bell in the years 1964 and 1966. Both for quantum physics and for this book, they are the most important advances made in our understanding of quantum mechanics since the creation of the theory itself. Before discussing these theorems, let us pause and take stock.

In every chapter of this book, we have had occasion to remark on various curious features of quantum theory. All are ways in which quantum mechanics *refuses to address certain issues*:

- In Chapter 1 we discussed how quantum theory never describes how a particle can make its way through two slits at the same time.
- In Chapter 2, in the context of the delayed-choice experiment, we pointed out that while quantum mechanics seems to imply that we can alter the past, it provides us with no explanation of how this could possibly be.
- In Chapter 3 we discussed how the uncertainty principle prevents us from attaining complete knowledge; there is always a certain "fuzziness" to the results of any measurement.
- Also in Chapter 3 we discussed how quantum mechanics does not provide explanations of events, but only speaks in terms of the probability of their occurrence. Indeed, the very idea that individual events have causes seems absent from the theory.
- In Chapter 4 we discussed how quantum theory implies that we can only know half of everything, rather than all of everything, as in classical thought.

Repeatedly we have emphasized that these are not trivial elements of the theory, which might be easily fixed. Rather, they are intrinsic to its very nature.

Also throughout our analysis, we have repeatedly asked what we are to make of this curious refusal. We have identified two possible views:

1. We should think of it as a limitation of the theory. It is pointing out that *quantum mechanics is incomplete*. There is such a thing as objective reality, and the theory is not telling us everything about it. Quantum mechanics is perfectly all right so far as it goes, but it does not provide the whole story.
2. There is nothing wrong with quantum mechanics at all. Remember—it is the *experiments* that are impossible to comprehend in any normal sense of the term. Even had quantum theory never been invented, these experiments could have been performed, and we would still find ourselves unable to understand them. Quantum theory's refusal to attempt to do so, far from being the theory's defect, is actually its greatest virtue.

At various points we have phrased the opposition between these two views in terms of a question: Does quantum theory (1) merely fail to offer a complete description of an extent, objective reality, or is it rather that (2) this reality simply does not exist?

Historically, (1) was Einstein's opinion, and (2) was Bohr's. The point of view expressed in (1) has come to be known as "realism," and the point of view expressed in (2) as "the Copenhagen interpretation." The running debate between Einstein and Bohr over this question has occupied many pages of this book, but it is important to emphasize that the issue here is not simply a disagreement between two individuals. Rather, at stake is the very nature of what we believe to be the goals of science—indeed, all of science, and not simply this one theory.

For decades it seemed impossible to see what the full implications of quantum mechanics might be on such fundamental philosophical issues as the nature or very existence of reality. Science had always presumed a world whose properties were independent of the observer and the act of observation: trees did, in fact, fall in the forest even if no one was present to hear the crash. Likewise, for the atomic world it seemed only reasonable that a self-consistent, if highly unusual, reality must underlie all the phenomena of the new physics. Einstein held firmly to this traditional vision of science, which sought to account for everything in terms of a complete microscopic theory, while Bohr felt that uncovering of the hidden machinery of nature was a hopeless and wrong-headed enterprise. Only predictions concerning measurable outcomes were significant for Bohr.

What could the hard evidence of physics contribute to this debate? At the outset, it seemed it could contribute nothing. Since the debate related only to how we regard quantum theory, and had no experimental consequences, most scientists were content not to think about the question very much. This was re-enforced by a theorem published in 1932 by the brilliant mathematician John von Neumann.[1] According to his theorem, it was impossible to construct a complete microscopic theory of the atomic

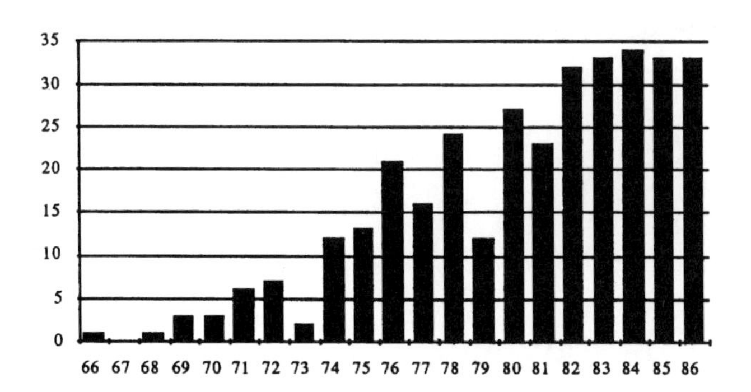

Figure 5–1 *Reception of Bell's Theorem.* Annual citations of Bell's theorem in the years following its announcement. The initial near-indifference only gradually gave way to a recognition of the theorem's importance. SOURCE: Reproduced with permission from L.E. Ballantine, Resource Letter I.Q.M.2, "Foundations of quantum mechanics since the Bell inequality," *Amer. J. Phys.*, vol. 55, p. 785 (1987).

world that would give predictions consistent with quantum mechanics. Philosophers were free to speculate about the deeper nature of the world, but it seemed that such activity would be purely philosophical, with no physical content. But in 1964 and 1966, two remarkable theorems were published by the young physicist John Bell[2] demonstrating that this view was wrong. Von Neumann's theorem was based on a faulty assumption, and Bell went on to show that not only could competing theories be invented, but that certain of them were open to experimental tests that would determine whether they were better than conventional quantum theory or not. What people had taken to be only a question of interpretation could be decided by a careful examination of the competing theories put to experimental tests in the usual way.

The implications of quantum mechanics have, in the meantime, become ever more transparent,[3] and in the 70s and 80s a series of experiments were carried out along the lines implied by Bell's result. As a result of this remarkable series of events, we now have unambiguous evidence that we must consider when thinking about the interpretation of quantum mechanics.

Bell's considerations were of two types. First, from theory alone, he showed a deep connection between the "context" of observation and the observed attributes of the quantum world. Second, Bell's 1964 theorem showed that competing theories could be experimentally tested. In the next chapter we will take up the actual experimental tests that have been based on this theorem.

Parenthetically, we should note that reaction to Bell's theorem followed an unusual pattern. For years after he discovered it, other physicists paid scant attention. In normal circumstances an important discovery is immediately followed by a burst of interest, in which many other papers are published dealing with it; later there is a gradual decline, signaling that the result has been incorporated into the fabric of the field. But this pattern is quite unlike that which greeted Bell's discovery. Figure 5–1, taken from Ballentine,[4] indicates the number of papers that made reference to his theorem. In this figure we see an initial near-total indifference, only gradually followed by a dawning recognition of the importance of Bell's theorem.

5.1 The EPR Argument

Bell's theorem is concerned with the so-called EPR argument. This argument was given by Albert **E**instein, Boris **P**odolsky and Nathan **R**osen[5] in 1935, and it is one of the most remarkable attacks on quantum theory ever launched. Recall that, according to quantum theory, measurements can be made of only one of any pair of complementary variables: position *or* momentum, energy *or* time. But the simultaneous measurement of both members of such a pair is impossible. The Einstein, Podolsky and Rosen paper argued that such measurements were quite possible, and it gave a simple description of how to carry them out. Thus, according to their analysis, it was possible to obtain a more complete description of physical reality than that provided by quantum mechanics. Their conclusion was that quantum theory was incomplete.

A colleague of Niels Bohr's, Leon Rosenfeld, has given us an account of Bohr's reaction to the EPR paper:[6]

> This onslaught came down upon us as a bolt from the blue. Its effect on Bohr was remarkable. ... A new worry could not come at a less propitious time. Yet, as soon as Bohr had heard my report of Einstein's argument, everything else was abandoned: we had to clear up such a misunderstanding at once. We should reply by taking up the same example and showing the right way to speak about it. In great excitement, Bohr immediately started dictating to me the outline of such a reply. Very soon, however, he became hesitant: "No, this won't do, we must try all over again ... we must make it quite clear ..." So it went on for a while, with growing wonder at the unexpected subtlety of the argument. Now and then, he would turn to me: "What *can* they mean? Do *you* understand it?" There would follow some inconclusive exegesis. Clearly, we were farther from the mark than we first thought. Eventually, he broke off with the familiar remark that he "must sleep on it."

The Einstein, Podolsky and Rosen argument has come to be known as "the EPR paradox." For decades, paper after paper was written in an attempt to resolve it, but not for thirty years was any real headway made on the matter. Bell's theorem, however, showed that an experiment was possible that could conclusively test whether the EPR argument was correct. In the early 1980s a series of such experiments were carried out. These experiments have conclusively shown that quantum mechanics is indeed correct, and that the EPR argument had relied upon incorrect assumptions.

But there are only two important assumptions that enter into the EPR argument, and one of them is that of reality: the assumption we have labeled (1) above. The other, known as locality, also seems hard to doubt. The implications of Bell's theorem and the experiments that test it constitute a remarkable insight into the nature of the physical world.

The Argument The EPR paper claimed to show how to measure *any* pair of complementary variables. Bell's theorem, on the other hand, was couched in terms of a particular version of the EPR paradox, developed by David Bohm.[7] For this reason we will concentrate on Bohm's version in what follows.

A particle's spin is customarily measured by means of a so-called Stern–Gerlach analyzer, diagrammed in Figure 5–2. On the other hand, such a device only measures one component of spin, that along the analyzer's vertical axis. Furthermore, recall that the operators for the x-component and the z-component of spin do not commute:

$$[S_x, S_z] \neq 0 \tag{5.1}$$

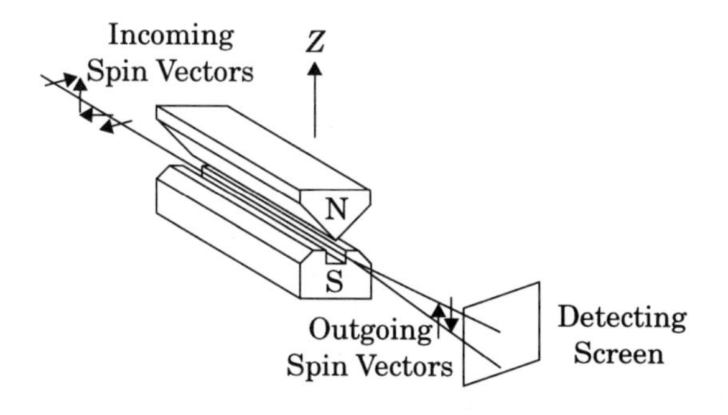

Figure 5–2 *A Stern–Gerlach Analyzer* measures the component of spin along the analyzer's axis, here labeled z. The magnets produce a nonuniform magnetic field that deflects those particles, so that those with differing spin components arrive at differing points on the detecting screen. The small arrows indicate the direction of spin of the incoming particles that would be revealed by measuring devices placed in their paths.

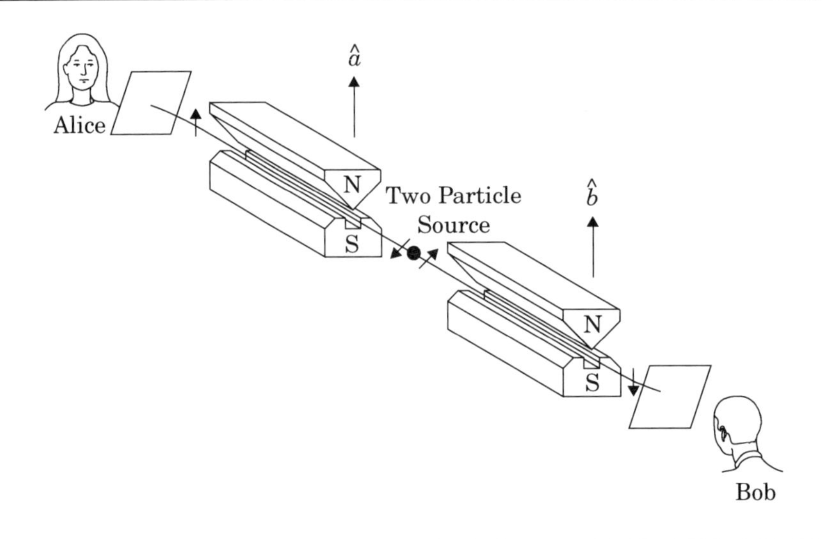

Figure 5–3 *The EPR Apparatus.* Alice can deduce the spin of the particle heading toward Bob without actually observing it.

so that measurements of S_x and S_z obey an uncertainty relation:

$$\Delta S_x \, \Delta S_z \neq 0 \tag{5.2}$$

So no apparatus can possibly measure all three components. In contrast, EPR argue that these components can be measured to arbitrarily high accuracy by use of the experimental apparatus sketched in Figure 5–3. This apparatus consists of three parts.

The first part is a device that shoots out two particles—always in opposite directions and always polarized with their spins pointing in opposite directions.* Although the EPR argument does not depend on the details of how these particles are produced, we note that such pairs of particles can be actually produced in the laboratory in a number of ways. One technique is to prepare an atom of positronium—an electron and a positron bound together—in a state of orbital angular momentum zero and spin angular momentum zero as well. One can then "ionize" the positronium atom, yielding the required pair.

The other two pieces of the experimental apparatus are Stern–Gerlach analyzers, which measure the component of particle spin along a certain

* This way of speaking implicitly assumes that such local properties can be properly assigned to particles—and this, as we shall see, is precisely what experiments reveal that we cannot do. To be more precise, we would say that, e.g., the particles' states are such that measurement of their spins always yield opposite results.

axis. One particle is sent toward the first analyzer, the other toward the second. They are at widely separated points in space: we will call the first "location A" and the second "location B." To make things specific, we will imagine two experimenters, Alice and Bob, operating the two analyzers. Alice and Bob are free to orient their analyzers in any direction. As the experiment begins, the emitter produces a pair of particles and sends them outward toward the two experimenters.

Suppose that initially Alice had chosen to orient her Stern–Gerlach analyzer as indicated in Figure 5–3: perpendicular to the line of flight of the approaching particle and pointing vertically upward along the z-axis. When the particle enters her analyzer, the device will give one of two answers: "spin up" or "spin down." Suppose, for the sake of definiteness, that in this particular run it yields "spin up." Since measurements on the two members of the pair of particles always yield opposite results, Alice concludes that Bob's particle has "spin down" along the z-axis. *In this way, Alice has measured the z-component of the spin of the particle heading toward Bob.* If they wish, Alice and Bob can test this conclusion by having Bob also orient his analyzer along the z-axis. They will find that every time Alice finds "spin up," Bob finds "spin down," and vice versa. But this test is not necessary other than to ensure that the experiment is functioning correctly.

EPR now introduce an essential point. They emphasize that locations A and B are widely separated in space, and that whatever goes on at one location can have no effect on what goes on at the other. While Alice's analyzer may have influenced the particle heading toward her, it cannot possibly have affected the particle heading toward Bob. The result Alice obtained could not have had any effect on the spin of Bob's particle. From this, EPR conclude that *Bob's particle must have had spin down along the z-axis even before Alice had made her measurement.* Her observation was certainly *required* in order to learn the spin of Bob's particle, but it cannot have *affected* this spin. The only function of her observation had been to find out about a pre-existing reality.

The remainder of the EPR argument is now simple. For suppose Alice had made a different choice of orientation of her analyzer. Suppose she had chosen not the z-axis but the x-axis. Precisely the same argument goes through: Alice can now measure the x-component of the spin of the particle heading toward Bob, and we are assured that this component must have existed prior to her measurement. Thus EPR conclude that both of the two complementary variables describing Bob's particle, S_z and S_x, exist and have definite values.

A slight variation of this argument can also be given. Let Alice orient her analyzer along the z-axis and Bob orient his analyzer along the x-axis. By the above argument, Alice can infer the spin along z of Bob's particle. But Bob can now directly measure the spin of his particle along x. Again, definite conclusions can be drawn about the two complementary variables, in opposition to the principles of quantum mechanics. However, this variant is less compelling than the first, since it is possible that Bob's measurement disturbed his particle.

Locality The EPR argument makes use of an assumption termed *locality*: the assumption that anything that happens at a given location has only local effects. Nothing that happens at A can have any effect on the state of affairs at B. Locality is an essential component of the EPR argument, for without this hypothesis it is possible to imagine that Alice's measurement could have forced Bob's particle into a new state. Thus, without the locality assumption, we cannot conclude that the spin of the particle heading toward Bob existed independently of Alice's measurement.

To make the locality hypothesis vivid, imagine that Alice lives on Earth, but that Bob lives on a planet located in a galaxy one million light years away. According to the theory of relativity, no physical effect from Alice's apparatus can propagate faster than the speed of light. Thus, for one million years after she performs her measurement, the state of affairs at Bob's location is perfectly "insulated" from Alice's experiment, and the locality assumption is justified.

We can always imagine, of course, that the theory of relativity is mistaken. But even this would not invalidate the locality assumption. For let Bob perform his measurement one year after Alice performed hers. In order for Alice's measurement to have any effect on the state of affairs at Bob's location, we would have to postulate some physical effect that travels one million times faster than light. Furthermore, we can always imagine Bob performing his measurement not one year, but one minute after Alice's—or, in the limit, arbitrarily shortly afterward. In this way, we can see that *the locality assumption is justified unless some physical effect is capable of traveling with infinite velocity*. Effects that do travel with infinite velocity give rise to so-called action at a distance. This phenomenon involves a radical revision of our ideas about physical reality, a revision Einstein, Podolsky and Rosen were unwilling to accept. (For an example of a theory that does include action at a distance, see Bohm's nonlocal interpretation of quantum mechanics, discussed in the next chapter.)

The Heisenberg uncertainty microscope illustrates that we always disturb an object in the process of observation. The essential trick that Einstein, Podolsky and Rosen used to get around this limitation was never to touch or look at Bob's particle. Rather, they studied it indirectly, by considering not one particle but two, and by studying only the other member of the pair. The locality principle ensured that this measurement could not have affected Bob's particle, and so guaranteed the reality of the property of Bob's particle, inferred by Alice's measurement of hers.

Reality and Hidden Variables As an analogy to the EPR method, imagine that you give a friend six seeds. Some are put in one box and the rest in another, identical to the first. The boxes are scrambled, such that neither of you knows which is which. Take one box to Moscow while your friend takes the other to New York. In Moscow, open the lid to your box and find two seeds. Since seeds cannot disappear or appear spontaneously (their number is conserved, just as is the spin of each particle in the EPR experiment), you immediately know that four are in the other box in New York. This knowledge is certain and instantaneous. No measurement was necessary on the distant box, and thus no disturbance, quantum-mechanical or otherwise, could have occurred to alter its seed count or render it uncertain. If you check by later counting the number of seeds in the other box, you will always find the correct number. You rightly deduce that there had always been four seeds in the New York box. *The only thing that changed through your observation was your knowledge of the real, pre-existing situation.*

Einstein, Podolsky and Rosen believed in the existence of such a reality. In their paper they proceeded cautiously, writing "If, without in any way disturbing a system, we can predict with certainty (i.e. with probability equal to unity) the value of a physical quantity, then there exists an element of physical reality corresponding to this quantity."[5] However, from his many writings and remarks, it is clear that all his life Einstein envisioned a world in which submicroscopic objects possessed real attributes that objectively existed. These are the "elements of reality" of the EPR paper. EPR formulated two conditions for the existence of these attributes: first, it must be possible to predict them with perfect accuracy; and second, the prediction must be based upon a measurement that exerts no disturbing influence on them. *EPR take the possibility of our making such a prediction concerning a quantity a test of the reality of that quantity.*

In our example, by means of measurements made of the S_z of her particle, Alice can infer the S_z of Bob's particle. If Bob chooses to, he can himself measure it and confirm that Alice's conclusions are invariably correct. Thus the first of these two conditions is met. Furthermore, the locality principle ensures that Alice's measurement could not have had any effect on Bob's S_z, which fulfills the second condition. Einstein, Podolsky and Rosen take these circumstances as evidence that this S_z must objectively exist. It must be a real attribute of the particle heading toward Bob—just as, say, its shape is a real, objectively existing property of a table.

The Einstein universe is one inhabited by real objects with real, persistent properties. The objects of that world, even if microscopic, should be understandable using concepts familiar to us from classical physics. But if quantum mechanics is taken as the true story, then a radical conceptual revolution is implied, one that entails a totally new understanding of the very nature of the scientific enterprise. This step Einstein was unwilling to take. He argued rather that, in any complete theory, there must be an element corresponding to each property of the real world—each "element of physical reality." According to EPR, quantum theory was clearly missing variables that would correspond to elements of physical reality such as S_x, S_y and S_z, and so was incomplete. As they saw it, if one possessed a complete theory instead of quantum mechanics, the ideas necessary to understand reality might be complex, but they would not be different in kind from those scientists have always used in the past. Such a new theory would go beyond quantum mechanics, and would treat the workings of the microscopic world in much the same way that classical mechanics treats the workings of the large-scale world. It would tell us all the things that quantum mechanics cannot: it would describe the trajectory a particle takes as it travels through a double-slit interference experiment, it would describe the real position and momentum of a particle being examined under a Heisenberg uncertainty microscope, and it would describe all three components of a particle's spin in the EPR device.

Such a theory is called a *hidden-variable theory*. (The name refers to variables such as position, momentum, direction of spin vector and the like, which are "hidden" from us.) In the point of view of Einstein, Podolsky and Rosen, when quantum mechanics predicts the expectation value of some observable, it is somehow averaging over all possible values these variables might have. The complete hidden-variable theory, on the other hand, would tell us about these quantities explicitly. Einstein wanted to find that theory.

There exists in physics a good analogue to this distinction between a partial theory and a deeper, more complete one: thermodynamics and statistical mechanics. Thermodynamics contents itself with considering quantities such as the pressure and internal energy of a gas. Statistical mechanics, in contrast, describes these quantities as arising from a deeper, hidden reality—from the motion of the molecules making up the gas—and shows how the description given by thermodynamics is a partial one, obtained by averaging over all possible motions of the molecules. In this analogy, thermodynamics corresponds to quantum mechanics, and statistical mechanics to the deeper, more complete hidden-variable theory that we wish to find.

Hidden-variable theories can be analyzed in two ways: first for their purely theoretical implications, and second for their experimental consequences. For decades it was thought that no experiment could distinguish between local hidden-variable theories and orthodox quantum mechanics. The difference was, therefore, thought to be only a matter of philosophical taste. This view persisted until Bell's 1964 theorem made it possible to experimentally distinguish between the two views. In addition, Bell proved a second theorem, first published in 1966 and subsequently improved upon by Kochen and Specker. This latter theorem made no experimental claims, but provided the basis for a new appreciation of quantum mechanics or any hidden-variable theory consistent with it. Before turning to Bell's justly famous 1964 theorem, we must explore his other theorem, which we will call the BKS theorem to avoid confusion.

5.2 The BKS Theorem and Contextuality

We have seen that, as a consequence of the uncertainty principle, quantum measurements can disturb a system in new and uncontrollable ways. Such disruptions occur when we measure one partner of a complementary pair, such as position and momentum.

In contrast, nothing prevents us from simultaneously determining the eigenvalues of observables as long as they are *compatible*. For example, one commonly gives the state of an atomic system by listing the values of a complete set of compatible observables, such as energy, orbital angular momentum, and so on. The mathematical statement of compatibility is, as we have seen, expressed through the commutation relationships that exist among the observables. If observables commute with one another, then they are compatible and can be given exact values simultaneously. If they fail to commute, then they are complementary and an uncertainty relationship governs the values they can take on.

However, from another standpoint, one formalized in the BKS theorem, interpretational difficulties arise even when we are working with compatible observables. In the nonquantum world it is perfectly permissible to consider hair color independently of height, weight or other "observables." Your hair color does not depend on whether someone is measuring your height or weight. Not so in the strange world of quantum mechanics.

Consider two sets of three observables: A, B, and C (hair color, height and weight) and A, L, and M (hair color, shoe size and gender). In the nonquantum world we can conceive of A (hair color) without concerning ourselves about B and C, or L and M. Hair color is well-defined regardless of which other personal attributes we care to observe. Not so in the quantum world. The "context" of the measurement (which is determined by our choice of B, C or L, M) is an important consideration for quantum systems. It turns out that, in general, the value of A (hair color) will depend on which other observations we make. This is even true when all the observables are compatible! Thus, this complication is not due to Heisenberg's uncertainty principle, but is an independent feature of quantum theory that has come to be called *contextuality*. The proof that quantum mechanics entails contextuality is the result proven by Bell, Kochen and Specker in their remarkable theorem. The full proof of this theorem is beyond the scope of this book, but we would like to sketch the essential elements of it, and especially discuss its implications.[8]

Sketch of the BKS Proof Consider a spin-1 quantum system that has components in three orthogonal directions: S_x, S_y and S_z. We know that the projection of a spin-1 system along any axis can give one of three results: eigenvalues -1, 0 or 1. The observables of interest to us are the squares of S_x, S_y and S_z, which therefore can have as eigenvalues 0 and 1. Two further facts are important. First, S_x^2, S_y^2 and S_z^2 commute with one another. In the language of our previous considerations, they are compatible. Nothing prevents us from measuring them simultaneously. Second, from the laws of quantum mechanics, we know that the sum of the squared spins is given by:

$$S_x^2 + S_y^2 + S_z^2 = s(s+1) = 2 \tag{5.3}$$

We now choose a particular triad of orthogonal directions against which to measure the spin squared. Because of Equation (5.3), two values of spin squared must be 1 and the other 0 in order to produce the value 2 as required, no matter how we choose the three mutually orthogonal directions. Choose another set of three directions. They too must lead to two values being 1 and one being 0. We can repeat this process as often as we like.

For a hidden-variable program to work, there must be a consistent way of assigning 1 or 0 to each direction so that when we pick a triad of orthogonal directions at random, we get results that reproduce quantum predictions. We also would like the added feature that the results lead to a consistent picture of the hidden realities that yield these results, regardless of which triad we happen to pick. If this is true, then it is possible to consider an act of measurement as uncovering values that already exist. This corresponds to our common-sense notion of the world and is the basic idea behind most (but not all) hidden-variable schemes. The BKS theorem shows that no hidden-variable theory of this type is possible. By a careful geometric argument, Bell, Kochen and Specker demonstrate that although one can choose each set of triads properly, by the end of the series an inconsistency has developed. They show that there is absolutely no self-consistent way to assign 1 or 0 to the various spin directions such that Equation (5.3) holds. The value you get for S_x, for example, may well depend on what directions you pick for S_y and S_z. To put it dramatically, the hair color you detect may well depend on whether you are simultaneously measuring shoe size and gender, or whether you are measuring height and weight.

Quantum mechanics is completely in agreement with the BKS theorem because quantum theory in no sense presupposes that the values that observables take on were pre-existing. In choosing one triad to measure, the experimenter must configure her apparatus in a particular way and not some other. Changing her choice of which three directions to measure requires a new experimental arrangement. Bohr insisted that one not "imagine" a pre-existing real world whose observables already possess real values: rather one should ask a theory to make statements only about those observables for which the apparatus is currently configured. Thus, in his view, we should discuss only one triad at a time. If one resists Bohr's stance, BKS places profound constraints on the kind of theory and interpretation we can consider. It must be contextual.

Naive hidden-variable models of the microscopic world are not "contextual" in the required way, and therefore fail to meet the elementary demands of quantum theory and the BKS theorem. Contextual hidden-variable theories are possible, as David Bohm has demonstrated, but then these are as mysterious in their own ways as quantum mechanics is in its. We will come back to this topic later.

We turn now to the more famous of Bell's two theorems and its experimental implications for the testing of hidden-variable theories.

5.3 Hidden-Variable Theories

The version of the EPR argument we have been discussing restricts attention to situations in which Alice and Bob orient their analyzers in parallel directions. Bell's theorem refers to a slight generalization, in which the two analyzers can be oriented in different directions. For this experiment, Bell's theorem shows that no hidden-variable theory obeying a few quite general conditions can possibly be created that duplicates all the predictions of quantum mechanics.

Figure 5–4 diagrams the new experiment. Alice's analyzer points along the $\hat{a}$-axis, Bob's along $\hat{b}$. Each time the emitter sends out a pair of particles, each analyzer responds—either with "spin up" or with "spin down." We can express these responses mathematically by defining two new quantities, A and B:

$A = +1$ if Alice's analyzer determines "spin up"
$A = -1$ if Alice's analyzer determines "spin down"

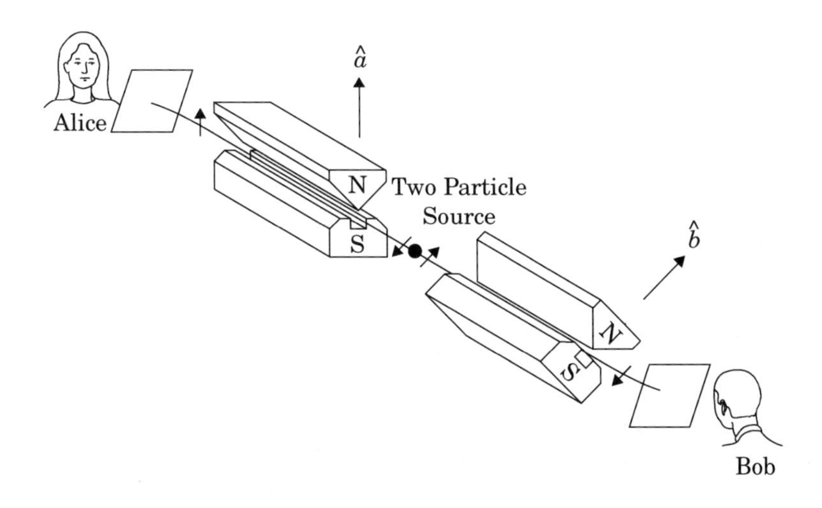

Figure 5–4 *Generalized EPR Apparatus* used in Bell's theorem. Alice's and Bob's analyzers are oriented along different directions $\hat{a}$ and $\hat{b}$.

$B = +1$ if Bob's analyzer determines "spin up"
$B = -1$ if Bob's analyzer determines "spin down"

Bell's theorem is concerned with the product AB. Clearly, it can only have two values, $+1$ or -1. The result $AB = +1$ implies that the two analyzers got the same answer (either both "up" or both "down"), while $AB = -1$ means the two analyzers got opposite answers. Recall that, in the EPR case, Alice and Bob are certain to get opposite responses, so that $AB = -1$. But since AB depends on the orientation of $\hat{a}$ relative to $\hat{b}$, this may not be true in general.

What are the predictions of quantum mechanics for this experiment? As usual, the theory makes no statements about the results obtained in any individual run. Rather, it predicts only statistical quantities. In particular, it can tell us the *expectation value of AB*. Let us call this E; because it depends on the orientation of the analyzers we write $E(\hat{a}, \hat{b})$. It can be shown that according to quantum mechanics,

$$E_{\text{QM}}(\hat{a}, \hat{b}) = -\hat{a} \cdot \hat{b} = -\cos(\phi) \tag{5.4}$$

where ϕ is the angle between $\hat{a}$ and $\hat{b}$.

How is this prediction to be compared with experiment? The expectation value of some quantity is the average value of that quantity, obtained by repeating an experiment many times. Alice and Bob must therefore choose some definite orientations $\hat{a}$ and $\hat{b}$, and leave their analyzers fixed along these directions. The emitter spits out a great number of pairs, for each of which Alice and Bob record A and B, and their product AB. They repeat the process many times, and then average the result. This will be the experimentally observed value

$$E_{\text{EXP}}(\hat{a}, \hat{b})$$

Finally, we need to formulate the predicted value of E according to our hidden-variable theory,

$$E_{\text{HV}}(\hat{a}, \hat{b})$$

This will be done by proposing a model for the reality underlying the experiment. That model will contain some quantities that are not known in any individual run of the experiment (analogous to the *actual velocities* of each molecule in a gas in statistical mechanics). Thus in our theory we will have to calculate the product AB for each possible value of the hidden variable, and then average over all its possible values to obtain $E_{\text{HV}}(\hat{a}, \hat{b})$ (analogous to the *pressure* in thermodynamics).

As we mentioned, Bell's theorem shows that no matter how hard we try, we will never be able to concoct a theory for which $E_{\text{HV}}(\hat{a}, \hat{b})$ equals

$E_{QM}(\hat{a}, \hat{b})$ for all $\hat{a}$ and $\hat{b}$. The theorem is remarkably general. It manages to prove this without considering any particular hidden-variable theory at all. Because of this great generality, it is often difficult to appreciate the theorem's significance. Therefore, before proceeding to a full discussion of Bell's theorem, we begin with a particularly simple example of a hidden-variable theory. We do so, not because the theory should be taken seriously—it will turn out to be false—but because in developing the theory, we will gain a clearer understanding of the issues involved in creating one.

Elementary Example of a Hidden-Variable Theory In this example, we imagine the objective reality underlying the experiment to be simply our naive classical concept of spin. We suppose that the particles emitted in the experiment are actually rotating. If we like, we can imagine the emitter to be a device that spits out two tiny pellets spinning in opposite directions. Each pellet is then characterized by a spin vector. We will imagine that, as each pellet flies toward its Stern–Gerlach analyzer, the direction and magnitude of this vector is fixed.

Figure 5–5 diagrams the configuration. In this figure, the solid lines indicate the view from the emitter looking toward Alice; $\hat{a}$ indicates the orientation of her analyzer, and $\mathbf{V}_a$ is the spin vector of the particle heading toward her. The angle between $\mathbf{V}_a$ and $\hat{a}$ is denoted by θ. (To make things simple, we will imagine that both $\mathbf{V}_a$ and $\mathbf{V}_b$ lie in the plane perpendicular to their lines of flight.) Similarly, the dashed lines give the view looking toward Bob. His analyzer points along $\hat{b}$; furthermore, since by hypothesis the spin vector of the particle heading toward him is opposite to that heading toward Alice, $\mathbf{V}_b$ is $-\mathbf{V}_a$. The angle between $\hat{a}$ and $\hat{b}$ is denoted by ϕ.

In this theory, the quantity we cannot predict is the orientation of $\mathbf{V}_a$ in any given run: *this orientation is the hidden variable.* Presumably, each time the emitter spits out a pair, the hidden variable changes. We will suppose it to be randomly distributed so that it is equally likely to point in any direction, and we will average over all possible directions.

Finally, we imagine that what each detector records is *the sign of the projection of the spin vector along its axis.* Thus A will be $+1$ if the spin vector of the particle heading toward Alice has a component along $\hat{a}$, and A will be -1 if the component points oppositely to $\hat{a}$. The same, of course, is true of B. From Figure 5–5 we see that

$$A = \text{sign}[\cos(\theta)] \tag{5.5}$$

and

$$B = \text{sign}[\cos(180 + \theta - \phi)] = \text{sign}[-\cos(\theta - \phi)] \tag{5.6}$$

so that

$$AB = \text{sign}[-\cos(\theta)\cos(\theta - \phi)] \tag{5.7}$$

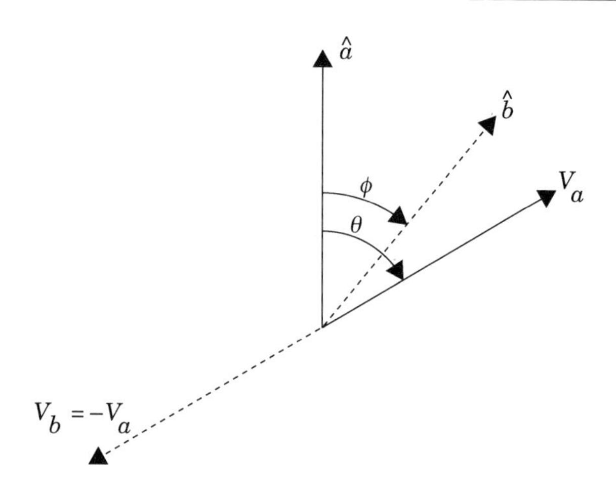

Figure 5–5 *Geometry of a Hidden-Variable Theory of Spin.* Alice's and Bob's analyzers point along $\hat{a}$ and $\hat{b}$; $\mathbf{V}_a$ is the spin vector of the particle heading toward Alice and $\mathbf{V}_b$ that of the particle heading toward Bob.

We must now compute the average value of AB over all possible values of the hidden variable θ. This is

$$E_{\mathrm{HV}}(\hat{a},\hat{b}) = \frac{1}{2\pi}\int_{-\pi/2}^{3\pi/2} AB\,d\theta \tag{5.8}$$

The integral is easy to compute because AB is always either $+1$ or -1, depending on θ. It is easy to see from Equation (5.7) that AB is given as listed in Table 5.1. We then find

$$E_{\mathrm{HV}}(\hat{a},\hat{b}) = \frac{1}{2\pi}\left\{\begin{array}{l} (+1)\left[\left(-\frac{\pi}{2}+\phi\right)-\left(-\frac{\pi}{2}\right)\right] \\ +(-1)\left[\left(\frac{\pi}{2}\right)-\left(-\frac{\pi}{2}+\phi\right)\right] \\ +(+1)\left[\left(\frac{\pi}{2}+\phi\right)-\left(\frac{\pi}{2}\right)\right] \\ +(-1)\left[\left(\frac{3\pi}{2}\right)-\left(\frac{\pi}{2}+\phi\right)\right] \end{array}\right\} \tag{5.9}$$

Table 5.1 The Function $AB(\theta)$

θ	AB
$-\pi/2$ to $-\pi/2+\phi$	$+1$
$-\pi/2+\phi$ to $+\pi/2$	-1
$\pi/2$ to $\pi/2+\phi$	$+1$
$\pi/2+\phi$ to $3\pi/2$	-1

and we finally find our theory's prediction for $E_{\text{HV}}(\hat{a}, \hat{b})$:

$$E_{\text{HV}}(\hat{a}, \hat{b}) = \frac{2}{\pi}\phi - 1 \tag{5.10}$$

where, we recall, ϕ is the angle between and $\hat{a}$ and $\hat{b}$.

Does the theory reproduce the observations? Turn first to the EPR case, in which $\hat{a}$ and $\hat{b}$ are parallel and Alice and Bob always get opposite answers. In this case AB is -1 in each run, so that its average value is -1. From Equation (5.10) we see that when ϕ is zero, $E_{\text{HV}}(\hat{a}, \hat{b}) = -1$. Note also from Equation (5.4) that the quantum-mechanical result $E_{\text{QM}}(\hat{a}, \hat{b}) = -1$ for $\phi = 0$ as well. So in the EPR case, our hidden-variable theory agrees with quantum mechanics, and both agree with experiment.

But this turns out not to be the case for other orientations of the analyzers. In Figure 5–6 we graph both predictions for E as a function of ϕ. We see that the hidden-variable prediction agrees with the quantum-mechanical one only for certain selected ϕ's. The EPR case of $\phi = 0$ turns out to be a special case.

Thus we have failed in our attempt to construct a hidden-variable theory that reproduces the predictions of quantum mechanics for every ϕ. Should this concern us? Perhaps not. Perhaps, by suitable tinkering and adjusting,

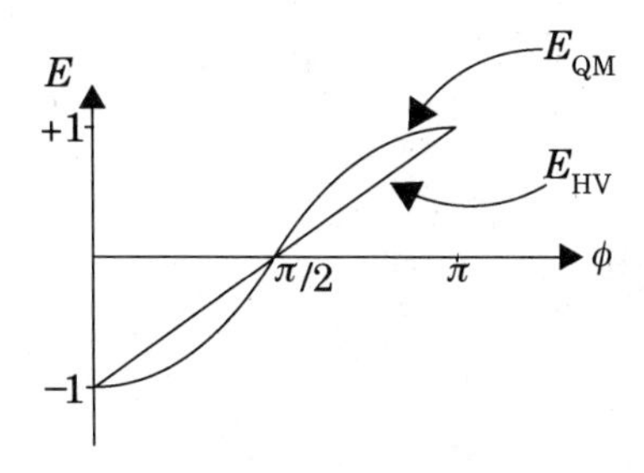

Figure 5–6 *Two Predictions for E;* the quantum-mechanical prediction E_{QM} and the hidden-variable prediction E_{HV}. They agree only for certain selected values of ϕ.

we might be able to modify the theory and bring it into agreement with quantum mechanics. This was the hope of the hidden-variable program. Not until Bell proved his theorem did people realize that these attempts were doomed to failure.

5.4 Bell's Theorem

Bell published his theorem (sometimes called "Bell's inequality") in 1964. Since that time several further inequalities have been proved, by Bell as well as by others, broadening and extending the first one's scope, and bringing it into a closer relationship with experimental possibilities.[9] Abner Shimony and others pioneered the effort to prove theorems that apply more closely to real experiments with detectors of finite efficiency. In another development, Greenberger, Horne and Zeilinger have proved a theorem concerning three correlated particles that demonstrates the same result but even more dramatically. But because of its immense historical importance, we will concentrate on Bell's initial version.

The theorem envisages a series of three experiments conducted by Alice and Bob. In the first, Alice orients her analyzer along $\hat{a}$, Bob along $\hat{b}$, and they measure $E_{\mathrm{EXP}}(\hat{a}, \hat{b})$. In the second, Bob rotates his analyzer to some new axis $\hat{c}$, Alice leaves hers untouched, and they determine $E_{\mathrm{EXP}}(\hat{a}, \hat{c})$. Finally, Alice rotates her analyzer to $\hat{b}$, and they determine $E_{\mathrm{EXP}}(\hat{b}, \hat{c})$. Bell's theorem is that, in any hidden-variable theory that makes the locality assumption, the Es will obey

$$|E_{\mathrm{HV}}(\hat{a}, \hat{b}) - E_{\mathrm{HV}}(\hat{a}, \hat{c})| \leq 1 + E_{\mathrm{HV}}(\hat{b}, \hat{c}) \tag{5.11}$$

It is easy to show that our simple hidden-variable theory developed above satisfies this inequality, as of course it must. It is also easy to show that, for certain settings $\hat{a}$, $\hat{b}$, $\hat{c}$ of the analyzers, the predictions of quantum mechanics obey Equation (5.11)—*but that for other settings they do not.* For instance, if we choose parallel settings, $\hat{a} = \hat{b} = \hat{c}$, the quantum-mechanical prediction (Equation (5.4)) is $E_{\mathrm{QM}}(\hat{a}, \hat{a}) = -1$, and Bell's inequality reads

$$\begin{gathered} |(-1) - (-1)| \leq 1 + (-1) \\ |0| \leq 0 \end{gathered} \tag{5.12}$$

which is the case. But if we choose settings in which $\hat{b}$ makes an angle of 60° to $\hat{a}$, and $\hat{c}$ makes an angle of 60° to $\hat{b}$, then $\hat{a} \cdot \hat{b} = \hat{b} \cdot \hat{c} = \frac{1}{2}$ and $\hat{a} \cdot \hat{c} = -\frac{1}{2}$.

$$\begin{gathered} |E_{\mathrm{QM}}(\hat{a}, \hat{b}) - E_{\mathrm{QM}}(\hat{a}, \hat{c})| = |(-\tfrac{1}{2}) - (\tfrac{1}{2})| = 1 \\ 1 + E_{\mathrm{QM}}(\hat{b}, \hat{c}) = 1 + (-\tfrac{1}{2}) = \tfrac{1}{2} \end{gathered} \tag{5.13}$$

which do not obey Bell's inequality.

From this we draw two conclusions. First, Bell's theorem shows that no local hidden-variable theory can reproduce all of the predictions of quantum mechanics. Thus the program of searching for a local hidden-variable theory "underlying" quantum mechanics will never succeed. Second, since experimental situations can be found in which the predictions of quantum theory differ from those of any hidden-variable theory, it is now possible actually to perform an experiment to distinguish between the two.

We now turn to a proof of Bell's theorem.

Proof of Bell's Theorem Any hidden-variable theory will make some definite prediction for A and B, the results of individual measurements made by Alice and Bob, once three things are specified: the orientations of their two analyzers, and the value of the hidden variable. In our simple theory, the prediction is Equations (5.5) and (5.6). Note that, in these equations, A depends on θ, the angle between the hidden variable and $\hat{a}$. *But A does not depend on* $\hat{b}$. This is just the locality assumption: the result of Alice's measurement cannot depend on anything Bob does. The same, of course, is true of Bob: B cannot depend on anything Alice does. Thus we can mathematically express the locality postulate as

$$\begin{aligned} A &= A(\hat{a}, \lambda) \quad \text{not} \quad A(\hat{a}, \hat{b}, \lambda) \\ B &= B(\hat{b}, \lambda) \quad \text{not} \quad B(\hat{a}, \hat{b}, \lambda) \end{aligned} \tag{5.14}$$

where we have used λ to indicate the hidden variable.

Note also that, in our simple theory, we wrote the expectation value of AB as the average of AB over all possible values of the hidden variable. The same will be true for any other hidden-variable theory:

$$E_{\mathrm{HV}}(\hat{a}, \hat{b}) = \int AB\, d\lambda \tag{5.15}$$

(In this expression we have omitted the 2π that occurred in the denominator of Equation (5.7). We do this purely for mathematical convenience, by requiring

$$\int d\lambda = 1 \tag{5.16}$$

Thus, in our simple example, λ corresponds to $\theta/2\pi$. We also note that Bell's theorem can be extended to the case of a nonuniform distribution of λs.)

Let us turn now to the EPR case. When the two analyzers are parallel, Alice and Bob get opposite answers in each individual run. In hidden-variable terms this means that

$$A(\hat{a}, \lambda) = -B(\hat{a}, \lambda) \tag{5.17}$$

We now write down the following quantity

$$E_{\mathrm{HV}}(\hat{a},\hat{b}) - E_{\mathrm{HV}}(\hat{a},\hat{c}) = \int [A(\hat{a},\lambda)B(\hat{b},\lambda) - A(\hat{a},\lambda)B(\hat{c},\lambda)]\, d\lambda$$

$$= -\int [A(\hat{a},\lambda)A(\hat{b},\lambda) - A(\hat{a},\lambda)A(\hat{c},\lambda)]\, d\lambda \qquad (5.18)$$

by using Equation (5.17). This can be factored to read

$$E_{\mathrm{HV}}(\hat{a},\hat{b}) - E_{\mathrm{HV}}(\hat{a},\hat{c}) = -\int A(\hat{a},\lambda)A(\hat{b},\lambda)[1 - A(\hat{b},\lambda)A(\hat{c},\lambda)]\, d\lambda \qquad (5.19)$$

because

$$[A(\hat{b},\lambda)]^2 = 1 \qquad (5.20)$$

since A and B are either plus or minus one. But, for the same reason, the factor

$$A(\hat{a},\lambda)A(\hat{b},\lambda)$$

is either plus or minus one, and so is certainly less than or equal to plus one. Thus if we simply drop it from the right-hand side of Equation (5.19) and take absolute values, we obtain

$$|E_{\mathrm{HV}}(\hat{a},\hat{b}) - E_{\mathrm{HV}}(\hat{a},\hat{c})| \leq \left| \int [1 - A(\hat{b},\lambda)A(\hat{c},\lambda)] \right| d\lambda \qquad (5.21)$$

But by Equations (5.15–5.17) this reads

$$|E_{\mathrm{HV}}(\hat{a},\hat{b}) - E_{\mathrm{HV}}(\hat{a},\hat{c})| \leq 1 + \int A(\hat{b},\lambda)B(\hat{c},\lambda)\, d\lambda$$

$$\leq 1 + E_{\mathrm{HV}}(\hat{b},\hat{c}) \qquad (5.22)$$

which is Bell's theorem.

Mermin's "Local Reality Machine" One of the many remarkable things about Bell's theorem is that, while it applies to a wide range of hidden-variable theories, it does not deal with any particular theory at all. Such generality is a great virtue—but at the same time, it makes the significance of the theorem, its truly enormous scope and impact, difficult to comprehend. But in 1985, N. David Mermin[10] described a thought experiment that made Bell's theorem far easier to appreciate. In this section we explore Mermin's work in some detail, for it makes particularly vivid the great significance of the theorem.

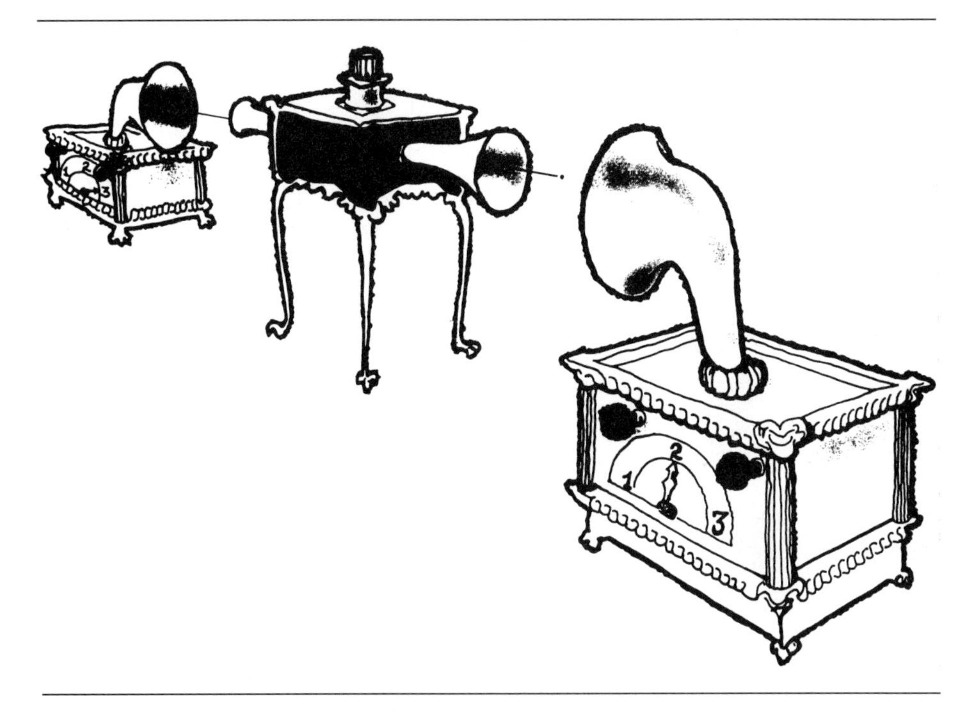

Figure 5–7 *Mermin's "Local Reality Machine."* SOURCE: Reproduced with permission from N.D. Mermin, "Is the moon there when nobody looks?," *Physics Today*, vol. 38, p. 38 (April 1985).

Mermin's example, which we have dubbed his "local-reality machine," is sketched in Figure 5–7. It bears some resemblance to the EPR experiment, in that it consists of an emitter and two detectors unconnected with each other. Mermin's detectors, however, differ from those of the EPR experiment, for each is equipped with a switch that can be set to one of three possible positions 1, 2, or 3. We are free to alter the settings of these switches in any way we wish: we can set both to 1, one to 2 and the other to 3, or whatever. Furthermore, mounted on top of each detector are two light bulbs, one red and the other green.

The emitter is supplied with a button. When it is pressed, each detector flashes one of its lights. Sometimes red is flashed, sometimes green; sometimes both detectors flash the same color, sometimes they flash different colors.

In Mermin's experiment, each time the emitter's button is pressed, we record (a) the setting of each switch, and (b) the color each bulb flashed. Thus the result of each run is a pair of numbers and a pair of colors. We then *independently and randomly* change the settings of the switches, and we press the button again. The fact that the switches are reset independently implies that sometimes they will be set the same and sometimes differently;

the fact that they are reset randomly means that 1, 2, and 3 will be chosen with equal frequency.

The full experiment consists of repeating this procedure a great number of times. When this is done, the results turn out to be as follows:

- When the two switches happen to be set the same, the light bulbs invariably flash the same color (half the time red, half the time green).
- If we pay no attention to the switch settings, and consider only the flashing of the lights, we find that the pattern is totally random. Half of the time the lights flash the same color, and half of the time they flash different colors.

That is all there is to Mermin's machine. Bell's theorem makes the extraordinary claim that absolutely no way exists to explain how it works in classical terms. To see how this impossibility arises, let us now try to imagine how it might work. We will attempt to concoct an explanation for the data, thinking in terms that Einstein would have liked—thinking, that is, in terms of some objectively real process taking place within it, a process that causally determines what happens. We therefore imagine that, whatever it is that the emitter sends forth, it possesses some property that makes the detectors do what they do. This property may be unknown to us, but it exists. Recall that such a property is just what we mean by a hidden variable.

Mermin's example is designed to persuade us that such a way of thinking is not going to work. No matter how hard we try, we are not going to be able to explain his experimental results in these terms.

Begin by concentrating on the first feature of the data. If only there were some form of connection between the two detectors—a wire leading from one to the other—it would be easy to ensure that, when both switches were set the same, the same colors would flash. But there are no such wires. How, then, can we understand it? One way is to imagine that *what travels toward one detector is the same as what travels toward the other.*

If this were to be the case, the situations at the two detectors would be twins. Their switch settings would be the same, and so would be the "things" arriving at them. The postulate of strict causality therefore ensures that the behavior of the two detectors will be identical: what one does, the other does. In this way, we can account for the first feature of Mermin's data.

How, then, can we understand the second feature? We need to think in more detail about the manner in which the "things" impinging on the detectors cause their lights to flash. Each detector has three possible states (its switch can be set to 1, 2, or 3) and for each state there are two possible things that can happen (a red or green flash). There are therefore eight possible combinations of settings and results. They are listed in Table 5.2.

Embodied in this table are the postulates of strict causality, objective reality, and locality. We are assuming that what a detector does is caused by (a) its internal state (i.e., its switch setting) and (b) some property of the "thing" impinging upon it (the hidden variable). Since this property

Table 5.2 Possible Responses of a Detector in Mermin's Thought Experiment

	Result of a run, if the switch is set to		
	1	*2*	*3*
I	R	R	R
II	R	R	G
III	R	G	R
IV	R	G	G
V	G	R	R
VI	G	R	G
VII	G	G	R
VIII	G	G	G

must cover all eventualities, we see that each "thing" emitted by the source must have one of eight such sets of properties. And finally, we are assuming that the behavior of each detector is caused by *nothing else*. In particular, it is not caused by anything having to do with the other detector; this is the locality assumption.

What might these eight properties be? There are many possibilities. For example, the "things" might be atoms and the hidden variable might be *the type of chemical element*. In this case, the entry "I" in Table 5.2 could correspond to hydrogen, "II" to helium, and so forth. The detectors could be built so as to measure which element was impinging upon them, and react as indicated in Table 5.2.

But this is not the only possibility. The hidden variable might be *trajectory*. Each detector might contain a target, divided into eight sectors as shown in Figure 5–8. We can imagine that the source emits something that travels along a well-defined path to the detector. The detector measures which sector it lands in, and again reacts as indicated in Table 5.2.

But in any case, will such a scheme be able to account for the data? We need to study every possible combination of circumstances. To begin, suppose that the "thing" heading from source to detector is of type I (hydrogen, perhaps, or a path aimed at sector I of a target). Table 5.2 tells us that, no matter how the switches are set, each detector then flashes red. Pass next to type II (helium, or a path aimed at sector II). Table 5.2 now tells us that we get red unless a switch is set to 3, in which case we get green. Proceeding in this way, we can map out the full set of possibilities. The results are enumerated in Table 5.3.

It is easy to see that the results set forth in this table obey the first property of the experimental data: whenever the switches are set the same, the lights flash the same colors. But do they obey the second property

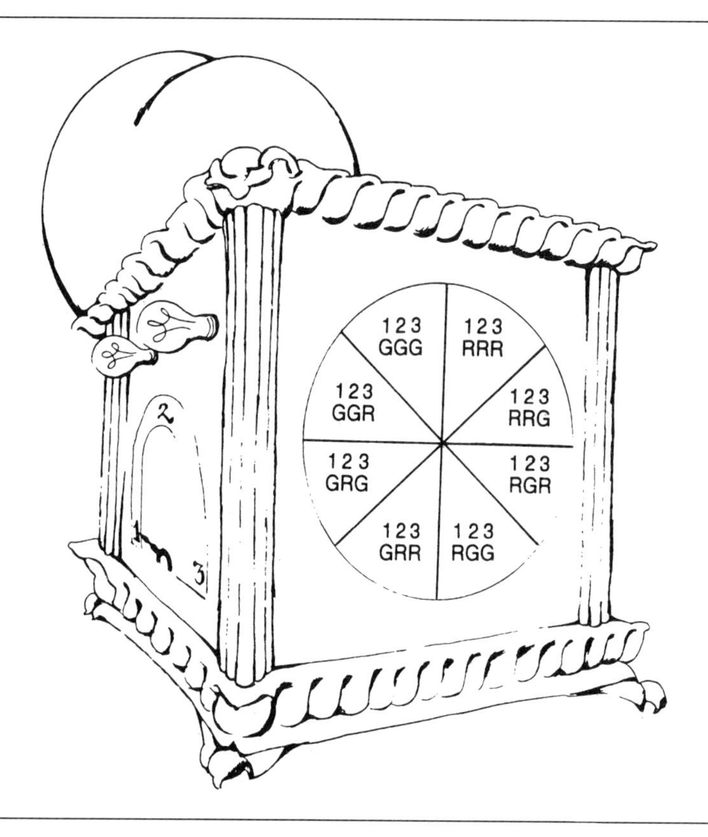

Figure 5–8 *One Way the "Local Reality Machine" Might Work.* Depending on which sector the particle strikes, and how the switches are set, the bulbs light up as indicated. SOURCE: Reproduced with permission from N.D. Mermin, "Is the moon there when nobody looks?," *Physics Today*, vol. 38, p. 38 (April 1985).

as well—that in all runs taken together, the lights flashed the same precisely half of the time? *We can easily show that they do not.* The proof proceeds simply by counting. At the bottom of Table 5.3 we have indicated, for each case, the number of switch settings in which the lights flashed the same color. Notice that in cases II through VII the lights flashed the same for 5 out of the 9 possible settings, whereas in cases I and VII they flashed the same for every setting. *Therefore, if the switch settings are random, the lights will flash the same color more than 5/9 of the time. But experiment reveals that they do not; they flash the same color half of the time.*

Our attempt to understand the workings of Mermin's machine has failed. Should we take this seriously? Is there *any* scheme that will account for the data? Before proceeding to the remainder of this discussion, we urge you, the reader, to lay this book aside, and try to concoct some method of doing so. You will not be able to do it.

Table 5-3 Possible Outcomes of Mermin's Thought Experiment

Switch setting on one detector	*Switch setting on the other detector*	*I*	*II*	*III*	*IV*	*V*	*VI*	*VII*	*VIII*
1	1	All red	RR	RR	RR	The same as IV, with R and G interchanged	The same as III, with R and G interchanged	The same as II, with R and G interchanged	All green
1	2		RR	RG	RG				
1	3		RG	RR	RG				
2	1		RR	GR	GR				
2	2		RR	GG	GG				
2	3		RG	GR	GG				
3	1		GR	RR	GR				
3	2		GR	RG	GG				
3	3		GG	RR	GG				
Number of switch settings that yield both colors the same		9	5	5	5	5	5	5	9

Discussion The proof that you will not be able to do it is Bell's theorem, adapted to the experiment under consideration.

How, then, can we understand the experimental data? We must give up one of the postulates that we had made. One such postulate is *locality*. In the context of Mermin's machine, locality is expressed by the fact that there are no wires connecting the two detectors; what happens at one detector is perfectly insulated from what happens at the other. As we argued above, were the wires to be present, it would be easy to account for the data. But recall that giving up on locality implies admitting that physical causes can propagate with a velocity not just greater than light, but infinite. While it is entirely possible to abandon this postulate, one must be aware of the consequences.

Our attempt also relied upon the postulate of *strict causation*; the postulate that the behavior of the detectors is determined in one fashion or another. We might be tempted to give up this postulate. But without it, the detectors would be quite literally free to do "whatever they pleased," and there would be no way to understand the perfect correlations seen in the data of the 11, 22 and 33 runs.

The only other postulate to give up is that of *reality*; the assumption that, whatever it is that travels from source to detectors, some real property is transmitted that causes them to behave as they do. Here, too, it is important to comprehend the significance of giving up this postulate—until the invention of quantum mechanics, all of natural science had made such an assumption.

There is, of course, one other way to account for the experimental data: *use quantum mechanics.*

We therefore turn to a more detailed description of the construction of Mermin's machine. The source is precisely the same as that of the EPR paradox: something that emits two electrons, with spins pointing in opposite directions. The detectors, in turn, are also the same as in the EPR paradox: they are Stern–Gerlach magnets that record the direction of the spin. On one detector, a red light bulb means "spin up" while green means "spin down"; on the other detector, just the opposite arrangement is used.

The only way in which Mermin's machine differs from the EPR thought experiment lies in the switches. They determine the *orientation of the Stern–Gerlach analyzers.* On each detector, a switch setting 1 causes it to be oriented straight up, 2 causes it to be orientated 120° from the vertical, and 3 causes it to be oriented 240° from the vertical. The EPR paradox dealt with the case in which both analyzers pointed in the same direction; i.e., similar switch settings. This is just what was covered in the first feature of the experimental data. The fact that both lights flashed the same color corresponds to the fact that if one detector indicates "spin up," the other is sure to indicate "spin down."

Bell's theorem, and Mermin's machine, broadened the discussion to include other possible orientations of the analyzers. Because it is somewhat involved, we will not give the proof here, but it can be shown that the full set of experimental data can be accounted for straightforwardly, using the principles of quantum mechanics.

Chapter 6

Testing Bell's Inequalities: Entangled States

In the last chapter we were concerned with Bell's proof that no local hidden-variable theory can be found that reproduces all the predictions of quantum mechanics. A consequence of this result is that, with a single experiment, one can test the viability of *any* common-sense theory of the type offered by classical physics. Such experiments have been done, and we will recount them in this chapter. They agree with quantum mechanics, and they disagree with local hidden-variable theories. Few developments in the history of physics have been of comparable significance for our philosophical understanding of the world.

These experiments are also part of a wider subject. The quantum state with which they work, and with which the EPR thought experiment is concerned, is but one instance of a general class known as entangled states. They have quite remarkable properties, which we will also recount.

What is an entangled state? The EPR thought experiment deals with a source that sends out two particles with opposite spins. We can write their state as:

$$\psi = \frac{1}{\sqrt{2}}[(\uparrow)_1(\downarrow)_2 + (\downarrow)_1(\uparrow)_2] \tag{6.1}$$

Here the subscript 1 describes the first particle and the subscript 2 describes the second. Equation (6.1) says that the state is a superposition of two terms: the first term describes particle 1 with spin up and particle 2 with spin down, and the second term describes the opposite case.

This is an entangled state. Note that it cannot be written as the product of two terms, the first describing particle 1 and the second describing particle 2,

$$\psi = \psi_1 \psi_2 \tag{6.2}$$

Mathematically, there is nothing very remarkable about this. But physically, it has extraordinary consequences. Nonentangled states are those for which we can properly think of particle 1 as fully described by ψ_1 and particle 2 by ψ_2; the system is a simple composite of these two parts. But an entangled state cannot be factored into the product of two wave functions, and consequently cannot be thought of as a composite system in any classical sense. The consequences turn out to be so remarkable that Schrödinger was led to say that entanglement was "not *one* but rather *the* characteristic trait of quantum mechanics."[1]

6.1 Tests of Bell's Inequalities

We begin with the actual experiments that have demonstrated the failure of Einstein's hopes for a local hidden-variable theory. Recall that, in 1951, David Bohm re-crafted the EPR paradox into its clearest form. In recent years his version, which once existed only as an abstract argument, has come to be realized in the laboratory; the EPR experiment is by now a thought experiment made real. Nowhere has it been performed more beautifully than in the Orsay lab of Alain Aspect and his collaborators outside Paris. In the two-year period 1981–82, Aspect and co-workers published three landmark papers detailing their tests of local hidden-variable theories via Bell's theorem.[2,3,4] Before turning to their work, we need to briefly examine other experiments that preceded it.

Bohm's version of the EPR experiment, which quickly became the canonical version, relies on two spin-1/2 particles that together form a spin-0 system. Recall that according to Bell's theorem, by making the appropriate measurements of the spin components for the two particles, the experimenter can distinguish between the validity of quantum mechanics (which violates Bell's inequality), and any local hidden-variable theory (which does not).

Early Work One pioneering experiment dealt with proton rather than electron spin.[5] Most subsequent work dealt with photon polarization, which proved easier to work with in the laboratory. For example, in one characteristic instance from 1975, experimenters studied a system comprised of a single electron and its antiparticle, the positron, which together formed a bound system known as positronium.[6] When these two particles interacted, they mutually annihilated with the emission of two gamma rays. By analysis of the gamma ray polarization, it was possible to test for a violation of Bell's inequality. Unfortunately, no efficient polarizers were available at

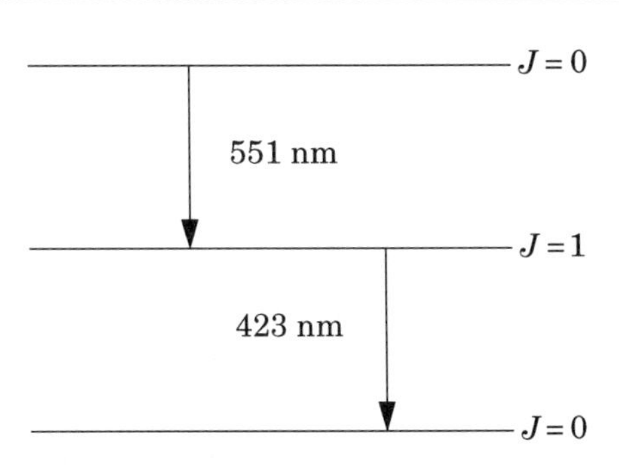

Figure 6–1 *Energy Level Diagram of Calcium* showing the states used in the production of entangled pairs of photons.

such high photon energies. As a consequence, the data had to be corrected using the very quantum theory the experiment was trying to test—not an ideal situation.

Two-Photon Entangled States Fortunately, far better experimental designs have been found. At present, the most successful experiments have worked with entangled states of photons produced by atomic cascades.[7] These cascades are produced by means of transitions between states in, for instance, atomic calcium. Calcium has two electrons outside a closed shell. Since both electrons are in *s*-states, and their spins are oppositely aligned, the ground state has a total angular momentum J (orbital plus spin) of zero. Figure 6–1 shows the energy levels for the ground state and relevant excited states. If we start in a higher-lying $J = 0$ state, two dipole transitions take the atom from its initial excited *s*-state, through an intermediate *p*-state ($J = 1$), to the ground state, which again has $J = 0$. Two photons are emitted in the process, one of wavelength 551.3 nm and the other of 422.7 nm. We now show that they are in an entangled state.

Note that the total change in the angular momentum of the atom is zero. Thus the two photons must have opposite angular momenta. But the spin angular momentum of a photon is related to its polarization state. The spin of a photon can only be aligned parallel or antiparallel to its direction of motion; parallel alignment corresponds to right-handed circular polarization, antiparallel to left-handed circular polarization. The two photons need not be emitted in opposite directions, but if we select those that are, conservation of angular momentum now requires that their handedness be the same. Therefore, they must have the same polarization: both right- or both left-circularly polarized (see Figure 6–2).

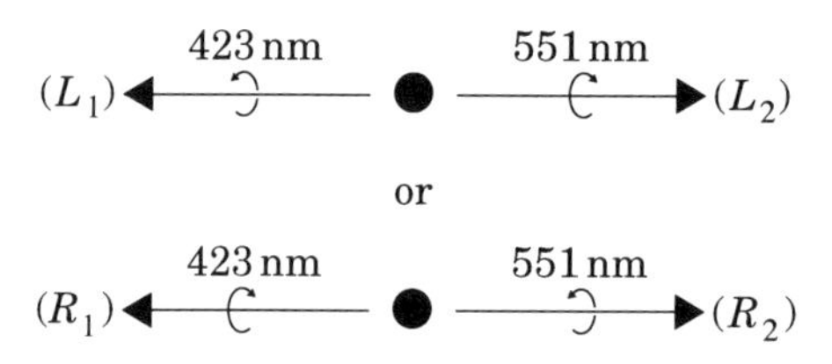

Figure 6–2 *Possible States of the Photons* emitted by the transitions illustrated in Figure 6–1.

Either will do. Of critical importance for our considerations is the degeneracy of the intermediate *p*-state. This state has three sublevels, which are the projections of J onto its quantization axis, usually labeled by $m = 1, 0, -1$. Because these three states are degenerate, we have the ambiguity needed for the creation of an entanglement between the two possibilities diagrammed in Figure 6–2. This entanglement is just the kind suited for tests of Bell's theorem.

The two decay paths pertinent for our purposes pass through either $m = 1$ or $m = -1$ on the way to the $J = 0$ ground state. They are illustrated in Figure 6–3a. In one case, the two emitted photons are both right-circularly polarized; in the other, they are both left-circularly polarized. Notice that this figure bears a striking resemblance to the classic two-slit interference experiment we have considered so many times before (Figure 6–3b). As in the interference experiment, two paths connect the initial and final states of the system. The difference, of course, is that instead of two spatially distinct trajectories, we now have two distinct decay paths. In a classical analysis, one or the other would be the "real" decay path. But in quantum mechanics, both paths exist, in an entangled state of two photons with correlated polarizations.

We can write down this state using a notation in which the symbol R_1 denotes photon number 1 with right-handed circular polarization, L_1 denotes photon number 1 with left-handed circular polarization, and the same for particle 2:

$$\psi = \frac{1}{\sqrt{2}}[(R_1)(R_2) + (L_1)(L_2)] \tag{6.3}$$

Notice the very strong similarity between this state and that of the EPR thought experiment, Equation (6.1). Equation (6.1) says that if the first particle is found to have spin up, then the second is sure to have spin down, and vice versa. Similarly, Equation (6.3) says that if the first photon has right-handed circular polarization, then so will the second; and similarly for left-handed polarizations. Furthermore, note that since R_1

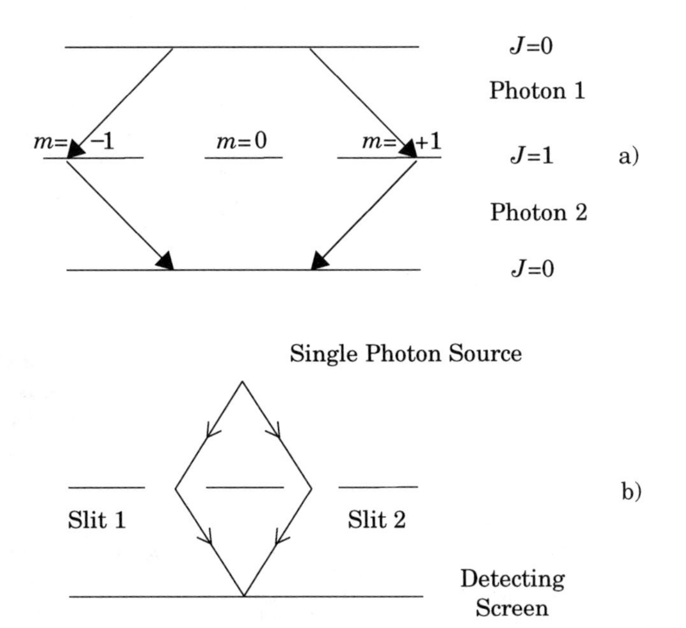

Figure 6–3 *Production of an Entangled State* in the two-photon decay of calcium. The decay can pass through either of the two intermediate $J = 1$ states, as illustrated in (a). Note the strong similarity between this and the classic two-slit interference experiment (b).

and R_2 (L_1 and L_2) travel in opposite directions, their total angular momentum sums to zero, as it must.

Already in 1972, Freedman and Clauser performed the first experimental test of Bell's theorem using an atomic cascade.[8] Their results disagreed with local hidden-variable theory, but were not taken as definitive. During the next ten years, refinements in both the experimental arrangement and the details of the theoretical analysis took place, culminating in the beautiful experiments of Aspect and co-workers.

Linear Polarization These experiments dealt not with circular, but with linear polarizations, H (horizontal) and V (vertical). But a circular polarization can always be expressed in terms of linear polarizations by[9]

$$\begin{aligned} R &= \frac{1}{\sqrt{2}}[(H) + i(V)] \\ L &= \frac{1}{\sqrt{2}}[(H) - i(V)] \end{aligned} \tag{6.4}$$

where $i = \sqrt{-1}$. If we substitute Equation (6.4) into Equation (6.3), we find that the two-photon entangled state becomes:

$$\psi = \frac{1}{\sqrt{2}}[(H_1)(H_2) - (V_1)(V_2)] \tag{6.5}$$

which says that if we find the linear polarization of photon 1 to be horizontal (vertical), then we will find that of photon 2 to be horizontal (vertical) as well. This is exactly the kind of correlation required for a test of Bell's theorem.

The theoretical analysis of the Aspect experiments is closely analogous to that we gave in the previous chapter for spin-1/2 particles. In the previous case we considered two experimenters, Alice and Bob, who measured the spins of the particles reaching them. If, for example, Alice obtained "spin up," she assigned $A = +1$, while "spin down" corresponded to $A = -1$. In the present situation we take $A = +1$ to mean "polarization parallel to Alice's polarizer," while $A = -1$ means "polarization perpendicular to Alice's polarizer," and similarly for Bob. As before, $\hat{a}$ and $\hat{b}$ denote the directions in which Alice's and Bob's polarizers point, and we are concerned with $E(\hat{a}, \hat{b})$, the expectation value of AB.

This expectation value is simply the sum of all the values AB can have, times the probabilities of obtaining them:

$$\begin{aligned} E(\hat{a}, \hat{b}) &= AB(++)P_{++}(\hat{a}, \hat{b}) + AB(--)P_{--}(\hat{a}, \hat{b}) \\ &\quad + AB(+-)P_{+-}(\hat{a}, \hat{b}) + AB(-+)P_{-+}(\hat{a}, \hat{b}) \end{aligned} \tag{6.6}$$

Here $P_{++}(\hat{a}, \hat{b})$ is the probability of obtaining the results $A = +1$, $B = +1$ when the polarizers are oriented along $\hat{a}$ and $\hat{b}$, and so forth. Similarly, $AB(++)$ is the value of AB in this circumstance. But clearly AB is $+1$ whenever Alice and Bob get the same results, and it is -1 when they get opposite results. Thus we find

$$E(\hat{a}, \hat{b}) = P_{++}(\hat{a}, \hat{b}) + P_{--}(\hat{a}, \hat{b}) - P_{+-}(\hat{a}, \hat{b}) - P_{-+}(\hat{a}, \hat{b}) \tag{6.7}$$

Standard quantum theory gives the following results for these probabilities:

$$\begin{aligned} P_{++}(\hat{a}, \hat{b}) &= P_{--}(\hat{a}, \hat{b}) = (\tfrac{1}{2})\cos(2\phi) \\ P_{+-}(\hat{a}, \hat{b}) &= P_{-+}(\hat{a}, \hat{b}) = (\tfrac{1}{2})\sin(2\phi) \end{aligned} \tag{6.8}$$

where, as in the previous chapter, ϕ is the angle between $\hat{a}$ and $\hat{b}$. If we substitute Equation (6.8) into Equation (6.7) we obtain the quantum-mechanical prediction for the expectation value:

$$E_{\text{QM}}(\hat{a}, \hat{b}) = \cos(2\phi) \tag{6.9}$$

Equation (6.9) is the analogue of the previous chapter's Equation (5.3). The two results are quite similar. (They are not identical because, of course, spin-1 photons are different than spin-1/2 particles.)

A note concerning polarization analyzers employed in real experiments. Two types exist: single-channel and two-channel. An example of the single-channel type is simply a sheet of Polaroid filter. Photons polarized parallel to the transmission axis ideally will always pass through, while those polarized perpendicular will always be absorbed. In contrast, two-channel analyzers make use of special optical devices that transmit both parallel and perpendicular orientations, but in different directions. The Glan prism is an example of a two-channel, linear-polarization analyzer. Experiments have been performed with both single- and two-channel analyzers. Figures 6–4 and 6–5 show the two types of experimental arrangements.

For the specific case in which both analyzers are oriented the same way, $\phi = 0$ and $P_{++} = P_{--} = \frac{1}{2}$. If the experiment were run with single-channel analyzers, then half the time the pair of photons would pass through both analyzers (P_{++}), and half the time the pair would be blocked (P_{--}). With two-channel analyzers, photodetectors sit at both output channels for both analyzers A and B, for a total of four detectors. In this case, either the parallel photodetectors or the perpendicular detectors fire in coincidence, and each do so half the time. As is evident from Equation (6.8), for parallel analyzer alignment it never happens that cross correlations occur; i.e., $P_{+-} = P_{-+} = 0$. Thus for $\hat{a} = \hat{b}$, photon detections in equivalent

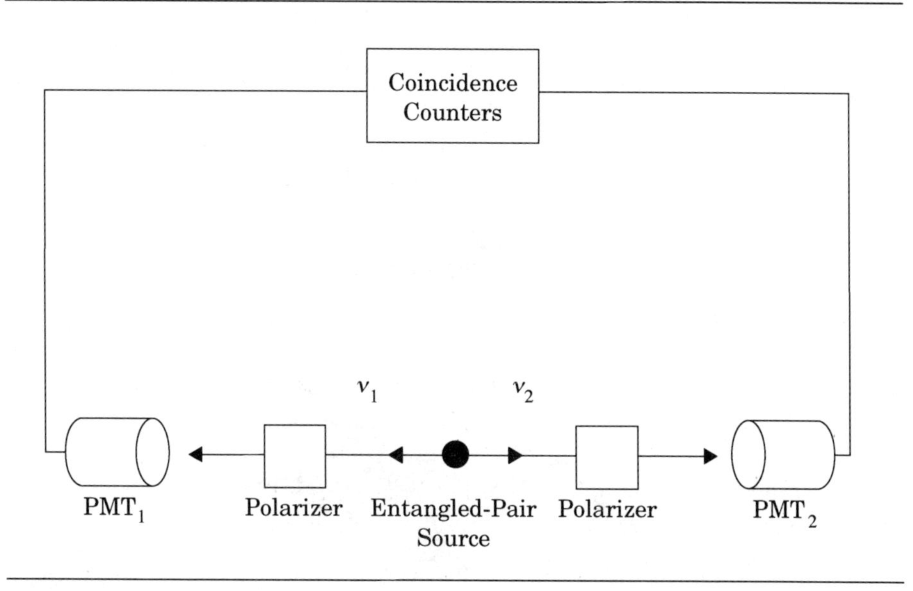

Figure 6–4 *Schematic Design of the First Aspect Experiment* testing Bell's inequality.[2]

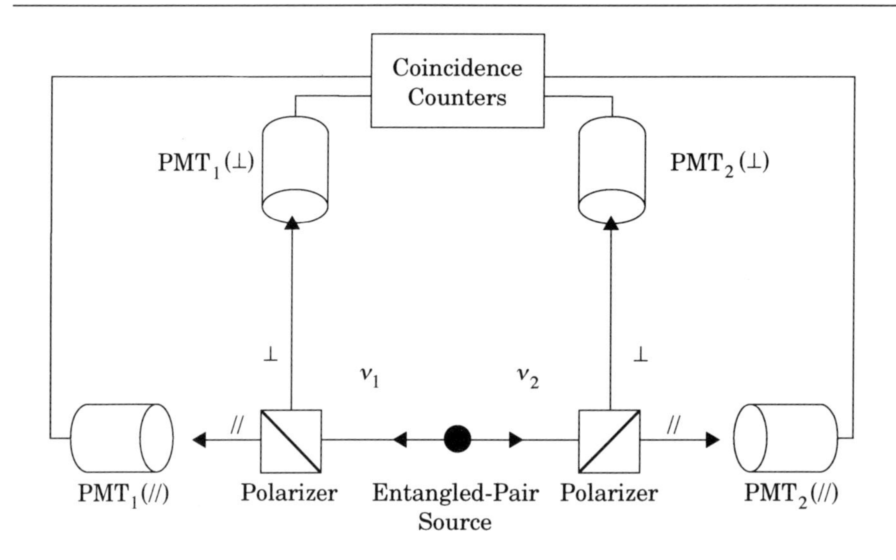

Figure 6–5 *Schematic Design of the Second Aspect Experiment* testing Bell's inequality.[3]

channels are completely correlated. Similarly, Equation (6.9) states that $E_{\text{QM}}(\hat{a}, \hat{b})$, the expectation value of AB, ranges from $+1$ to -1. When E is $+1$ or -1, there is a complete correlation between the results of measurements made by Alice and Bob; when E is 0, there is none. These results are the photon analogue of the EPR correlations among spin-1/2 particles we discussed in the previous chapter.

Clauser, Horne, Shimony and Holt have derived an analogue of Bell's theorem applicable to the present situation. They consider two orientations of $\hat{a}$ and two of $\hat{b}$, and they form the quantity S given by

$$S = E(\hat{a}, \hat{b}) - E(\hat{a}, \hat{b}') + E(\hat{a}', \hat{b}) + E(\hat{a}', \hat{b}') \tag{6.10}$$

The quantity S is formed from the results of four measurements of the expectation value E, each with a different pair of polarization analyzer orientations. They showed that, for a very broad class of hidden-variable theories that are local and realistic in the sense we defined in the previous chapter, the value of S_{HV} is constrained to lie between -2 and $+2$. But quantum mechanics can predict values of S beyond this range. In particular, if we take the case diagrammed in Figure 6–6, then

$$S_{\text{QM}} = 2\sqrt{2} = 2.83 \tag{6.11}$$

which is in clear violation of the hidden-variable limit.

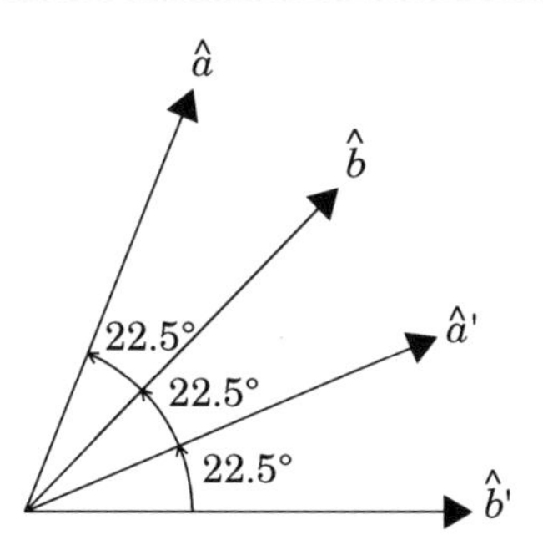

Figure 6–6 *Orientation of Analyzers* for which quantum mechanics predicts a strong violation of the generalized Bell inequality $-2 < S < 2$.

The question remains, of course, which prediction is correct. The Aspect experiments were designed to answer this question.

The Aspect Experiments As in the early experiment by Clauser and Freedman, Aspect and his collaborators chose the calcium cascade as their photon source. An atomic beam of calcium was excited by light from two lasers to the upper state via two-photon absorption. Using state-of-the-art techniques, Aspect and co-workers were able to achieve coincidence rates of over 100 per second, permitting them to attain unprecedented statistical accuracy in a matter of minutes. Three different and increasingly sophisticated experiments were performed:

A. using one-channel analyzers;
B. using two-channel analyzers;
C. using time-varying analyzers.

(A) In the experiment using single-channel analyzers,[2] the photons were either transmitted through the polarizers or lost to the system. Detection took place in only a single pair of detectors, one for the first photon and one for the other. Figure 6–7 shows a comparison between the data and the predictions of standard quantum mechanics. These data violate Bell's inequalities by nine standard deviations, and therefore provide strong evidence against local hidden-variable theories.

(B) Single-channel experiments are incomplete, since they do not detect those photons with polarization perpendicular to the transmission axis of the analyzers. If photon detectors were perfect, this would not be a problem. But in reality, all detectors are somewhat inefficient, and can fail to register a photon even though one has arrived. Therefore, in the first experiment, the failure of a detector to register a photon might not have been evidence that the photon's polarization was perpendicular to the polarizer axis; it might

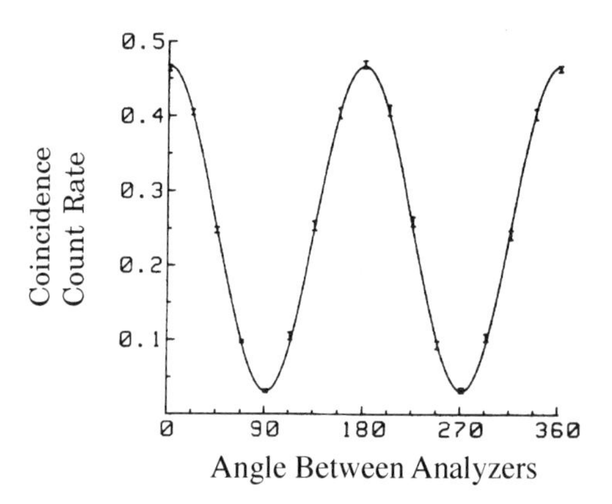

Figure 6–7 *Results of the First Aspect Experiment* testing Bell's inequality. The curve drawn through the data points is not a best fit to the data, but a prediction of quantum theory. SOURCE: Modified with permission from A. Aspect, P. Grangier and G. Roger, "Experimental tests of realistic local theories via Bell's theorem," *Phys. Rev. Lett.*, vol. 47 (7), p. 460 (1981), published by The American Physical Society.

have been due to detector inefficiency. In the second experiment, this shortcoming was circumvented by employing a more elaborate scheme, which detected photons of both parallel and perpendicular polarizations. With this addition, direct comparisons could be made to the Bell inequalities for $E(\hat{a}, \hat{b})$.

About a year after their first paper, in July of 1982, Aspect, Grangier and Roger reported the results of this experiment.[3] The experimental arrangement was shown in Figure 6–5. Using the data from all four detectors, the four required coincidence rates could be measured with high precision for all orientations of the polarizers. The violation of Bell's inequalities was now an extraordinary 40 standard deviations. A comparison of the predicted and measured polarization correlation is shown in Figure 6–8.

(C) Although these experiments offer compelling evidence against local hidden-variable theories, both suffer from one small but critical flaw: they are static. This leaves open the possibility that the orientation of the analyzer at one end of the apparatus could be signaled somehow to the analyzer at the other, or alternatively, to the source emitting the particles. Nothing we know of physics predicts that such a signaling occurs, but neither does anything explicitly forbid it.

In particular, the postulated influence need not travel faster than light. Indeed, since the experimental arrangement is static, such a signal speed

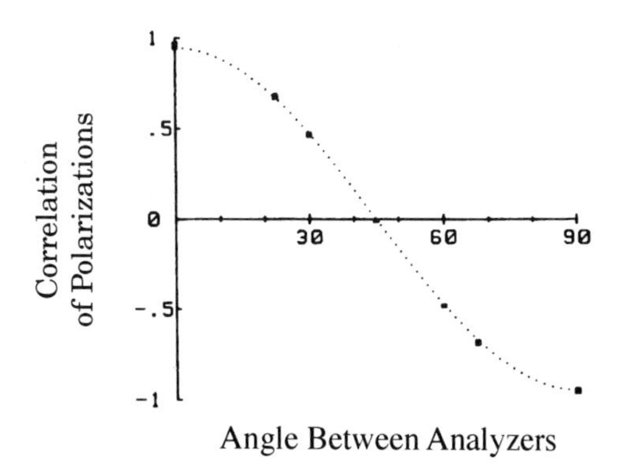

Figure 6–8 *Results of the Second Aspect Experiment* testing Bell's inequality. The curve drawn through the data points is not a best fit to the data, but a prediction of quantum theory. SOURCE: Modified with permission from A. Aspect, P. Grangier and G. Roger, "Experimental realization of Einstein–Podolsky–Rosen–Bohm Gedanken experiment: A new violation of Bell's inequalities," *Phys. Rev. Lett.*, vol. 49 (2), p. 91 (1982), published by The American Physical Society.

may be quite small. This is in contrast to the type of signaling Einstein, Podolsky and Rosen rejected when they made their locality assumption. They were concerned with an influence on Bob's result due to the *outcome of Alice's measurement*, as opposed to an influence due to the *orientation of her analyzer*. Since the two measurement results may be simultaneous, that signaling would have had to be instantaneous.

But Bell's theorem explicitly assumes such a signaling not to occur. Equation (5.14) of the previous chapter, which expresses one of the assumptions made in Bell's proof, states that the result of each measurement does not depend on the orientation of the other analyzer. So, if such a signaling were occurring in the above two experiments, the inequality derived by Bell would no longer hold. Apparently nonlocal correlations could be appearing in the data merely due to signaling between the analyzers.

The way out of this difficulty had already been foreseen in 1957 by David Bohm and Yakir Aharonov.[10] It was to rapidly change the analyzer orientation. In their final experiment, Aspect, Dalibard and Roger[4] performed the experiment Bohm and Aharonov first suggested, thereby closing the door on possibilities of this sort.

Their experiment assumed the principle of relativity to be valid, so that the purported signal could not travel faster than light. Their basic idea was then simply to change the experimental arrangement on a time scale short compared with the time it took light to travel from one end of the apparatus

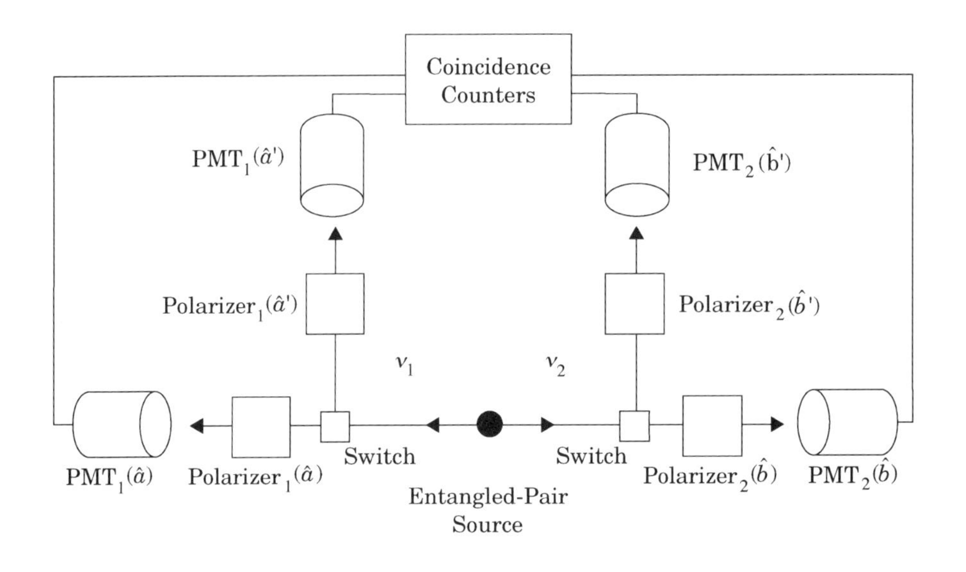

Figure 6–9 *Experimental Arrangement of the Third Aspect Experiment* testing Bell's inequality.[4] High-speed switches change the experimental arrangement on a time scale short compared to that required for any signal to propagate from one analyzer to the other.

to the other. Their photon source was, once again, a calcium cascade; but now the polarization analyzers and detectors were separated by a much longer distance, nearly 40 feet. This implied a travel time of at least 40 nanoseconds for the purported signal to travel between one analyzer and the other. They then placed a high-speed acousto-optical switch in each flight path just before the analyzers (Figure 6–9). This device provided them with the means for switching the flight path of each photon between two polarizers, each preset to a different orientation.

The acousto-optical switches made use of the diffraction of light from a standing wave in water. Transducers at both ends of a water cell vibrated 25 million times per second, i.e., with a period of 40 nanoseconds. This created a standing wave in the water much like that on a vibrating string. The density variations that this caused in the water created corresponding changes in the index of refraction. Because these variations were periodic in space, the experimenters had created the equivalent of a rapidly fluctuating phase grating. The photons Bragg-scattered off it through a small angle (about 0.3 degrees). Furthermore, since the grating was created by a standing wave, it formed, disappeared, and then re-formed twice in each acoustical cycle. Therefore, twice during the 40-ns cycle, the standing wave passed through zero amplitude and the optical beam passed through the water undeflected; and twice the standing wave was at its maximum and the light was fully deflected.

As shown in Figure 6–9, polarization analyzers of different orientations intercepted both the deflected and undeflected beams, and this on both sides of the apparatus. Thus the experimenters could switch between four analyzers and detectors, and they could do so in a time short compared to the 40-ns travel time for the hypothesized signals between them. The Bell inequality for this experimental arrangement, if violated, would provide compelling evidence that "common-sense," realistic theories consistent with relativity must be excluded from serious consideration.

Aspect's group ran the time-varying experiment for various polarizer orientations. Figure 6–10 shows a direct comparison of the predictions of quantum mechanics with the data they obtained. The agreement is superb. Analyzing this data for the set of orientations that yields the greatest predicted disagreement between quantum mechanics and other theories gives a violation of Bell's inequalities of 5 standard deviations. This implies a probability of less than 1% that the data could be consistent with a local realistic theory.

Comments Subtle and delicate objections have been raised to the design of and assumptions underlying the Aspect experiments. But at the time of this writing, most workers in the field believe that these objections are not fatal. If this view is correct, it is fair to say that their metaphysical

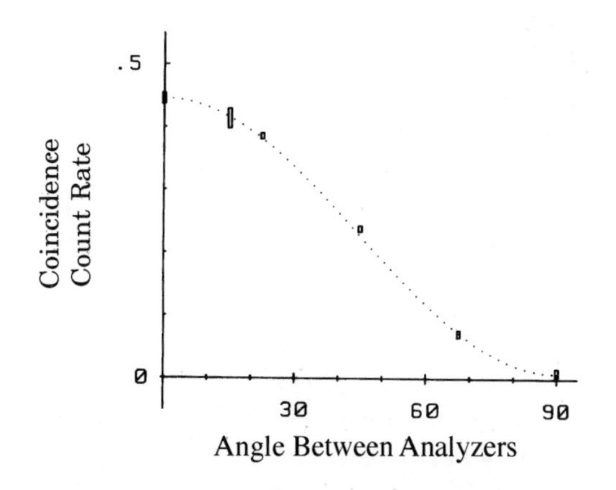

Figure 6–10 *Results of the Third Aspect Experiment* testing Bell's inequality. As before, the curve drawn through the data points is not a best fit to the data, but a prediction of quantum theory. Modified with permission from A. Aspect, J. Dalibard and G. Roger, "Experimental test of Bell's inequalities using time-varying analyzers," *Phys. Rev. Lett.*, vol. 49 (25), p. 1804 (1982), published by The American Physical Society.

implications are profound. The experimental tests of Bell's inequalities, such as those we have recounted in this chapter, go so far as to change the very way we should think of physical existence at its most fundamental level. No longer is it possible to think of the microworld in the terms Einstein, Podolsky and Rosen advocated. Rather we must think in terms of nonlocality, and/or we must renounce the very idea that individual objects possess discrete attributes. But since Galileo's description of primary qualities, all of science has held to the idea of definite attributes for individual objects.

In 1987, the elderly Nobel physicist E.M. Purcell delivered a lecture at Harvard University on the philosophical implications of quantum mechanics.[11] In it, he expressed his delight at having lived long enough to see a philosophical problem settled in the physics laboratory. It is rare indeed to see this happen, but the experimental tests of Bell's theorem have done just that.

6.2 Bohm's Nonlocal Hidden-Variable Theory

Bell's theorem, and the experiments based upon it, have provided convincing evidence that a local hidden-variable theory will never be able to account for the full range of quantum phenomena. But this does not eliminate all theories that attribute objective properties to the microworld. In fact, the very first hidden-variable theory offered as an alternative to quantum mechanics was nonlocal, and it had been proposed long before Bell proved his theorem. In 1952, David Bohm did what many thought impossible: he provided a complete theory in which particles had well-defined positions and trajectories at every instant of time, and yet which accounted for all quantum phenomena.[12] In place of the vague language of quantum mechanics, Bohm offered an account that had many of the trappings of classical physics. But there was one extraordinary difference: his theory was radically nonlocal. Historically, it was while thinking of this very nonlocality in Bohm's theory that Bell discovered his famous theorem.

Bohm's theory is able to account for quantum phenomena because in many ways it is identical to ordinary quantum mechanics. Indeed, he always referred to it as a new *interpretation* of quantum mechanics, rather than a whole new theory in its own right. In particular, quantum systems are still described by a wave function that obeys the Schrödinger equation. But Bohm gives this wave function a new interpretation. In his theory, particles are purely classical objects: they have definite positions and velocities, they move along well-defined paths through space, and they are never in "many places at once." But these particles are acted upon by a force that depends on the wave function.

Bohm begins with the Schrödinger equation:

$$i\hbar \frac{\partial \psi}{\partial t} = -\frac{\hbar^2}{2m} \nabla^2 \psi + V\psi \tag{6.12}$$

By expressing the wave function in polar form, $\psi = R\exp(iS/\hbar)$, he divides the Schrödinger equation into two, one for S and the other for R. He then notices that the equation for S is simply the classical equation of motion for a particle with momentum $p = \nabla S$, but now moving in a novel, two-part potential. In addition to the usual classical potential, V, an additional term appears, which one can interpret as a "quantum potential" Q:

$$Q = -\frac{\hbar^2}{2m} \frac{\nabla^2 R}{R}. \tag{6.13}$$

All the features of quantum mechanics are caused, in Bohm's view, by the quantum potential.

We began this book by presenting the classic double-slit experiment as evidence for the radically incomprehensible nature of the quantum world. But Bohm reinterprets this experiment, and others like it, in terms of particles moving along perfectly definite trajectories. The only difference is that these trajectories are influenced, not only by the slits themselves, but also by the quantum potential. The quantum potential for the experiment is shown in Figure 6–11. Notice the broad plateaus and deep valleys. These valleys correspond to regions where Q changes quickly, leading to a strong quantum force. This force guides the particles into the interference maxima and away from the minima. Assuming a Gaussian distribution of initial particle positions, those to one side of the median go through one slit, while those on the other side pass through the other. Each particle passes through one slit or the other, not both as we are tempted to say in the conventional quantum-mechanical account. The actual theoretically determined trajectories are plotted in Figure 6–12.

What happens if we suddenly close one slit? The wave function downstream from the slits instantly changes, so that the quantum potential does, too. Now the particles are exposed to a different quantum force, which changes their trajectories. Bohm shows that such nonlocal effects in his theory cannot be used to violate the limitations of special relativity. Nonetheless, we are called on to view both slits as relevant to the path of each particle, even though each particle passes through only one.

The particle positions and velocities in Bohm's account are, of course, precisely the hidden variables of which Bell's theorem treats. How then can his theory be maintained, given Bell's result? Because it is radically nonlocal. This nonlocality becomes evident if we consider his theory of

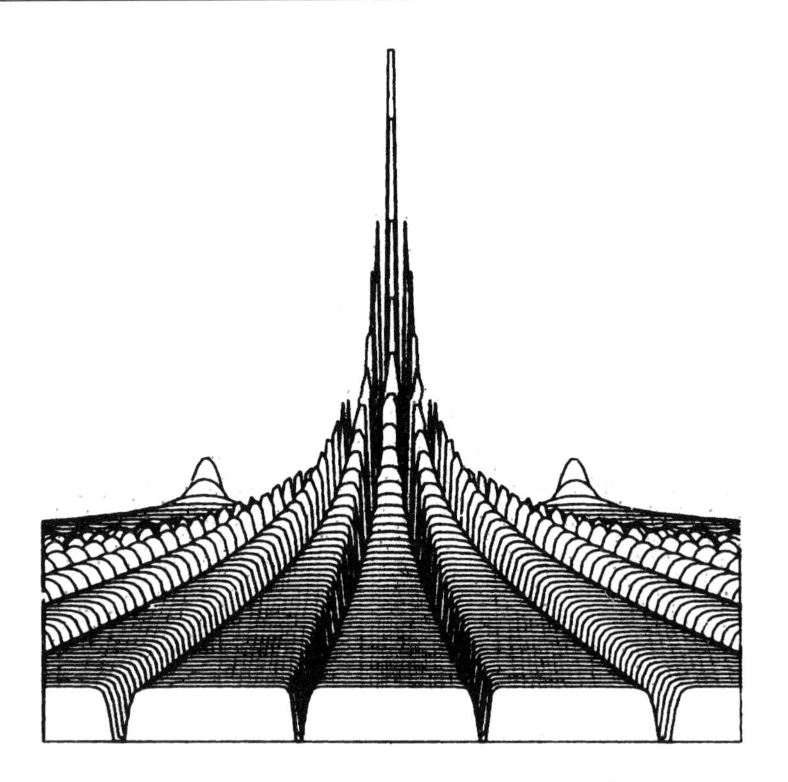

Figure 6–11 *Quantum Potential* of the two-slit interference experiment, in Bohm's nonlocal hidden variable theory. SOURCE: Reproduced with permission from C. Philippidis, C. Dewdney and B.J. Hiley, "Quantum interference and the quantum potential," *Nuovo Cimento B*, vol. 52B, ser. 2, no. 1, pp. 15–28 (1979). Copyright Societá Italiana di Fisica.

several particles. The wave function is now

$$\psi = \psi(\mathbf{r}_1, \mathbf{r}_2, \mathbf{r}_3, \ldots, t) \tag{6.14}$$

where $\mathbf{r}_1$ is the coordinate of particle 1, $\mathbf{r}_2$ that for particle 2, and so on. The force equation for particle 1 is

$$m\mathbf{a}_1 = \nabla_1[V + Q] \tag{6.15}$$

where ∇_1 represents the gradient taken with respect to r_1. But the quantum potential is now

$$Q = -\frac{\hbar^2}{2m}\frac{(\nabla_1^2 + \nabla_2^2 + \cdots)R}{R} \tag{6.16}$$

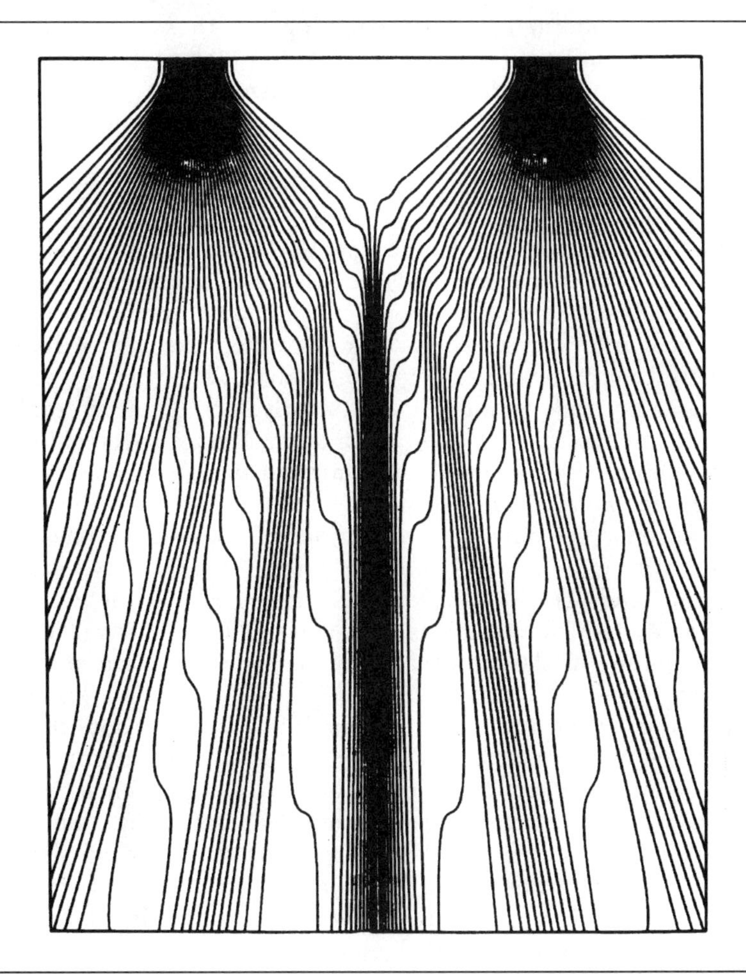

Figure 6–12 *Particle Trajectories* in the two-slit interference experiment, in Bohm's nonlocal hidden variable theory. SOURCE: Reproduced with permission from C. Philippidis, C. Dewdney and B.J. Hiley, "Quantum interference and the quantum potential," *Nuovo Cimento B*, vol. 52B, ser. 2, no. 1, pp. 15–28 (1979). Copyright Societá Italiana di Fisica.

We see that Q depends on the coordinates of all the particles in the system, so that the force on particle 1 does too: *the force on any particle depends on the positions of all the others.*

Notice also that this radically new nonlocal interaction between particles does not diminish as they are moved farther and farther apart. Presumably, the effects of any given particle on the overall wave function must diminish with distance from that particle. But R appears both in the numerator and in the denominator of Q; if R is multiplied by some small constant, corresponding to the reduction of these effects at great distances, this constant factors out of the quantum potential. So *the nonlocality contained in Bohm's theory extends over arbitrarily large distances.* Each particle in the system responds to information from the whole system.

But a yet deeper nonlocality exists within Bohm's theory, one which confounds a mechanical view of existence.[13] An example will clarify. The interaction between the Moon and the Earth is "pre-assigned," in the sense that it is completely specified once the law of interaction (universal gravitation in this case) and the positions of the two bodies are specified. All mechanical interactions share this character: the law of interaction and the spatial relations are sufficient to analyze the entire system.

But this is not true quantum-mechanically. The quantum analogue of the Earth–Moon system is the hydrogen atom. Here a specification of the law of interaction (the Coulomb potential) and the positions of the proton and electron are *not* sufficient to specify the particle trajectories. This is because Q depends not only on the positions of the two particles, but also on their wave functions. Thus the two particles might have exactly the same positions and velocities, but on the one hand be in the ground state, or on the other hand be in an excited state. The functional form for Q would be different in the two cases, so that the forces on the particles would be too.

Since the wave function reflects everything about the system (including even a superposition of internal states of the atom), Bohm and co-workers maintain that it is impossible to reduce such a problem to separable parts interacting with each other, as required by all mechanical models. Their interpretation of quantum theory goes beyond simple non-locality, and calls upon us to see the world as an undivided whole. Even in a mechanical world of parts, the interactions between the parts could, in principle, be nonlocal but still be mechanical. Not so in the quantum universe.

It is important to realize that Bohm's theory, and the more conventional account of quantum theory we have given up to this point, both argue for nonlocality. Bohm's theory has the advantage of providing an explicit account of how this occurs, but at the cost of introducing a new quantum potential that differs fundamentally from traditional potentials in physics.

6.3 The Mystery of the EPR Correlations

Recall the analogy we gave in Chapter 5 to the EPR paradox:

> As an analogy to the EPR method, imagine that you give a friend six seeds. Some are put in one box and the rest in another,

> identical to the first. The boxes are scrambled, such that neither of you knows which is which. Take one box to Moscow while your friend takes the other to New York. In Moscow, open the lid to your box and find two seeds. Since seeds cannot disappear or appear spontaneously,... you immediately know that four are in the other box in New York.

Notice now an apparently trivial fact. If this experiment is repeated over and over again, the number of seeds in each box will be different every time—but if we add together the numbers found in the two boxes, we will get six every time. Let us refer to this regularity as an "EPR-like correlation." How can this correlation be understood? In this case, the explanation is trivial: each time the experiment was conducted, we began with the same number of seeds, and the number of seeds is a conserved quantity.

Turn now to an EPR experiment of the type we have been describing. Two photons are emitted at the outset; one travels toward Alice, the other toward Bob. If their polarization analyzers are oriented along the same direction, then every time Alice and Bob perform measurements, they get identical results. They never get opposite polarizations. This is an "EPR correlation"—and how are we to explain *it*?

Prior to Bell's theorem and the experiments we have just recounted, the explanation would have been equally trivial. We simply would have postulated that the photons heading toward Alice and Bob had identical polarizations. If they had started off with angular momentum zero, and if angular momentum was conserved, then in the absence of external torques we would find the final angular momentum to be zero as well, guaranteeing their polarizations to be identical. *But the polarizations of the two individual photons are precisely what we mean by local hidden variables*—and we now know that these cannot exist.

In the analogy of the seeds, the hidden variable was the fraction of seeds traveling to Moscow and New York. In the world of classical physics, we are certainly allowed to postulate that such a fraction exists. Furthermore, until quantum mechanics came along, nearly everyone was sure that similar quantities existed for the microworld. Einstein was sure of this—this was his assumption of reality. Measurements, to him, revealed the pre-existing state of affairs. But the significance of the experiments that test Bell's inequalities is that we are no longer allowed to make this assumption.

We cannot account for the EPR correlations by postulating that the two photons emitted by the source toward Alice and Bob carry definite local properties. We must therefore think about the correlations in some other way. They point to a remarkable and entirely nonclassical connection between the state of affairs at Alice's and Bob's detectors. Furthermore, if it were proper to think of this mysterious connection as traveling with some velocity, notice that this velocity would have to be infinite. This is because Bob may be any distance at all from Alice, and he may make his measurement arbitrarily shortly after she does.

This new connection is quantum nonlocality.

6.4 Does Quantum Nonlocality Violate the Principle of Relativity?

It is important to distinguish the quantum nonlocality we are considering here from the nonlocality that Einstein, Podolsky and Rosen rejected in formulating their paradox. Their assumption of locality was the assumption that nothing done at any one location—nothing done by Alice—can have instantaneous causal effects at another location—at Bob's detector. If this assumption were dropped, we would certainly be violating relativity's principle that no physical cause can travel faster than light. But the quantum nonlocality that gives rise to EPR correlations cannot be thought of as transmitting any physical causation from Alice to Bob.

This is because, as Alice prepares to measure the polarization of the photon heading toward her, she cannot control what result she is going to get. She will find the answer to be either "horizontal" or "vertical," and nothing she can do will affect the outcome. Suppose, conversely, that she could do something to control this outcome. Then she would also be able to control the result of Bob's measurement. She could force his photon to have horizontal polarization by forcing hers to have horizontal polarization. This sort of control is exactly what we mean by physical causation and, as we have seen, it would propagate with infinite velocity. But because Alice is unable to exert this control, no physical causation is involved in the EPR correlations. And precisely because of this, we are saved from superluminal communication between Alice and Bob.

The sort of nonlocality that EPR rejected, the nonlocality that involves physical causes traveling with infinite velocity, arises from the so-called "action at a distance." The physicist and philosopher Abner Shimony has called the different sort of nonlocality that we are considering here "passion at a distance." It is a wonderfully evocative phrase. Physical causation operating over great distances necessarily involves some sort of action—but Alice and Bob, as they make their measurements, are utterly passive. Yet even though they are passive, unknown to them, a subtle quantum connection links their results.

It is also easy to show that, even though it involves some kind of instantaneous connection, "passion at a distance" cannot be used to send a message faster than light. At first sight, it might seem that it can. We might think that we can imagine a scheme whereby the two photons heading toward Alice and Bob could be used to carry messages between them. Alice and Bob might have agreed between themselves, for instance, that the receipt of a photon with horizontal polarization means "I am feeling fine," while the opposite polarization means "I am miserable." If so, whenever Bob receives a photon with horizontal polarization, he would know—instantaneously—that his partner was in good shape. But this scheme will not work. Indeed, the reason is the same as given above: Alice cannot control the outcome of her *own* polarization measurement, and thus cannot cause Bob's measurement to take on a particular value. Therefore, she can do nothing to control the "message" he gets.

In fact, if Alice and Bob conduct their individual experiments over and over again, each will find that the results are perfectly random. Alice will simply receive a random string of "horizontals" and "verticals," and so will Bob. Surely, no message is contained in a random list!

This points to one of the most curious elements of the quantum nonlocality responsible for the EPR correlations. If Alice pays attention only to the results of her own measurements, she will not even be *aware* of the fact that her particle is so intimately connected with Bob's. She is receiving a random string of "horizontals" and "verticals"—and this is precisely what she would be receiving were the source emitting not entangled pairs, but merely individual photons. Only if she compares her results with Bob's will the two of them discover the extraordinary fact that, even though the results of their individual measurements were random, a hidden regularity was present.

It is, indeed, something of an ominous situation. Imagine that you are conducting experiments on what appears to you to be an isolated particle. But is it an isolated particle? Even though nothing is touching it, even though nothing else is even near, it might be entangled with some other particle. Indeed this other particle, so intimately connected with yours, could be located on a planet orbiting a star in a distant galaxy, of which we are at present entirely unaware. Furthermore, there is no local experiment you can perform to tell whether or not this is the case. While in actual practice the EPR correlations are difficult to maintain over great distances, nothing in principle prevents such a situation from occurring.

Finally, how are Alice and Bob to compare their data, and so discover the perfect correlation? On the one hand, Alice and Bob might travel toward one another. If they do so, they must travel at velocities less than that of light. Alternatively, Alice could broadcast a (normal) message to Bob, containing the results of her measurements; when he gets it, Bob would then make the comparison. But this broadcast itself involves a message traveling at or below the velocity of light. In either case, no violation of the relativity principle has occurred.

What is going on in all this? How can a nondeterministic connection be maintained over arbitrary distances, and in a way that maintains perfect correlations? In the world of classical physics, the answer would have been trivial, but in the quantum world it will have to accommodate the tests of Bell's inequalities. Furthermore, recent experiments have probed the nature of this quantum nonlocality yet farther; they reveal it to be far different, and far richer, than classical thinking would have permitted.

6.5 Quantum Nonlocality: A New Source and a New Experiment

In the EPR experiments we have described so far, the calcium cascade has played an essential role. It was the physical process that produced the state required for tests of Bell's inequalities. Alain Aspect perfected this source, and he went on to use it in an important series of experiments that examined the physics of entangled states. But around 1985, Leonard Mandel of the University of Rochester realized that a second and even more powerful source of entangled states exists. Through a process known by the intimidating name of "spontaneous parametric down conversion," a single ultraviolet photon can fission into two if it is passed through certain crystals. Moreover, the two down-converted photons are in an entangled state perfectly suited to a whole range of new experiments. We will consider only two from the many the Rochester group and others have performed, dramatizing the nonlocal character of quantum physics.

Before going on to the experiments, we should spend a moment considering the down-conversion process itself. In empty space, a photon cannot "break into pieces," but in a suitable medium something like this can happen. Already in 1970, Burnham and Weinberg undertook to examine the nature of the secondary light produced when intense laser light passed through certain nonlinear crystals such as KDP and lithium iodate.[14] Most of the incident light passed straight through, but a small fraction was converted into a rainbow of colors that surrounded the primary beam in a cone. It was a beautiful effect, but its most salient feature was hidden from casual view, and only became apparent after a detailed theoretical treatment of how spontaneous down-conversion takes place.

As the name implies, the down-converted photons arise "spontaneously." Like spontaneous emission in individual atoms, the process is quantum in nature. We should, therefore, consider what is happening one photon at a time.

A single incident photon arrives at the nonlinear crystal. Through its interaction with the crystal, a small but finite probability arises for it to disappear and for two others to arise simultaneously in its place. Energy and momentum ($\mathbf{p} = \hbar\mathbf{k}$) must be conserved, which means that:

$$\begin{aligned} \mathbf{k}_0 &= \mathbf{k}_1 + \mathbf{k}_2 \\ \omega_0 &= \omega_1 + \omega_2 \end{aligned} \tag{6.17}$$

But there are many, in fact, infinitely many pairs of photons that meet these constraints. As always, where such possibilities exist, quantum physics exploits them. Classically we would imagine that one photon pair with well-defined properties is produced by each incident photon. But quantum-mechanically, a superposition state is produced instead. Indeed, the superposition contains infinitely many terms, corresponding to the continuous range of possible values of energy and momentum of the down-converted photons.

Experimentally, out of the myriad possible pairs, one or two are usually selected. Each pair is chosen by first picking a direction for the first photon, by inserting a pinhole somewhere in the cone of secondary light. Having chosen one photon in this way, its partner can be found by searching on the opposite side of the primary beam until a coincidence signal is located. With pairs of photons produced this way, a range of remarkable experiments can now be performed. We will consider the pioneering work of Ghosh and Mandel.[15]

Their apparatus is diagrammed in Figure 6–13. A and B are the two down-conversion beams produced in the nonlinear crystal. They are picked out by pinholes located exactly opposite each other relative to the primary beam. Now, while the pinholes are small, they are not of infinitesimal size, so that each beam actually has a certain spread. Thus the photon from each pinhole can strike the screen over a small but finite area.

In their first experiment (Figure 6–13a), a single, tiny photodetector was moved along the screen. When this was done, its count rate was found *not* to exhibit an interference pattern. Rather, its count rate was constant. But why? After all, the two members of the pair are generated together in time, and from a coherent laser source. Already we see an anomaly whose explanation requires us to think in a new way. We will delay discussion of this remarkable result until we have considered the second part of their experiment (Figure 6–13b).

In it, the single photodetector was replaced by a pair of detectors: D_1 at x_1 and D_2 at x_2. When they varied the position of the first detector, its count rate was found to be constant. The same was true for the second detector. But Ghosh and Mandel then connected the two detectors to a coincidence counter, which registered a count only if D_1 and D_2 fired simultaneously. They found a clear variation, of exactly the type that we would expect from interference.

But what is interfering? In a normal double-slit experiment we have learned to think in terms of a superposition of probability amplitudes for the single photon traveling both paths to the detector. Here we must consider two photons in an entangled superposition state. The detector at x_1 could fire because it received a photon from either A or B; similarly, the detector at x_2 could fire because it received a photon from B or A. The superposition we are considering is:

$$\psi = \frac{1}{\sqrt{2}}[(1)_{A1}(0)_{A2}(0)_{B1}(1)_{B2} + e^{i\theta}(0)_{A1}(1)_{A2}(1)_{B1}(0)_{B2}] \qquad (6.18)$$

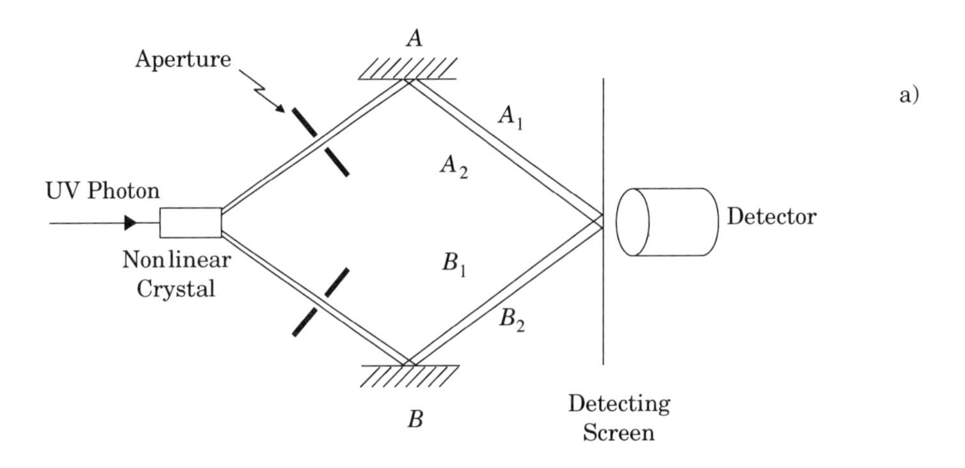

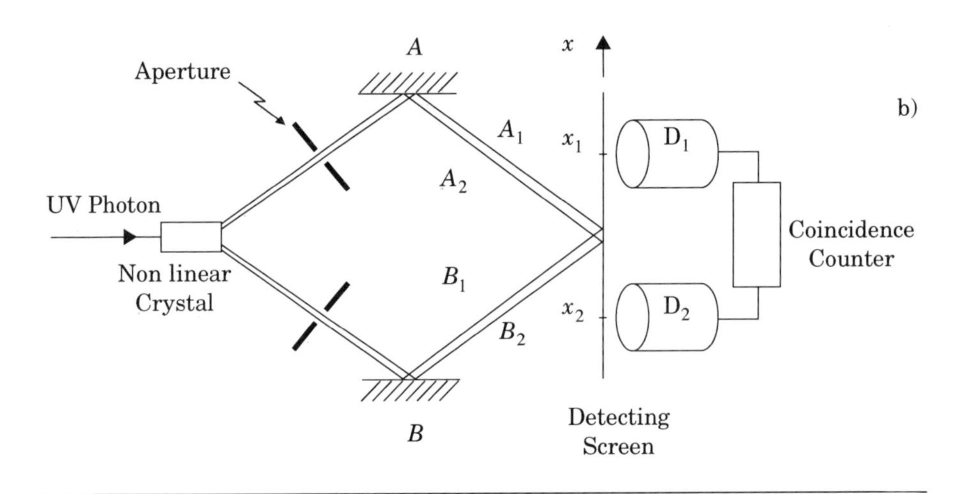

Figure 6–13 *The Ghosh–Mandel Experiments.* A single photon entering the nonlinear crystal splits into a pair. Each member of the pair can strike the detecting screen over a small but finite area. Moving along the screen is (a) a single detector and, in (b), a pair connected to a coincidence counter.

Here a "1" indicates that a photon is present in the indicated mode and a "0" indicates that it is not. Thus the first term in Equation (6.18) means that one photon has arrived at D_1 along path A and the other has arrived at D_2 along path B. The second term describes the opposite possibility; and in keeping with the fundamental principles of quantum mechanics, we add the two probability amplitudes before calculating the probabilities of detection for the entire system. Detailed calculations show that no interference for single photon detection is predicted, but two-photon coincidence interference with 100% visibility is predicted.[15]

The remarkable thing about this experiment is that, as the phase changes by moving the detectors, the individual count rates do not change at all. Both detectors receive photons at a steady (although random) rate. Only if detections at x_1 and x_2 are compared via a coincidence counter does the interference pattern emerge. Lacking this comparison, it is not even possible to find out if the phase is being changed! In this regard, the Ghosh–Mandel experiment is similar to the EPR thought experiment, in that the two observers must actually compare their data in order to realize that anything interesting is going on.

The nonlocal effect exhibited by the Ghosh–Mandel experiment is quite remarkable, and it is impossible to understand classically. For example, let D_1 be fixed, and move D_2 smoothly along until it reaches an interference minimum. As this is done, both D_1 and D_2 will continue receiving counts at a steady rate. Nevertheless, once D_2 has reached the interference minimum, none of its counts will occur at the same *time* as those recorded by D_1 (in an ideal experiment). Conversely, if D_2 is now moved to an interference maximum, many of its counts will. Somehow, even when there is no communication between D_1 and D_2, the photons arriving at each detector "know about" those arriving at the other.

6.6 Comments on Quantum Nonlocality

The thought experiment of Einstein, Podolsky and Rosen and the Ghosh and Mandel experiment we have recounted here illustrate the extraordinary nature of entangled states. The lesson they teach is that it is not appropriate to think of these states as consisting of two separate particles with their own individual properties. Rather, the two particles are tangled together into a seamless unity.

This is why no interference was observed in the first part of the Ghosh–Mandel experiment. Classically, interference arises when two waves with a definite phase relationship between them strike the same detector. But a phase describes a relationship between two things, and a down-conversion pair—and, more generally, every entangled state—is actually a single thing.

This thing, for which there is no classical counterpart, exists at many different locations at once. Its attributes are in some sense mingled together. The different locations over which it extends are in a strange intimate contact—a contact that carries neither messages nor physical causation, but that always exists and can lead to instantaneous correlations. Clearly, if we take quantum mechanics seriously as making a statement about the real world, then the demands it places on our conventional thinking are enormous. Hidden behind the discrete and independent objects of the sense world is an entangled realm, in which the simple notions of identity and locality no longer apply. We may not notice the intimate relationships common to that level of existence, but, regardless of our blindness to them, they persist. Events that appear to us as random may, in fact, be correlated with other events occurring elsewhere. Behind the indifference of the macroscopic world, "passion at a distance" knits everything together.

Chapter 7

Schrödinger's Cat

In 1935 Erwin Schrödinger published an article[1] in which he presented an extraordinary paradox. His treatment of this paradox was remarkably brief—it occupies no more than a single short paragraph of a dense, sixteen-page paper. But so striking are its consequences, that it has continued to concern and fascinate physicists to this day.

Schrödinger expressed his paradox in terms of a thought experiment, and he explicitly described it as a "quite ridiculous" one. He certainly did not advocate performing the experiment. It does not need to be performed; its function, rather, is to fix our thoughts on a situation crafted so as to dramatize most clearly the paradoxical nature of quantum theory. Since then, it has come to be known as "Schrödinger's cat paradox."

Here is a translation of that remarkable paragraph:[2]

> One can even set up quite ridiculous cases. A cat is penned up in a steel chamber, along with the following diabolical device (which must be secured against direct interference by the cat): in a Geiger counter there is a tiny bit of radioactive substance, so small that *perhaps* in the course of one hour one of the atoms decays, but also, with equal probability, perhaps none; if it happens, the [Geiger] counter tube discharges and through a relay releases a hammer which shatters a small flask of hydrocyanic acid. If one has left this entire system to itself for an hour, one would say that the cat still lives *if* meanwhile no atom has decayed. The first atomic decay would have poisoned it. The ψ-function of the entire system would express this by having in it the living and the dead cat (pardon the expression) mixed or smeared out in equal parts.

In modern language we would say that after the hour has passed, the state of the cat is a superposition of two terms, one representing a living cat, and the other a dead one. If we represent the state by C,

$$C = \frac{1}{\sqrt{2}} [\psi_{\text{alive}} + \psi_{\text{dead}}] \tag{7.1}$$

7.1 What Is the Cat Paradox?

Schrödinger's thought experiment is remarkably subtle. There is a good deal of confusion, even among practicing physicists, as to where the paradox actually lies. Let us attempt to express it.

The first question is: What does the superposition given by Equation (7.1) mean? It is difficult to be sure. Should we say that it describes a cat that in some peculiar sense is both alive and dead at the same time? What could this possibly mean? But there is more to the paradox than our difficulty in deciding what the superposition state given by Equation (7.1) actually means. For after the hour has passed, let us now step forward, open the box, and *look* at the cat. When we do so, all of these questions drop away, for what we see will not correspond to any of these bizarre possibilities. Rather we will see something entirely prosaic—nothing more than a cat; maybe dead, maybe living.

Thus one's first thought is that the paradox is that the superposition given by Equation (7.1) does not represent what we see when we observe the cat. Indeed, it does not represent anything we have ever seen. Clearly, Schrödinger's paradox can be reformulated for any situation involving two mutually exclusive possibilities. Thus a tossed coin will land either heads or tails, but never some mysterious combination of both and neither. Similarly, if I am standing inside a room with two open windows and throw a baseball, and if the baseball ends up lying on the lawn outside, then it must have passed through either one or the other window. So we might be tempted to say that the cat paradox is that *in the macroscopic world we always observe either one or the other of two, mutually exclusive circumstances, but never both.*

But a little thought reveals that this will not do, for the same is true when we directly observe the microworld. We can demonstrate this by creating an example that has all the essential features of Schrödinger's example, but that pertains to subatomic particles. Consider the case of an electron that might have its spin up or, with equal probability, down. The state of the electron is written as

$$\psi = \frac{1}{\sqrt{2}} [(\uparrow) + (\downarrow)] \tag{7.2}$$

The superposition given by Equation (7.2) is just as difficult to interpret as that given by Equation (7.1): all of the unresolved questions we asked about Equation (7.1) pertain with equal force to Equation (7.2). But if we do not concern ourselves with these questions, and simply proceed to measure the spin of such a particle, we obtain a perfectly sensible answer—either up or down, with equal probability. (This is because a fundamental tenet of quantum mechanics is that, if we measure any observable, we will get only results corresponding to the various possible eigenvalues of the operator corresponding to that observable.) And this is exactly what we observe when we open the door and look at Schrödinger's cat: each time we look we find the cat either living or dead, and if we were to repeat the experiment over and over again, we would find the two outcomes occur with equal frequency.

A clue to the correct statement of the cat paradox can be found in one of the macroscopic examples we gave above: the baseball, which, when thrown through a wall pierced by two windows, passes through one or the other but never both. But electrons can perfectly well pass through two windows at once! The phenomenon of interference demonstrates this fact. We have already analyzed interference experiments extensively in previous chapters. Recall that, if we were to directly observe the path of each electron, we would observe it passing through one or the other of the two slits—just as, when we observe the cat, we find it either living or dead—and in this circumstance, no interference pattern will appear. But if we choose *not* to observe the electron's path, we do obtain interference.

After nearly three-quarters of a century of quantum mechanics, we have gotten used to the fact that the microworld exhibits quantum properties. *The real cat paradox is that the macroscopic world of our daily experience does not. We never observe in it anything corresponding to interference between dead and living cats.*

7.2 Superpositions and Mixtures: A More Technical Statement of the Cat Paradox

This correct formulation of the cat paradox involves the distinction we drew in Chapter 3 between *quantum uncertainty* and *classical ignorance*. If we were to present Schrödinger's thought experiment to a person not versed in quantum mechanics, what would that person say about the state of the cat after the hour had passed? He would say that the cat was either dead or alive, and that it was not possible to predict which. And this, of course, is just the situation of classical ignorance. It is like saying that an electron possibly passes through one slit, or possibly the other, but that it did not pass through both.

Technically, classical ignorance cannot be described as a simple quantum state, but rather requires a distinct treatment known as a mixture. We say that a group of N particles is described by a mixture if N_1 of them are actually in the state ψ_1 and N_2 of them are actually in the state ψ_2, where $N_1 + N_2 = N$. The mixture describes a state of whose nature we are unsure—not for any reasons involving quantum-mechanical uncertainty, but simply because of classical ignorance. The quantum state of each of the N particles is definitely ψ_1 or ψ_2, but we do not happen to know which.

We can elucidate the distinction between superpositions and mixtures in the context of the two-slit interference experiment by writing ψ_1 as the wave function describing a particle that has passed through slit 1, and similarly ψ_2 as the wave function describing a particle that has passed through slit 2. Interference will be observed if the state is a superposition. Alternatively, we can imagine a different experiment in which the source is designed to emit some particles *only* toward one slit and other particles toward the other, but never both. The ensemble of particles will be described by a mixture. Furthermore, because each particle passes through only one slit, interference will not occur. This is a very general point: *superpositions allow for interference, but mixtures do not.*

We therefore arrive at a more formal statement of the cat paradox: *were we actually to perform the experiment many times, the state of the ensemble of cats would be represented by a mixture. But quantum mechanics says it should be represented by a superposition.* More generally, the paradox is that all aspects of the macroscopic world we daily observe are described by mixtures, whereas quantum theory says they should be described by superpositions.

7.3 Further Discussion of the Difference Between Superpositions and Mixtures: Spin

The distinction between superpositions and mixtures has observable consequences, but these consequences do not always lead to an interference pattern. Here is a second example, involving spin.

Let us imagine that we have a box containing a large number of spin-1/2 particles. The box is pierced by a tiny hole, which allows the particles to escape one by one, and each such particle we pass through a Stern–Gerlach apparatus. This apparatus is oriented along the z-direction, and so it allows us to determine the z-component of each particle's spin. If the experiment is performed a large number of times, we find ourselves obtaining the result $+\frac{1}{2}\hbar$ half the time and $-\frac{1}{2}\hbar$ half the time.

But now notice that there are two possible ways this result might have come about. On the one hand, each particle in the box might be in a superposition state

$$\psi = \frac{1}{\sqrt{2}}[(\uparrow)_z + (\downarrow)_z] \tag{7.3}$$

Alternatively, half the particles in the box might have spin up, and the other half spin down, i.e., they might form a mixture. How can we determine which of these two alternatives is the case? The method is to rotate our Stern–Gerlach analyzer so that it points, not along the z-direction, but along the x-direction. What do the above two alternatives predict if this is done? In what follows we will need the following mathematical relations concerning spin-1/2 superpositions (all of which follow directly from Equation (7.17) below):

$$\frac{1}{\sqrt{2}}[(\uparrow)_z + (\downarrow)_z] = (\rightarrow)_x \tag{7.4}$$

$$(\uparrow)_z = \frac{1}{\sqrt{2}}[(\rightarrow)_x + (\leftarrow)_x] \tag{7.5}$$

$$(\downarrow)_z = \frac{1}{\sqrt{2}}[(\rightarrow)_x - (\leftarrow)_x] \tag{7.6}$$

Equation (7.4) states that the first of our two possible alternatives corresponds to an eigenstate of spin along the x-axis. Thus *if the state is the superposition given in Equation (7.3), every particle will be found to have its spin along the positive* x*-axis*. But the second alternative will not! In the case of the mixture, Equation (7.5) will pertain to half of the particles in the box—those whose spin is really up. For them, our measurement of the x-component of the spin will be equally likely to result in a positive or a negative value. For the other half of the particles in the box, Equation (7.6) obtains, and we get precisely the same result. Thus, *if the state is a mixture, measurements of the* x*-component of the spin will have equal numbers of positive and negative results.*

The fact that such an experimental procedure exists emphasizes the difference between superpositions and mixtures. We also wish to note that this is no abstract exercise, but rather corresponds to experimental reality, for a neutron spin experiment has actually been performed illustrating these issues.[3]

7.4 Why Is Quantum Behavior Not Observed in the Large-Scale World?

Although the cat paradox has exerted a perpetual fascination over many physicists since its publication in 1935, it is fair to say that not all physicists shared in this fascination. This is because until recently it could not be experimentally tested. In most macroscopic circumstances the difference between quantum and classical behavior—between superpositions and mixtures—is far too small to be experimentally observed. We now turn to a discussion of several reasons why this is so; afterwards, we will describe recent experiments in which these reasons have been circumvented, and preliminary laboratory versions of Schrödinger's cat have been constructed.

One's first thought might be that the cat paradox poses no real difficulty because quantum mechanics does not even apply to the large-scale world. After all, the theory was invented to account for submicroscopic objects such as atoms, photons and the like; it is a theory of the small, and was never intended to apply to the large.

The difficulty with this is that, according to quantum mechanics itself, the theory does indeed apply to the large-scale world we inhabit. Nowhere in the rules of quantum mechanics is there to be found a statement that the Schrödinger equation applies only to small things. Indeed, according to its tenets, the Schrödinger equation applies to cats and baseballs just as well as electrons.

Why, then, do cats and baseballs not exhibit quantum behavior? There are a variety of reasons. We will consider three simple ones and, in the next section on decoherence, a more complex one.

Interference Return to the example of a baseball thrown at a wall pierced by two windows. Why does the baseball not exhibit interference? Recall from Chapter 1 that successive interference maxima arise whenever the path lengths from the two slits differ by one de Broglie wavelength. But the de Broglie wavelength is $\lambda = h/p$, where p is the momentum. If an object of mass, say, $\frac{1}{2}$ pound = 0.23 kg is thrown at, say, 20 miles per hour = 8.9 m/s, its de Broglie wavelength works out to a mere 3.2×10^{-34} m. Thus the spacing between successive interference maxima is far smaller than the dimensions of even an atom! Such a rapidly varying interference pattern is experimentally indistinguishable from a purely uniform probability of finding the baseball anywhere. Thus, if real baseballs—or any other macroscopic objects—do in fact exhibit interference, we would never know it.

Uncertainty Principle All microscopic objects are subject to the uncertainty principle. Macroscopic objects are too, but its effects turn out to be so small as to have no practical consequences. Suppose, for instance, that we ask how well a baseball can be localized. Let us say, for the sake of argument, that we know where it is to an accuracy of one hundredth of an inch. Using this for Δx in the uncertainty relation

$$(\Delta x)(\Delta p_x) = \frac{\hbar}{2} \tag{7.7}$$

we obtain, for a mass of $\frac{1}{2}$ pound for the baseball, $\Delta v = 9.1 \times 10^{-31}$ m/s. This "jitter" in the baseball's velocity is so small as to be entirely unobservable. We can justifiably speak about the trajectory of a baseball, but not an electron.

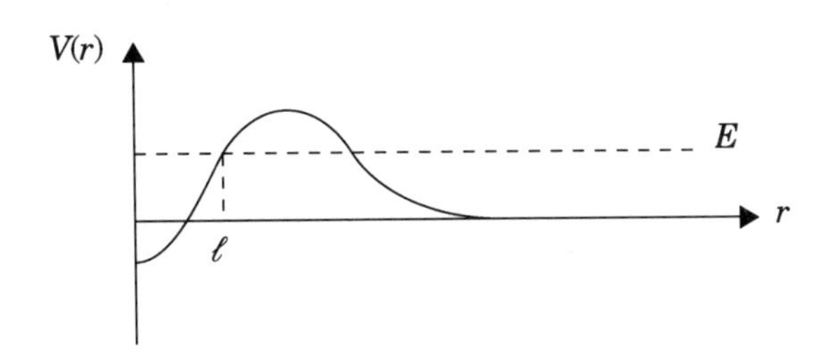

Figure 7–1 *Potential Energy* of an alpha particle of energy E in an atomic nucleus. Classically, it should be trapped within the region $0 < r < \ell$, but the phenomenon of radioactivity proves that in fact it is able to escape.

Quantum Tunneling Tunneling is another purely quantum effect with no classical counterpart. We will analyze it in some detail here, both in order to understand why it is not observed in the large-scale world, and because recent laboratory realizations of Schrödinger's cat involve the phenomenon.

Historically, quantum tunneling was first invoked by Gamow[4] and by Gurney and Condon[5] to account for alpha radioactivity, the emission of alpha particles by unstable atomic nuclei. These treatments thought of the alpha particle as being trapped in an attractive potential well—the nucleus—by the nuclear force. The difficulty in understanding radioactivity arose from the fact that the attractive nuclear potential was known to be significantly greater than the kinetic energy of the alpha particles. Thus the alpha particles should be trapped within the nuclei. Figure 7–1 diagrams the situation; the kinetic energy of the alpha particle inside the well is not sufficient to allow it to "climb the hill" and escape. But the phenomenon of radioactivity demonstrates that it does. Gamow, Gurney and Condon, by applying quantum mechanics to the situation, showed how this comes about.

Figure 7–2 presents a schematic view of the problem. A wave is incident from the left on a potential barrier whose height V_0 exceeds the particle energy E. In regions I and III the potential $V(x) = 0$ in the Schrödinger equation, and its solutions are the well-known plane waves

$$\begin{aligned} \psi &= A_1 e^{ikx} + A_2 e^{-ikx} \quad \text{in I} \\ \psi &= A_5 e^{ikx} + A_6 e^{-ikx} \quad \text{in III} \end{aligned} \tag{7.8}$$

where $k = \sqrt{2mE/\hbar^2}$ and the constants A are to be determined by the boundary conditions. Similarly, in region II, the potential $V(x) = V_0 > E$ and the solutions of the Schrödinger equation are

$$\psi = A_3 e^{\rho x} + A_4 e^{-\rho x} \tag{7.9}$$

where $\rho = \sqrt{2m(V_0 - E)/\hbar^2}$.

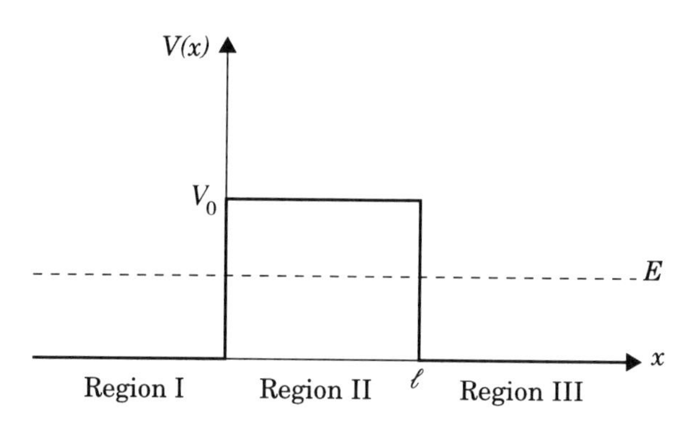

Figure 7–2 *Schematic View of the Trapping Potential* illustrated in Figure 7–1.

What question do we want to ask of these solutions? Begin with a beam of particles incident from the left in region I: we want to find out what fraction of them penetrate the barrier into region III, there to continue traveling in the same direction. In Equations (7.8)–(7.9), the quantity A_1 is the amplitude of the wave incident from the left. Similarly, A_5 is the amplitude of that fraction of the wave that has penetrated the barrier and continued on in the same direction. The square of their ratio will be the fraction we desire. Classically, we expect this fraction to be zero; what does quantum mechanics say?

To find the coefficients A, we invoke boundary conditions. They are: (1) $A_6 = 0$: this sets the initial condition that the incident wave is coming in from the left rather than the right, and (2) both the wave function and its first derivative must be continuous at the boundaries $x = 0$ and $x = l$. It is straightforward to show that these conditions lead to the relation

$$\text{Fraction that penetrate} \equiv \left|\frac{A_5}{A_1}\right|^2 = \frac{16E(V_0 - E)}{V_0^2} e^{-2\rho\ell} \tag{7.10}$$

for $\rho\ell \ll 1$.

To apply this result to the phenomenon of radioactivity, we need to know how often the alpha particle "tries" to escape its potential well. How rapidly does it move within the nucleus? By the uncertainty principle, its momentum must be of order $P = h/\ell$, where ℓ is the nuclear diameter, so its velocity is $v = h/m\ell$ and the time required to cross the nucleus is $\ell/v = m\ell^2/h$. For a typical diameter of a large nucleus, several tens of Fermis, this works out to several times 10^{-20} seconds.

Measured half-lives of alpha-unstable nuclei span an enormous range, from millionths of a second to tens of billions of years. As an example, let us concentrate on a half-life of one year. In this interval of time, the alpha particle strikes its potential barrier about 10^{27} times; thus to account for this half-life, we require the probability of tunneling from Equation (7.10) to be $10^{-27} = e^{-62}$. It is easy to show that, for plausible values of ℓ, E and V_0, Equation (7.10) does indeed yield such values. Furthermore, because the exponential factor in Equation (7.10) varies so rapidly, relatively slight variations in these parameters can also account for the great range in half-lives.

Thus quantum mechanics accounts for the phenomenon of alpha-radioactivity. We should note, however, as we did in Chapter 1 when we discussed the phenomenon of interference, the deficiencies in the quantum account. The alpha particle, trapped in its potential well, is precisely analogous to a prisoner trapped in a cell whose door has been welded shut. Nowhere does the theory explain how the prisoner manages the magical feat of escaping. All it tells us—and it does so correctly—is roughly how long the prisoner must wait before inexplicably finding himself free.

Let us now apply just the same analysis to a macroscopic version of quantum tunneling. To be specific, we concentrate on the case of the escape of a prisoner from a cell. Equation (7.10) is still valid, but we will see that now the rate of quantum tunneling it predicts is so slow that the phenomenon is never expected to occur in any realistic circumstance.

To find the probability of escape we need to estimate the relevant parameters in Equation (7.10). Some are easy: the prisoner's mass is on the order of 100 kg, and the thickness ℓ of the walls enclosing him perhaps a meter. A more delicate part is estimating the potential V_0 in which he is trapped. Let us guess that a projectile, if fired at the prison wall at a velocity of one thousand miles per hour, would be capable of shattering it. Such a projectile, with mass perhaps 10 kg, has a kinetic energy of order 10^6 J, which we can identify with V_0. As for E, it represents the prisoner's kinetic energy as he restlessly paces back and forth within the cell. If he is pacing at a few miles per hour, then E is of order 10^2 J.

With these numbers, the probability of tunneling out of the jail cell is

$$\text{Probability of escape in a single try} \cong 10^{-10^{38}} \qquad (7.11)$$

But if the prisoner paces back and forth, never sleeping, for the rest of his life, he will encounter these walls roughly 10^8 times. Thus we see that the probability of his escaping from the cell in this magical way is vanishingly small. Indeed, had the prisoner been pacing throughout the entire history of the universe since the big bang, approximately 20 billion years, the probability would still have been vanishingly small.

Thus we conclude that quantum tunneling, like interference and the uncertainty principle, plays a great role in the microworld, but no appreciable role at all in the large-scale world.

7.5 Decoherence

In the previous section we argued that, although the principles of quantum mechanics do indeed apply in the large-scale world that we inhabit in our daily lives, their consequences are unobservable. Interference effects, the uncertainty "jitter," and tunneling rates are too small in the everyday world to be observed. The notion of decoherence, on the other hand, takes exception to this. Proponents of decoherence claim that Schrödinger's cat, and indeed all other macroscopic objects, are effectively *not* described by superpositions, but rather by mixtures. Thus, they claim, Schrödinger's paradox is in fact not a paradox.

The essential element behind decoherence is the recognition that, unless extraordinary precautions are taken in the laboratory, large objects are never isolated from their environments. Furthermore, these environments are continually and erratically fluctuating. Electrons, atoms, and the like can be studied in isolation—they exist in a vacuum, so to speak. But cats and baseballs are perpetually buffeted about. As it sits in its box, Schrödinger's cat is ever so slightly shaken by seismic waves from an earthquake in Peru. A tiny breath of wind disturbs the flying baseball's path. Indeed, in this regard even the perpetual microscopic jittering back and forth of the atoms of which large-scale objects are composed can be thought of as part of this continual erratic fluctuation. And the consequence of this fluctuation is that, for all practical purposes, superpositions are converted into mixtures.

A further essential element of the notion of decoherence is that it is to some degree an illusion. The total system consists of *both* the cat *and* its environment—and this total system is truly in a superposition state. But when we think about the cat, we are thinking of merely part of the total system, and this part is effectively described by a mixture. In this way, the notion of decoherence does not invalidate the general principle that quantum mechanics applies to all things, big as well as little.

How does the incessant fluctuation in an object's environment convert its state from a superposition into a mixture? The basic ideas behind the process can be understood with the help of a simple illustrative example, due to H. Bernstein (unpublished).

We will need a few mathematical facts about spin-1/2. The states

$$(\uparrow)_z \quad \text{and} \quad (\downarrow)_z \tag{7.12}$$

form a complete set, using any spin-1/2 state which can be expressed. Let us write down their most general superposition:

$$u = \alpha(\uparrow)_z + \beta(\downarrow)_z \tag{7.13}$$

where

$$|\alpha|^2 + |\beta|^2 = 1 \tag{7.14}$$

Let us now simply define two new constants, θ and ϕ, through

$$\begin{aligned} \alpha &\equiv \cos\left(\frac{\theta}{2}\right) e^{-i\phi/2} \\ \beta &\equiv \sin\left(\frac{\theta}{2}\right) e^{i\phi/2} \end{aligned} \tag{7.15}$$

These are two equations in two unknowns, and they could be solved for θ and ϕ in terms of α and β if we wished. The solution is cumbersome, however, and we will have no use for it, so there is no need to bother. (It is worth noting, though, that

$$|\alpha|^2 + |\beta|^2 = \cos^2\left(\frac{\theta}{2}\right) + \sin^2\left(\frac{\theta}{2}\right) = 1 \tag{7.16}$$

so the normalization condition [Equation (7.14)] is automatically fulfilled.)

What is the purpose of this transformation? It can be shown that the state u is in fact an eigenstate of the spin along a new axis, one pointing in the $\hat{u}$ direction, as illustrated in Figure 7–3. Thus we conclude that the

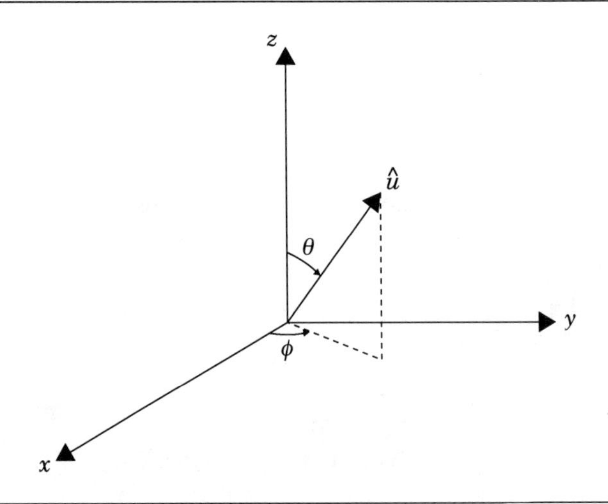

Figure 7–3 *Spin Geometry*. The most general superposition of spins can always be reduced to an eigenstate pointing along the $\hat{u}$ direction, in which θ and ϕ are given in terms of the coefficients of the superposition.

most general possible superposition of our basis states describes a spin pointing purely in some definite direction, and it is even possible to write down this direction in terms of the coefficients of the superposition.

If we specialize to spins restricted to the xy plane, we can set $\theta = 90°$ and Equations (7.13)–(7.15) reduce to

$$u = A[(\uparrow)_z + e^{i\phi}(\downarrow)_z] \qquad \text{where } A \equiv \frac{1}{\sqrt{2}}\, e^{-i\phi/2} \tag{7.17}$$

$$(\text{since } \cos 45° = \sin 45° = 1/\sqrt{2})$$

which is the result we will need in what follows. (Incidentally, we can get Equation (7.4) above from this result if we set $\phi = 0$; similarly, we can get Equations (7.5)–(7.6) by setting $\phi = 180°$.)

Bernstein's illustration of decoherence involves a game, which goes as follows. I have a machine that spits out electrons. They are traveling along the z-axis, and I guarantee that their spins are perpendicular to this axis—that is, their spins point along some direction in the xy plane. Your task is to find that direction.

How do you do it? You are equipped with a Stern–Gerlach apparatus that is oriented perpendicularly to the incoming beam of electrons. This apparatus splits the beam into two, one whose spins are up along the axis running from the north to the south poles of the magnets, and the other whose spins are down along this axis. Hold up your measuring device to my beam of electrons and orient its magnets along some randomly chosen direction in the xy plane. You will find some of the electrons traveling along its upper path and some along the lower.

Now rotate your apparatus to some other randomly chosen axis, making sure that it still lies in the xy plane. Still you find some electrons taking the upper path and some the lower. But as you continue rotating your apparatus this way and that, eventually you will find one particular direction with the important property that *every* electron passes along the upper path.

With this last step you have won the game. The direction you have found is the $\hat{u}$-direction of Figure 7–3. Furthermore, we know that if you continue swinging your apparatus this way and that, you are eventually sure to win—for, as we have seen, every superposition state corresponds to an eigenstate pointing purely along some direction. In order to find it, all you must do is keep trying.

But there is another wrinkle to the game. Upon my machine a switch is mounted, which so far has been in the "off" position. Now I flip it to "on." (The switch could equally well be labeled "isolated from environment," and "not isolated from environment"; or alternatively, "superposition" and "mixture.") Once I do so, no matter how you turn your Stern–Gerlach apparatus, you *never* find a direction for which all the electrons pass along one of the two paths. More than that; no matter how you orient it, half the electrons turn out to traverse the upper path and half the lower.

Note that this result is incomprehensible if the state of the electrons emitted by my machine is described by a superposition, for a superposition always corresponds to an eigenstate along some direction. Thus my machine suddenly seems to be violating the rules of quantum mechanics. It is not, of course. Rather it is now converting its output, which used to be a superposition, into a mixture.

Here is how my machine works. Inside is a gun that emits electrons. When the switch is "off," these electrons' spins are invariably oriented along a definite axis in the xy plane. But when the switch is "on," the machine does something more. Now just prior to emitting each electron, it spins a roulette wheel. The outer rim of this wheel, rather than being marked off in the usual fashion, is labeled in degrees. Thus, when the wheel's marble comes to rest, it does so having randomly specified a certain angle. Call that angle ϕ. The machine now proceeds to rotate the electron's spin by the angle ϕ away from its initial position—and it then fires the electron off into space. Thus, with the switch "off," my machine emits electrons whose spins all point in the same direction; but with the switch "on," the spins are random.

(It is now easy to see why you found equal numbers of electrons traversing the upper and lower paths of your Stern–Gerlach apparatus when my switch was "on." Had you happened to guess the angle ϕ correctly, you would have found all electrons traversing the upper path. But you were equally likely to have guessed 180° away from ϕ, in which case you would have found all electrons traversing the lower path. Similarly, had you happened to guess 90°, or 270° away from ϕ, you would have found equal numbers of electrons traversing the two paths because of Equations (7.5) and (7.6). And finally, had you happened to choose some angle a away from ϕ, you would have obtained some definite ratio between the upper and lower paths—but had you chosen the complement of a, you would have obtained the opposite ratio. By symmetry, for a random set of guesses on your part, you would have found a random distribution of traversals of the two paths.)

Mathematically, there are two ways to describe the state of the electrons emitted by my machine with the switch "on." First, this state is described by the superposition (7.17), but the angle ϕ is randomly re-set prior to each emission. We know, however, that each choice of ϕ corresponds to an eigenstate along the ϕ axis, so a second way to describe the state is to say that each individual electron is in a quantum state ψ_0, or ψ_1, or $\psi_2, \ldots$, or ψ_{359} where

$$\begin{aligned} &\psi_0 \text{ is the state where spin is oriented up along the } \phi = 0 \text{ axis} \\ &\psi_1 \text{ is the state where spin is oriented up along the } \phi = 1^\circ \text{ axis} \qquad (7.18) \\ &\vdots \qquad\qquad\qquad\qquad\qquad\qquad\qquad\qquad \vdots \end{aligned}$$

each with a probability of 1/360. And this description is a mixture. We have reached the following crucial insight: *a superposition with randomly fluctuating coefficients is equivalent to a mixture.*

This, then, is how decoherence operates: by continually and erratically changing the coefficients of a superposition. But how does it do so—and what has all this to do with interactions between the system and its environment?

Here is how my roulette wheel works. It is meant to model the results of the interaction between the electron emitted by my machine and a complex environment. The "environment" is an external magnetic field applied to the electron. Like the real environment, this field is continually and erratically fluctuating. We know that, because the electron possesses a magnetic moment, it has an interaction energy with this magnetic field

$$V_{\text{interaction}} = \gamma B_z S_z \tag{7.19}$$

where γ is the electron's gyromagnetic ratio, B_z is the z-component of the magnetic field, and S_z is the z-component of the electron's spin, which is $+(\hbar/2)$ for spin up, and $-(\hbar/2)$ for spin down.

The two terms in the superposition (7.17), the one having spin up and the other spin down, therefore have different interaction energies with the environment. Now, it is a general principle of quantum mechanics that, if the energy of a particle is E, and its initial state is $\psi(0)$, then after a time t has elapsed the state has evolved to

$$\psi(t) = \psi(0)\, e^{-iEt/\hbar} \tag{7.20}$$

Thus the two terms in the superposition evolve in time differently. Furthermore, because B_z is fluctuating erratically, so is their time evolution. It is by exploiting this randomly fluctuating difference that we can make the coefficients in the superposition fluctuate, so as to turn it into a mixture.

The electron gun emits particles whose spins initially all point along the $\phi = 0$ direction. With $\phi = 0$, Equation (7.17) describing their state reads

$$u(0) = \frac{1}{\sqrt{2}}[(\uparrow)_z + (\downarrow)_z] \tag{7.21}$$

The first term in Equation (7.21) has a time dependence

$$e^{-iEt/\hbar} = e^{-i\gamma B_z t/2} \tag{7.22}$$

but the second term, because its spin points in the opposite direction, has a different time dependence:

$$e^{-iEt/\hbar} = e^{i\gamma B_z t/2} \tag{7.23}$$

So if the external magnetic field acts for a time t before the electrons are finally emitted, their ultimate state will be

$$u_{\text{upon emission}} = \frac{1}{\sqrt{2}} e^{-iEt/\hbar}[(\uparrow)_z + e^{i\gamma B_z t/2}(\downarrow)_z] \tag{7.24}$$

Thus the angle ϕ is to be identified with $\gamma B_z t/2$ and, because B_z is fluctuating, so is ϕ. We see that the coefficients of the two terms in the superposition are randomly fluctuating. And because they are doing so, the superposition has been converted into a mixture.

How long does this take? An illustrative example will make clear that decoherence is a spectacularly rapid process for macroscopic objects. Consider a body at rest on the surface of the Earth. Imagine that it shifts about ever so slightly. Because it has done so, it has moved to a slightly higher or lower elevation, and so shifted its gravitational potential energy. This will cause the phase factor appearing in Equation (7.24), $Et/\hbar$, to fluctuate. If the shifting about is random, the resulting fluctuation in this phase will wipe out quantum coherence.

If the mass M shifts its elevation by H, its gravitational potential energy has changed by MgH, where g is the acceleration due to gravity. Then, after a time $t = \hbar/MgH$, the phase factor has altered significantly. If the mass M is, say 100 kilograms, and H is on the order of the dimensions of a single atom—10^{-10} m—then this occurs in the extraordinarily short time of 10^{-27} seconds! Thus even the smallest of motions will have an extraordinarily rapid effect.

This completes our discussion of Bernstein's elementary model of decoherence. Its essential elements have been as follows. (I) The environment in which any system is embedded is constantly and irregularly fluctuating. (II) If a system is described by a superposition, the different terms in this superposition will interact differently with the environment. In particular, they will have different interaction energies. Therefore, (III) the time evolution of each of the terms in the superposition is constantly and irregularly fluctuating—and (IV) this is indistinguishable from a mixture.

7.6 Laboratory Realizations of Macroscopic Quantum Behavior

The quantum-mechanical tunneling of elementary particles, or of simple four-particle systems such as alpha particles, is commonplace. But the tunneling of prisoners out of their cells is fantastically improbable. Where is the dividing line between the possible and the impossible? Can we create large-scale systems that display quantum behavior? It is clear from the above discussion that this is no easy task. Some means must be found to circumvent in such systems the smallness of the de Broglie wavelength and of the uncertainty "jitter," and the slowness of tunneling.

Furthermore, as we have seen from our discussion of decoherence, large-scale systems that we hope will reveal quantum behavior must be highly "insulated." This insulation must be from both their own internal microscopic states and from the rest of the world. Each can be regarded as comprising the quantum system's environment. Insulation is necessary because appreciable interactions between a system and its environment destroy the coherence required for quantum effects.

This implies that such macroscopic objects cannot be things we are familiar with from daily experience—cats, for example. Nevertheless, recent experiments have actually succeeded in demonstrating quantum behavior in certain carefully designed macroscopic objects. We turn now to a discussion of this subject.

At the beginning, we must carefully distinguish between two kinds of macroscopic quantum behavior. All objects are made of atoms, which obey the laws of quantum theory. Usually this deep structure is washed out and the system behaves classically. In some instances, however, the behavior of a macroscopic object will exhibit certain features precisely because of the underlying quantum behavior of its constituent atoms. Indeed, the very existence of matter as we know it is an example, for as we saw in Chapter 3, the existence of atoms follows from the uncertainty principle. Superconductivity and the specific heat of solids are two other examples of deviation from classical expectations; both arise for purely quantum-mechanical reasons.

The large-scale behavior of these systems therefore reflects the laws of their underlying quantum particles taken collectively. In such situations one has indeed an incursion of quantum mechanics into the macroscopic world. But it is a relatively modest incursion. The variables used to understand the phenomena are still microscopic ones. In contrast, the effort to realize a laboratory version of Schrödinger's cat is in fact far more ambitious. A truly macroscopic quantum phenomenon requires that we create a large-scale system that is described by *its own wave function as a whole* and that evolves according to *its own Schrödinger equation.*

The distinction between *microscopic* and *macroscopic variables* is essential to the discussion of macroscopic quantum behavior. A single electron can be described within quantum theory by a simple set of variables: position, spin, and so forth. These are microscopic in that they apply to the single elementary particle. A prisoner pacing back and forth in a cell is comprised of a vast number of distinct atoms and molecules, each with its own set of microscopic variables. One way to think of the tunneling of the prisoner from his cell would be to treat each atom separately. We could calculate the probability for each to tunnel through, and then multiply them all together to find the probability that all atoms in the prisoner's body will tunnel through at once. Such a calculation would be in the spirit of the first of the two types of macroscopic quantum behavior that we are distinguishing.

But this would hardly be macroscopic tunneling in the more profound second sense. Rather it would be a calculation of the likelihood of many microscopic events taking place simultaneously. In order to speak of macroscopic quantum behavior in the deeper sense we need to describe the entire aggregate of particles—i.e., the prisoner—by a single wave function. This is done by introducing a new concept: *macroscopic variables.*

This was, in fact, the calculation we had performed. In our discussion above of macroscopic tunneling, we entirely disregarded the fact that the prisoner was composed of a large number of particles. Instead, we treated him as described by a single variable—the position of his center of mass. Such a position is an example of a macroscopic variable. Note in this regard that the macroscopic variable has a somewhat abstract character; in reality, a prisoner does not consist of a single 100-kg particle at all. Similarly, in what follows we will encounter macroscopic variables that do not correspond to any obvious physical constituent of the laboratory "Schrödinger's cat."

Conditions for the Existence of Macroscopic Quantum Behavior In order for a macroscopic variable to be a quantum variable with its own wave function and Schrödinger equation, three stringent conditions need to be met.

First, the macroscopic variable must be well decoupled from the motion of the microscopic degrees of freedom. Failing this, the quantum state corresponding to a particular value of the macroscopic variable decays too quickly.

For example, the atoms in a swinging pendulum may be engaged in their own microscopic motion, but the center of mass of the whole system is decoupled from such internal motion, and swings only according to the gravitational field. In this example, the angle between the vertical and the pendulum would be the macroscopic variable. Clearly, it is well "insulated" from the positions and velocities of the atoms making up the pendulum. Alternatively, consider what would happen were these microscopic motions to have a significant effect on the motion. Because of their incessant jiggling, the pendulum would swing erratically; the macroscopic variable would no longer move according to the gravitational field alone.

Formally speaking, there is always an interaction between the macroscopic and the microscopic degrees of freedom of any system. Because of this interaction, the macroscopic variable can never remain forever in one of its eigenstates. Rather, if placed in such a state, it eventually decays to another. If the interaction is weak, however, the decay is slow, which we require for macroscopic quantum behavior to be observable.

In many ways the microscopic degrees of freedom describing a system can be thought of as "the environment" in which the macroscopic variable moves. And the effect of its environment on a system is, of course, the phenomenon of decoherence.

Second, the temperature must be low. Even when a macroscopic variable, say X, is decoupled from microscopic ones, we require an experimental situation for which different values of X lead to measurably distinct values of $\psi(X)$. This adds a second crucial constraint, that the temperature be low enough so that thermal motion does not wash out the quantum effects we are looking for. Were the temperature too high, the thermal energy would exceed the spacing between energy levels of the system. In this circumstance the system would not be in a single eigenstate, and we would be unable to determine if the macroscopic variable was indeed governed by the Schrödinger equation.

If the system we are considering is a pendulum, the scale is set by its natural vibrational frequency ω. For the simple harmonic oscillator, the spacing between energy levels is $\hbar\omega$. If, for example, ω is on the order of one Hertz, then by the Planck relation the energy associated with this frequency is $\hbar\omega$, or about 10^{-34} J. The temperature must therefore be so low that $kT < 10^{-34}$, where k is Boltzmann's constant. This implies that the temperature must be less than 10^{-11} K! While this is clearly an impossible constraint for pendulums, using modern cryogenic techniques and electronic analogues to the massive pendulum, the required temperature is no longer so impossibly low.

Third, the motion of the macroscopic variable must be controlled by a microscopic energy. The correspondence principle is well known in quantum mechanics. It states that the properties of a highly excited quantum system are indistinguishable from those of classical mechanics. This is related to the so-called correspondence limit, which states that when the characteristic potential energy of a system is large compared to the spacing between energy levels, then the predictions of quantum mechanics must be identical to those of classical mechanics. Clearly this would make it impossible for us to see a difference between the two.

We are therefore required to keep the potential energy of the system very low, $V \ll \hbar\omega$. It is easy to verify that most familiar potentials, such as gravity or electromagnetism, are far too large to obey this relation. We must therefore construct a system insensitive to these, and only sensitive to a microscopic energy. If we succeed, then that microscopic energy will control the motion of the macroscopic variable, which we hope will display quantum-mechanical behavior.

The theorist A.J. Leggett has performed a careful analysis of possible experimental strategies for the two important classes of experiments meant to address these questions.[6] He identified two likely candidates: so-called Macroscopic Quantum Tunneling (MQT), and Macroscopic Quantum Coherence (MQC) experiments. We now turn to them.

Macroscopic Quantum Tunneling: SQUIDS As Leggett predicted, the first experiments that showed convincing evidence for MQT used Superconducting

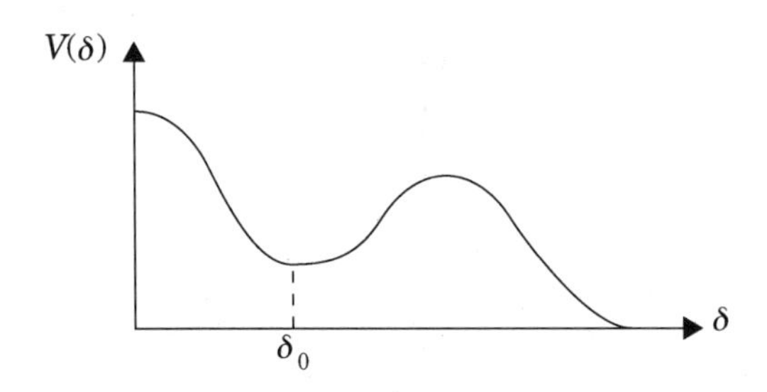

Figure 7–4 *Macroscopic Quantum Tunneling*. The potential energy of a SQUID is shown as a function of the phase difference δ of the wave function across the insulating barrier. Classically, we would expect the system to be trapped in the region δ close to δ_0. Experimentally, however, it is not.

Quantum Interference Devices, or SQUIDs for short. A SQUID is a ring of superconducting metal, such as niobium, that is broken in one or more places by a thin insulating barrier. Individual electrons can tunnel across such a barrier in the usual quantum-mechanical fashion. At low temperatures an additional phenomenon can occur in certain materials: superconductivity. Superconductivity depends on a remarkable phenomenon in which electrons pair up, forming so-called Cooper pairs at temperatures of a few Kelvins.* The electrical resistance plummets to zero below this temperature. In this state, it is the Cooper pairs that tunnel across the junction.

However, if the insulating barrier is sufficiently thin, something even more remarkable happens: the Josephson effect.[7] The state of the superconductor on either side of the barrier, or Josephson junction, is given by a wave function. For thin barriers, the tail of the wave function stretches across the junction and into the other superconducting region. In this situation it can be shown that the tunneling current of Cooper pairs depends only on *the phase difference* δ of the wave function across the junction. Furthermore, it can occur in the absence of an applied voltage; even with no potential difference across the junction, a direct current can flow. This is the Josephson effect.

It can be shown that, for a suitable setup of the SQUID system, the variable δ plays exactly the role of the position of an alpha particle in a radioactive nucleus. Figure 7–4, which is much like the tunneling barrier we examined earlier, shows the potential as a function of δ for the SQUID system. Notice the shallow potential well in which the SQUID can be "trapped." At high temperatures the state can hop over the barrier, but as

* The theory of high-temperature superconductors is not yet known, nor even whether they also rely on the formation of Cooper pairs.

the temperature is reduced, there comes a point at which kT is less than the barrier height. In this circumstance it is classically impossible for the SQUID to get over the barrier; the phase difference δ should be constrained to a narrow range of values close to δ_0.

Nevertheless, in 1988 Clarke, Cleland, Devoret, Esteve and Martinis[8] found that it is not. They observed the phase difference across a SQUID suddenly making a transition away from δ_0. The only way this could have happened is by quantum tunneling.

At this stage, a subtle but essential point needs to be made. Since the electron is a spin-1/2 particle, it is a fermion. But a Cooper pair is comprised of two such particles, and has therefore integer spin. It is a boson. Bosons do not obey the Pauli exclusion principle, so that many Cooper pairs can occupy the same quantum state if this is energetically favorable. At very low temperatures, this is exactly what happens. The Cooper pairs that make up the superconductor all collapse into the lowest energy state, forming a so-called Bose condensate. The wave function for the system describes the state of the condensate as a whole. In this case, δ is not the phase difference between individual Cooper pairs, but that between the entire condensate wave function on one side of the junction and the other. In recognizing this, we make a transition to the truly macroscopic description we distinguished above. We should no longer think of the phase difference as a microscopic variable pertaining to individual pairs, but rather speak of the phase difference across the junction for the SQUID as a whole. Thus, δ has now become a macroscopic variable. By analogy to the pendulum's center-of-mass coordinate, we use δ to describe the state, not of the separate microscopic particles, but of all the Cooper pairs taken collectively.

In this circumstance, the phase difference δ becomes a quantum-mechanical operator with an associated wave function. Recall that we have already emphasized that often the macroscopic variable has only a very abstract physical significance. This is clearly the case here, since the wave function describes the motion of a purely fictitious particle, whose abstract coordinate is δ.

Experimenters Clarke, Cleland, Devoret, Esteve, and Martinis put it this way:[8]

> In Josephson tunneling the passage of each Cooper pair is controlled by the difference δ in the phase of the pair across the barrier. Since the condensate in any piece of superconductor is characterized by a single phase, the phase difference δ for all pairs must be the same. Thus δ is "macroscopic" in the sense that it is the single variable that completely specifies the state of the junction, that is, of all the Cooper pairs. [But] in the process of macroscopic quantum tunneling it is the [fictitious] particle associated with the phase difference δ that tunnels as opposed

to the tunneling of individual Cooper pairs that occurs in Josephson tunneling.

In their experiment, Clarke et al. found exactly the behavior predicted by quantum mechanics. At low temperatures, macroscopic quantum tunneling of the SQUID to new values of δ dominated over classical thermal processes. The measured rates for quantum tunneling of the macroscopic variable δ were in excellent agreement with theoretical predictions.

As icing on the cake, Clarke et al. went one step further. The potential well can be made deep enough to support three discrete energy levels. This means that one should be able to see transitions between them. The group used a microwave spectroscopic technique to search for these transitions, and found them right where they were expected.

We re-emphasize that, for both the tunneling and excitation phenomena, we are *not* dealing with individual particles, but with the whole SQUID whose state is describable by the single macroscopic variable, the junction phase difference. A SQUID may not weigh in at two hundred pounds, like some inmates, but to the eye of a physicist, the escape of the SQUID phase δ from the confines of its potential well is just as dramatic as any prison escape. After all, not a spoonful of earth was disturbed. Instead, δ simply disappeared from within the well, and re-appeared on the outside.

Macroscopic Quantum Coherence In our discussion of Schrödinger's cat, we contrasted the concept of a *superposition* of two states with a *mixture* of them, in which the probability of finding the first state is 1/2 and the probability of finding the other is also 1/2. Although no one will ever find a real cat in a superposition state, macroscopic systems exist that appear to approach the bizarre situation described by Schrödinger. Again we begin by considering a well-studied microscopic quantum system, and then search for a macroscopic analog.

The ammonia molecule NH_3 has two stable geometrical arrangements, as sketched in Figure 7–5. The only difference between configurations I and II is the position of the single nitrogen relative to the three hydrogen atoms in the tetrahedron. The energies associated with the two configurations are obviously identical. Classically, we might imagine that ammonia comes in one configuration or the other—a mixture. But quantum mechanically this is not the case. Evidence points to a picture in which the molecule is in a superposition state of I and II.

The potential function for ammonia has two minima, as shown in Figure 7–6. We can think of configuration I as associated with the state of the molecule when it is in the left-hand well, and configuration II when it is in the right. Classically, the two configurations are separated by an insurmountable barrier; if we prepare the molecule in configuration I, it should stay there. But once again quantum tunneling enters the picture. It is found that, if we prepare the molecule in configuration I, inversion of

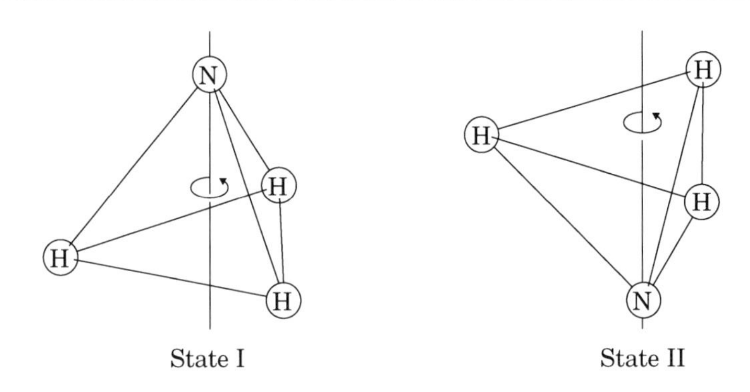

Figure 7–5 *Two Possible States of the Ammonia Molecule.* The energies of the two states are identical.

the tetrahedron to configuration II does indeed take place. Once on the other side, it tunnels back, and so on, cycling at a definite frequency. In Figure 7–7 we graph the probabilities of finding the molecule in its two states as a function of time. Notice that a quarter of the way through the cycle it is in exactly the Schrödinger-cat superposition state.

We now search for a macroscopic analog of the ammonia molecule, and find it in the form of some of the world's tiniest magnets. Many biological organisms contain the magnetic protein ferritin. In an interesting series of experiments, David Awschalom and co-workers at the University of California in Santa Barbara have examined the changing orientation of the magnetic poles of these tiny magnets. They have good evidence for what appears to be a small but still macroscopic version of the ammonia molecule's quantum-mechanical inversion process.[9]

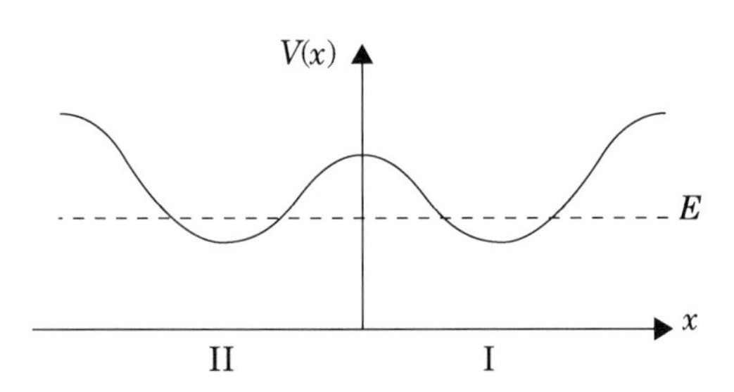

Figure 7–6 *Energy of the Ammonia Molecule* as a function of the nitrogen atom's position. (x labels the nitrogen's distance from the plane containing the three hydrogens.)

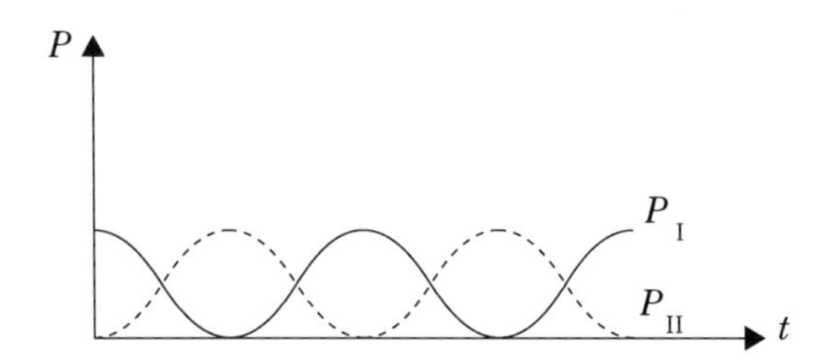

Figure 7–7 *Quantum Oscillation* of the ammonia molecule between its two possible states. P_{I} is the probability of being in state I, P_{II} that of being in state II.

Ferritin can be made in various sizes, ranging from 2 to 7 nanometers in diameter. Although small, these are macroscopic by atomic standards: they contain of order 10^6 cubic Bohr radii. The details of their magnetic properties are somewhat subtle, but for our purposes it is sufficient to know that when placed in very small fields, of about 10^{-9} tesla, two equivalent states exist corresponding to two orientations of the magnetization (or its antiferromagnetic equivalent, the Neel vector). The potential function for this *macroscopic* variable looks exactly like that of the ammonia molecule. At temperatures below 200 mK, where thermal activation across the barrier is impossible, Awschalom and co-workers detected a resonance in the magnetic susceptibility that one would expect for macroscopic quantum tunneling. Detailed analysis showed that its resonance frequency scales with the size of the magnets in a manner consistent with MQT.

This is as close as we have gotten at present to realizing Schrödinger's cat in the laboratory. If we think of the two magnetization directions as corresponding to alive and dead, then we have the equivalent of a cat that coherently and persistently transits back and forth between life and death. With these and similar experiments, we have made stunning progress in extending the range of quantum mechanics into the macroscopic domain of everyday life.

Chapter 8

Measurement

In this final chapter, we encounter a new situation. Throughout this book, we have found quantum mechanics adequate to deal with the extraordinary nature of the quantum world as revealed by modern research. But in this chapter, we will describe a topic that quantum theory finds exceedingly difficult to deal with. Indeed, many physicists believe that the theory *cannot* deal with it; and that its failure to do so points to a grave defect in the theory.

The topic to which we refer is the act of making a measurement. Which measurement? Any measurement. The acts that pose such problems for quantum mechanics can be as simple and commonplace as the excitation of a single atom by a single photon. Alternatively, they can be as complex and monumental as the appearance in a giant detector at CERN of a new subatomic particle. It is not this measurement or that measurement that has raised so much controversy among those who study the foundations of quantum mechanics: it is the very concept of measurement.

We will also see that measurements play a radically different role in the quantum world than they do in the classical world. Classically, measurements have an essentially passive nature: they find out about a pre-existing reality. But quantum-mechanically, their role is far more active.

8.1 The Measurement Problem

The Collapse of the Wave Function Let us begin our discussion of measurement by returning to a phenomenon we discussed in Chapter 2 on photons. There we wrote

> If we think of light as a wave, then when it falls on photographic film we might liken it to an ocean wave hitting the beach. Nothing

> prevents an ocean wave from hitting the sand simultaneously along its full extent. By analogy, one might expect light falling on film to expose it uniformly along its entire wavefront. But this is not what happens. When examined carefully, one finds that individual grains of silver halide have been blackened, one at a time.

In Chapter 2 we were concerned with whether this phenomenon, the darkening of individual grains rather than all of them at once, constituted evidence for the existence of photons. Here we wish to look at it in a different way: *the blackening of each silver halide grain apparently constitutes a measurement of the location of a photon.* After all, were a photon *not* present at a given location, the grain located there could never have been exposed. Furthermore, since this blackening is caused by the interaction between a photon and an individual atom in the grain, the measurement is a particularly simple one: each photon is being detected by a single atom.*

Let us examine this measurement more carefully. We imagine a beam of light whose intensity corresponds to that of a single photon. Figure 8–1 diagrams the situation. Light of a very low amplitude is incident upon a strip of film. Which atom will register an event? Of course we do not know. What we *do* know is that, by the usual rules of quantum mechanics, the probability of this happening is proportional to $\psi^*\psi$ at every point in space. If the wave function is very broad, as illustrated in Figure 8–1, this will be effectively constant across the film. So each grain in the film strip is equally likely to be exposed.

We emphasize that Figure 8–1 diagrams the situation *prior to the measurement.* In Figure 8–2 we diagram the situation *after* the measurement. In this figure, the black dot represents the atom that has registered an event. But notice something else about this sketch. In it, *the wave function has changed its shape.* What used to be a broad wave packet representing the photon extending across the film has collapsed to a single sharp peak centered on the atom that registered the event.

Why has this happened? Imagine that it had not. Imagine that, after the measurement, the wave function still had its old form. Then $\psi^*\psi$ would be nonzero at various other locations across the film. But this means that *there would be a finite probability of finding the photon somewhere else—somewhere other than where it was found to be.* But this is impossible.

This sudden change is known as "the collapse of the wave function." It is easy to see how the name comes about: ψ has "collapsed" from the broad wave illustrated in Figure 8–1 to the narrow peak of Figure 8–2. How quickly does this happen? The measurement is made at some definite time

---

* In reality, several photons are required to blacken a grain. Modern photodetectors, on the other hand, can detect individual photons, and the discussion we outline here can be extended to their operation in a straightforward fashion.

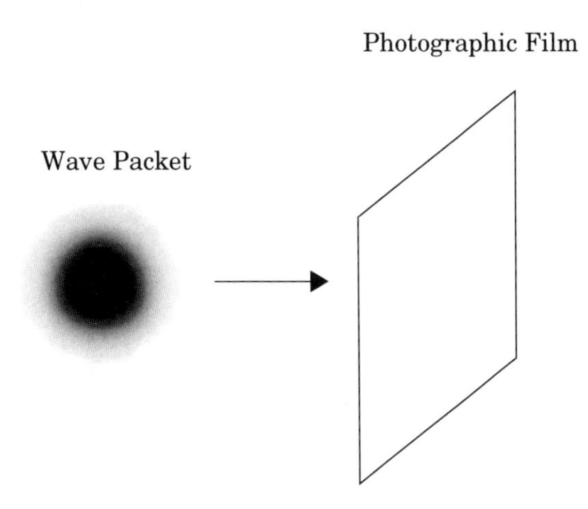

Figure 8–1 *A Wave Packet of Light Incident on a Strip of Photographic Film.* The wave function describing the packet is very broad, but because it contains a single photon, only one silver halide grain will be exposed.

and at a definite place. We can then imagine a second measurement occurring arbitrarily soon after the first, and arbitrarily far away. If the wave function at this second time and place had *not* dropped to zero, this second measurement would have a finite probability of finding the photon. But this cannot be, since a photon cannot travel arbitrarily rapidly. We conclude that *the collapse must take place instantaneously over all space.* If we wish to think of it as propagating with some speed, that speed is infinite.*

The remarkable nature of the collapse of the wave function can be dramatized by slightly changing our example. Imagine that the photon was produced at some known location and at a known time, but suppose that the wave function is spherical, as illustrated in Figure 8–3. Imagine that all space is populated by silver halide grains, each one of them functioning as a detector. We produce the photon, sit back, and wait. Which grain will blacken?

Suppose it turns out that we end up waiting five hours before the light is finally detected. By this time, it has traveled an enormous distance. Indeed, the wave function of Figure 8–3 has spread out to encompass the entire solar system! Let us say that the grain that ultimately detects the photon turns out to lie on Neptune. In this case, the collapse of the wave function caused by this detection extends over literally billions of miles. The wave function

---

* In this case, the photon is destroyed in the process of detection. Our discussion has therefore, a gap in it. This can be filled by considering a measurement that does not destroy the particle it detects.

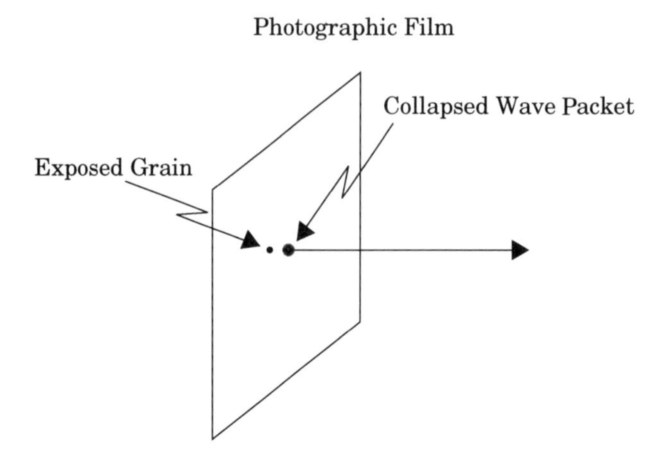

Figure 8–2 *Once a Grain Has Been Exposed*, the wave function shrinks to a narrow peak centered on the exposed grain, a process known as the "collapse of the wave function."

drops to zero inside the Sun, and over the surface of the Earth, and on Mars and Venus and throughout the asteroids. And this extraordinary transformation happens in literally no time at all.*

The phenomenon of the collapse of the wave function is not limited to this one example. It occurs for measurements of every type. To illustrate this, let us consider a second example, in which what we measure is the direction of spin of an electron. Suppose that initially the electron is in the spin state

$$\psi_{\text{before measurement}} = \frac{1}{\sqrt{2}}\left[(\uparrow)_z + (\downarrow)_z\right] \tag{8.1}$$

And suppose that a measurement is made in which the spin is found, let us say, to be "up" along the z-axis. This instantaneously collapses the state to

$$\psi_{\text{after measurement}} = (\uparrow)_z \tag{8.2}$$

for a precisely analogous reason: had this not occurred, a second measurement, made arbitrarily shortly after the first, would have a finite probability

* We are not considering the relativity of simultaneity. If one takes this into consideration, one can show that no contradiction arises from the standpoints of different frames of reference in relative motion.

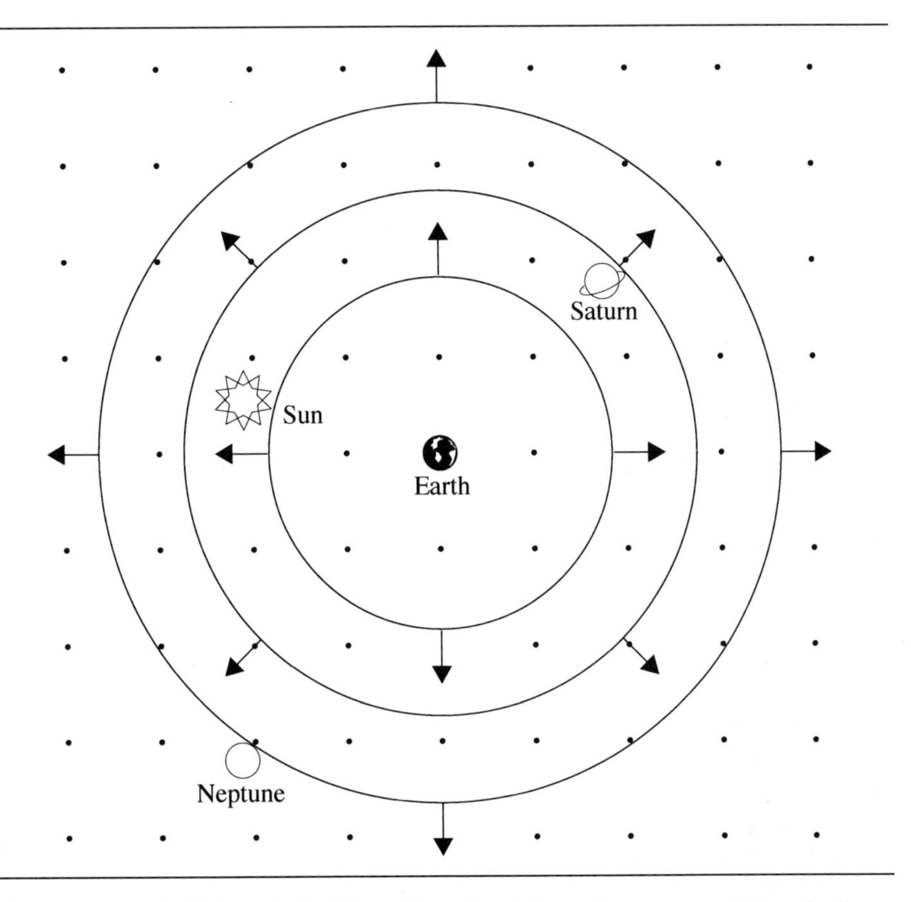

Figure 8–3 *Collapse of the Wave Function* takes place over arbitrarily large regions, and it does so instantaneously.

of obtaining the opposite result. But this would imply an infinite torque acting on the electron, which is impossible.

On the other hand, in this instance there is less reason to call the transformation a "collapse." For this reason, some workers refer to the transformation as the "reduction of the state": the superposition (8.1) is "reduced" to the form given by Equation (8.2).

Is the Collapse of the Wave Function Described by the Schrödinger Equation? The collapse of the wave function is a striking phenomenon, and the arguments we have given above make clear that it must occur. But remarkably, this collapse is *not* predicted by quantum mechanics. In particular, as we now show, it is not described by the Schrödinger equation. We therefore turn to the quantum-mechanical theory of the means by which

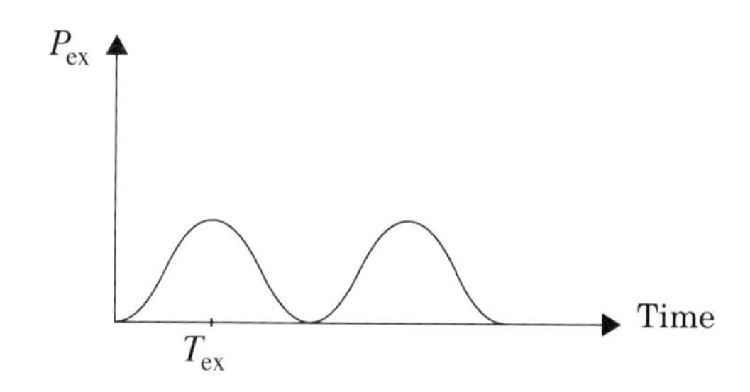

Figure 8–4 *Probability of Exciting an Atom* exposed to a sinusoidal perturbation, if it is initially in its ground state.

light causes a silver halide grain to darken: we will show that what this theory has to say about the phenomenon is inadequate.

The only thing light can do to an individual atom in a grain is to excite it. The darkening must in some way follow from this excitation. How, then, does quantum theory describe the excitation of an atom by light? Various discussions can be given, at varying levels of sophistication: we will treat the light as a classical wave. We therefore imagine an atom, initially in its ground state, that is subjected to a sinusoidal perturbation. Although in most practical situations this perturbation is relatively weak, we will treat the case of a strong field in order to connect our discussion with that of Section 8.2 on the quantum Zeno effect. No essential differences are introduced by making this shift.

Under these conditions, one can calculate P_{ex}, the probability of finding the atom in its excited state. The result is sketched in Figure 8–4. From this sketch we see that P_{ex} starts out equal to zero, implying that at the instant the perturbation commences—the instant the light wave turns on—the atom is definitely in its ground state. Thereafter P_{ex} smoothly rises, implying a gradually increasing probability of finding the atom to be excited. Over the long term, P_{ex} oscillates, implying a periodically increasing and decreasing probability of finding the atom excited: these are known as Rabi oscillations. For certain experimental parameters, P_{ex} can reach 1, implying a 100% probability of exciting the atom.

Thus the atomic state can be written

$$\psi = \alpha_{gd}\phi_{gd} + \alpha_{ex}\phi_{ex} \tag{8.3}$$

where α_{gd} is the coefficient of the ground state ϕ_{gd} and α_{ex} is the coefficient of the excited state ϕ_{ex}. The probability P_{ex} that we graphed in Figure 8–4 is just α_{ex}^2, while α_{gd}^2 is simply $(1 - \alpha_{ex}^2)$. We sketch these squared coefficients in Figure 8–5. We see that α_{gd}^2 smoothly drops initially, while α_{ex}^2 correspondingly rises.

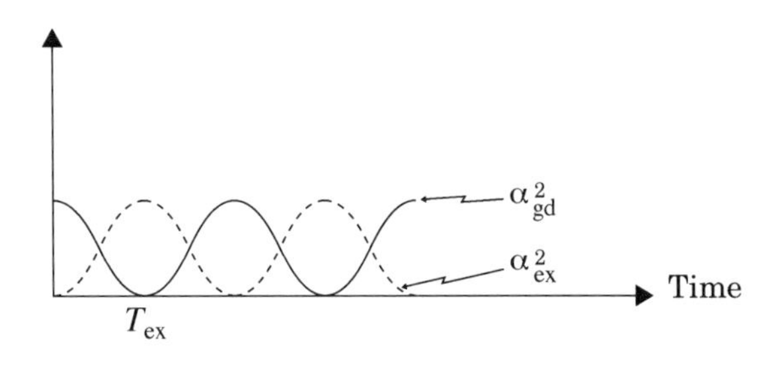

Figure 8–5 *Coefficients of the Superposition* of ground and excited states of the atom of Figure 8–4.

This is what quantum theory has to say about the excitation of an atom by light. It is *all* the theory has to say. Indeed, what is most remarkable about this treatment is the number of things it has left out. For instance, if our atom began in a ground state and ended up in an excited state, it must have made a transition between the two. But nowhere does the theory even mention this transition. (The reader might think that the transition occurs when the probability of being in the excited state reaches 1. But this is not so: the transition has a perfectly finite chance of having occurred long before this time. Indeed, it could have occurred at any time at all, other than $t = 0$. The theory is simply silent on this issue.)

Furthermore, this transition is a vitally important event. After all, it is presumably the cause of the collapse of the wave function, or is at least intimately related to it. But here too the theory is silent: the reader will have noticed that nowhere has our treatment even mentioned this collapse. It simply lies outside of the range of issues treated by the Schrödinger equation. And this turns out to be the case in general; in no instance does the application of the Schrödinger equation to a process yield up a discussion of the collapse of the wave function associated with that process.*

We conclude that the collapse of the wave function occupies an anomalous position within quantum mechanics. It is required by the fact that observations occur, but it is not predicted by quantum theory. It is an additional postulate, which must be made in order that quantum mechanics be consistent.

Before we close, two caveats are necessary. In the preceding chapter we described the phenomenon of decoherence. This is a phenomenon that emphatically *is* predicted by quantum mechanics, and some workers argue

---

*Recent advances in experimental techniques, pioneered by Hans Dehmelt, have allowed individual transitions to be studied in the laboratory. Reference 1 describes these techniques and discusses some of the ambiguities in their interpretation.

that decoherence accounts for the collapse of the wave function. We will return to this question below.

We must also mention the view, held by certain workers in the field, that the wave function has no physical meaning at all. Rather they hold that the wave function should be understood as describing *our information about a system.* In this view, the collapse of the wave function has no particular significance. Consider in this connection the question of whether it will rain at noon tomorrow. The weather bureau might predict that, say, there is a 30% chance of rain on the following day. Suppose we then wait till noon arrives, go outside and look. In the instant we become aware of the weather, the 30% probability "collapses"—to 100% if we find it to be raining, and to 0% if we find that it is not. No one is surprised by such behavior. On the other hand, we should note that most physicists regard a change in the wave function as corresponding to a physical process, as opposed to a change in our knowledge of that process.

Quantum Theory of Measurement: The Infinite Regress The argument of the previous section was that the Schrödinger equation does not describe the collapse of the wave function caused by a measurement. We now ask what the Schrödinger equation *does* describe. We will find an astonishing result: *according to the Schrödinger equation, measurements never happen.* Rather, what happens is an infinite regress.

We begin by pointing out a hidden oversimplification we have made up to now. Recall that, in our above discussion, we were attempting to measure the location of a photon by monitoring the upward transition of an atom: what we found was that, rather than telling us about this transition, the Schrödinger equation merely predicted that the atom went into the superposition state (8.3). In fact, however, the final state is not a simple superposition but an enormously complex *entanglement.* The configuration we analyzed was a single atom in the presence of a photon. But the configuration we should have analyzed was an entire collection of atoms—all the atoms in the photographic film—together with the photon.

To deal with this problem we need to write down a factor describing the state of the first atom, a second factor describing the state of the second atom, and so on until we have covered every atom in the film—and then a final factor describing the photon. If the Schrödinger equation is applied to this problem, it predicts a complex state. The first term of this state consists of

- a factor describing atom #1 in the superposition (8.3);
- factors describing all the other atoms in their ground state;
- a factor describing the photon at the location of atom #1.

Similarly, the second term is

- a factor describing atom #2 in the superposition (8.3);
- factors describing all the other atoms in their ground state;
- a factor describing the photon at the location of atom #2.

and so forth. Clearly, this final state is an entanglement. Just as clearly, it is exceedingly difficult to work with. So, for the purposes of clarity, let us consider an even simpler problem—the problem of measuring, not a photon's location, but its energy. The advantage of this shift is that it allows us to work with a detector that really does consist of a single atom, as opposed to the strip of film that consists of many.

In fact, we will consider an even simpler problem: a measurement whose sole function is to tell us whether the photon's energy is very great or very small. The detection process, as before, is an excitation, but now it is an excitation of a particular sort: an ionization. If the photon is of high energy, the atom will be ionized by it; but if the photon's energy is low, the atom will not. What does the Schrödinger equation predict if it is applied to this problem? It predicts that

$$\psi = \alpha\omega_{\text{low}}\phi_{\text{neutral}} + \beta\omega_{\text{high}}\phi_{\text{ionized}} \tag{8.4}$$

where α and β are coefficients.

Equation (8.4) corrects Equation (8.3). But all the dissatisfaction with Equation (8.3) that we had expressed applies as well to our new result. We set out to perform a measurement of a photon's energy—but rather than doing this, the Schrödinger equation has informed us that a peculiar state has developed, a state for which there is no classical analogue, and which hardly seems to have anything to do with a measurement.

But we need not stop here. We could determine the photon's energy if we could find out whether the atom was ionized or not. So let us turn our attention to this problem. An ionized atom possesses a net electric charge, and charges respond to electric fields. So perhaps we can measure the photon's energy by applying an electric field to the atom and seeing what it does. If the photon had high energy, the atom will be deflected by the field; if it had low energy, the atom will go straight. What does the Schrödinger equation predict?

Perhaps the reader will not be surprised to learn that the Schrödinger equation does *not* predict anything that we might interpret as a clean measurement. Rather it predicts a yet larger entanglement—not an entanglement of two factors, but of three:

$$\psi = \alpha\omega_{\text{low}}\phi_{\text{neutral}}\chi_{\text{goes straight}} + \beta\omega_{\text{high}}\phi_{\text{ionized}}\chi_{\text{deflects}} \tag{8.5}$$

To determine whether the atom was deflected by the electric field, we can place a detector of atoms in the undeflected beam. If this detector catches an atom, the photon had low energy; and if it does not, the atom had high energy. But, here too, all that develops is a yet larger entanglement:

$$\begin{aligned}\psi = {} & \alpha\omega_{\text{low}}\phi_{\text{neutral}}\chi_{\text{goes straight}}D_{\text{catches atom}} \\ & + \beta\omega_{\text{high}}\phi_{\text{ionized}}\chi_{\text{deflects}}D_{\text{does not catch atom}}\end{aligned} \tag{8.6}$$

The further we go in our analysis, the larger does the entanglement grow. *But at no point does a measurement occur.* Rather, what occurs is an infinite regress.

Termination of the Infinite Regress: The Projection Postulate What *would* constitute a measurement of the photon's energy? Notice that in the very last step of our analysis, an important transformation has occurred: we have included a macroscopic measuring device. The conundrum presented to us by the quantum theory of measurement is that this device is predicted to be in an ambiguous state: a superposition. But in reality, we know perfectly well that, if it is working correctly, a detector never behaves in such an obscure fashion. It either detects the atom, or detects its absence.

In order to make this happen, in order to perform a measurement, we need to terminate the infinite regress at some stage, and replace the entanglement by a single term. But this cannot be done by the Schrödinger equation. It is necessary, therefore, to divide the time evolution of a quantum system into two distinct parts. The first lasts from the instant a quantum state is prepared until the moment just prior to the act of measurement. During this period of time, the system evolves in a precisely specified manner according to the time-dependent Schrödinger equation, in which the forces acting on the system are included through the potential energy function $V(r)$:

$$-\frac{\hbar^2}{2m}\frac{\partial^2\psi}{\partial x^2} + V(r)\psi = i\hbar\frac{\partial\psi}{\partial t} \tag{8.7}$$

The result is an ever-increasing entanglement.

But the act of measurement stands in sharp contrast to this orderly time development. No potential energy function, no Hamiltonian, exists for measurement; no equation analogous to the Schrödinger equation describes its evolution in time. Within orthodox quantum mechanics, measurement is an acausal process that, in a very real sense, falls outside the theory.

The mathematician von Neumann described the problem thoroughly in his classic text *Mathematical Foundations of Quantum Mechanics.*[2] From him we have inherited an ad hoc mathematical device to get around the problem of the infinite regress. In place of the dynamical Equation (8.7), von Neumann described the *projection postulate*. This is the postulate that, when a measurement occurs, the entanglement is replaced by a single term. The wave function of the quantum system is "projected onto" the various possibilities provided by the detector, with a probability of projection given by the square of the coefficient multiplying each of the terms of the entanglement.

In the context of the example we have been considering, the projection postulate is that, at the moment of measurement, the state is collapsed either onto

$$\psi = \omega_{\text{low}}\phi_{\text{neutral}}\chi_{\text{goes straight}}D_{\text{catches atom}} \tag{8.8}$$

(with probability α^2) or onto

$$\psi = \omega_{\text{high}}\phi_{\text{ionized}}\chi_{\text{deflects}}D_{\text{does not catch atom}} \tag{8.9}$$

(with probability β^2). Notice that, in both Equations (8.8) and (8.9), the detector is left in a perfectly well-defined state—and this is just what we mean by a measurement.

We emphasize that the projection postulate is nothing more than a mathematical statement of the postulate of the collapse of the wave function. To see this, return to our model problem, in which the broad wave of Figure 8–1 was incident on the photographic film. As we saw earlier, the evolution described by the Schrödinger equation leads to a state consisting of a sum of terms, each describing a photon at a different location. The projection postulate, in turn, picks out a single term, one describing the photon at a definite location—and this is just the collapsed state illustrated in Figure 8–2.

We also emphasize that the projection postulate does not correspond to a real, physical process. Rather it is a purely mathematical procedure, which gets us from the causal language of quantum mechanics to experimental probabilities in a way that agrees with experiment. In so doing, as Heisenberg put it, what was probable becomes actual. But how does this occur? The answer is the subject of much contention.

The projection postulate presents us with a distasteful state of affairs. One dissatisfying feature is that we do not understand how the projection comes about. But a further dissatisfying element is that *sometimes the postulate is not needed.* In certain situations the postulate is required in order to make a measurement, but in other situations it is not! We will illustrate this point by returning to our above analysis of a photon whose energy can be either quite large or quite small. We will discuss three situations. In the first two, a measurement will occur quite naturally, within the framework of the orderly evolution described by the Schrödinger equation. Only in the third will the Schrödinger equation prove to be insufficient, and the postulate will be required.

How is such a photon produced? It is produced by the decay of an atom whose energy-level diagram is similar to that illustrated in Figure 8–6. The decay of such an atom from level 2 to level 1 produces a photon of low energy; that from 3 to 1 produces one of high energy. *In case I* we prepare a single atom in a well-defined state—either level 2 or level 3. The decay of this atom produces our photon. Via the series of experiments we have outlined above, its energy can be determined. If the photon's energy is low, Equation (8.8) describes the final state; if it is high, Equation (8.9).

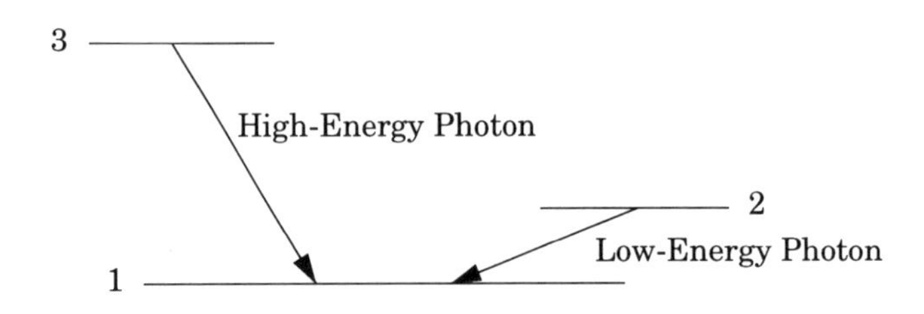

Figure 8–6 *Production of a Photon of Indeterminate Energy* occurs via the decay to the ground state of a three-level atom.

This is very like a classical situation, in which the outcome of a measurement stands in direct correspondence with the state of the system prior to the measurement. The initial state may not be known to us beforehand, but the outcome of the measurement reveals it to us. And finally, notice that at no stage have we been forced to invoke the projection postulate: the measurement has been effected solely as the result of the time-dependent Schrödinger equation.

In case II we prepare a collection of such atoms, some in level 2 and some in level 3. Suppose for the sake of argument that 10% are in 2 and 90% in 3. Such a collection is, of course, simply the mixture we have already encountered. Once again, we measure the emitted photons, allowing sufficient time for the entire ensemble of atoms to decay. Since each individual atom is described as in the previous case, the result of each measurement is perfectly straightforward, and once again the projection postulate is not required. We will not be able to predict in advance which energy each particular photon will have, but this is no cause for concern. We simply do not have sufficient information—even in the classical universe, it is seldom possible to predict an event with this kind of certainty. But we do know that we will find 10% of the decay photons to be of low energy and 90% of high energy. Results like this lend support to our conventional understanding of reality as having an independent existence and well-defined attributes, regardless of the act of measurement.

Notice that, in both cases I and II, the initial state of the atom or atoms corresponds directly to one of the eigenstates of the detection apparatus. As long as this is true, measurement in quantum mechanics does not contradict our naive view of reality. However, as we have seen time and time again, the special feature of quantum mechanics is that it allows states other than simple eigenstates. The situation changes dramatically if we consider them.

In case III we prepare a collection of atoms, each one of which is in the superposition state given by

$$\phi = \sqrt{0.1}\phi_2 + \sqrt{0.9}\phi_3 \tag{8.10}$$

We saw in Chapter 4 that the phenomenon of quantum beats gives clear evidence that even single atoms can be prepared in such states. When such a state decays, the emitted photon is in a superposition state of its own:

$$\phi = \sqrt{0.1}\omega_{\text{low}} + \sqrt{0.9}\omega_{\text{high}} \tag{8.11}$$

If we now seek to measure the energy of this photon, the infinite regress we encountered above will result—an infinite regress that can only be terminated by invoking the projection postulate.

Here lies the nub of the problem. In case III the outcome of the series of measurements we perform will be identical to that produced in case II: 10% of the photons will turn out to be of low energy and 90% of high. In this case, however, we have no theoretical understanding of how the measurements came about. Furthermore, what is it that distinguishes the pathological case III from the well-behaved cases I and II? Only the choice of initial states to be studied! Those that happen to coincide with the eigenstates of our measuring apparatus will not require the extra projection postulate. Finally, notice that measuring devices exist whose eigenstates are not those of energy, but correspond to more complex superpositions of energy eigenfunctions—and if we substitute these devices for our previous ones, the need for the projection postulate will evaporate. Surely this is a most unsatisfactory state of affairs!*

8.2 The Active Nature of Measurement in Quantum Mechanics

Measurements play a radically different role in quantum mechanics than they do in classical physics. Classically, the function of measurement is to learn about a pre-existing reality. The classical world exists: by observation, we find out about it. But, as we have seen, in the quantum world objects do not exist in anything like so simple a sense as do the objects of the classical world. Correspondingly, in quantum theory measurements have a radically different function than they do in classical physics.

In an evocative phrase, Bohm has described a quantum state as a "set of potentialities." Following up on this point of view, Shimony and others advocate thinking of measurements as *actualizing one of these*

---

* This discussion has assumed that we are able to choose which of the three states to prepare. But a careful analysis shows that the task of *preparing* a state is subject to the same infinite regress as that of *determining* what it is. It is not so clear, therefore, what we mean by saying that the state "is" such-and-such. On the other hand, no matter what the state, a device can be imagined for which it is an eigenstate, and another device can be imagined for which it is not. Thus this difficulty can be evaded by couching our discussion in terms of the measuring apparatus we elect to use, as opposed to the state we elect to prepare.

potentialities. Speaking more loosely, we might say that measurements do not so much find out about reality as create it. We will give three examples to illustrate what these formulations mean. Before doing so, however, we wish to point out the relevance of this point of view to the delayed-choice experiments. We have several times written of these experiments as "altering the past." But in the present view, we would rather say that *the state of affairs discovered in the experiment had not even existed until the final measurement had occurred.*

Mixtures and Superpositions In the previous chapter we introduced the concept of a mixture, and we showed that there is a real physical difference between a mixture and a superposition. We illustrated this difference by means of a thought experiment:

> Let us imagine that we have a box containing a large number of spin-1/2 particles. The box is pierced by a tiny hole, which allows the particles to escape one by one, and each such particle we pass through a Stern–Gerlach apparatus. This apparatus is oriented along the z-direction, and so it allows us to determine the z-component of each particle's spin. If the experiment is performed a large number of times, we find ourselves obtaining the result $+\frac{1}{2}\hbar$ half the time and $-\frac{1}{2}\hbar$ half the time.

In our discussion, we noted that there are two ways this could have come about: the box could have contained a mixture, or it could have contained a superposition. As we showed, one could find out which was the case merely by rotating the Stern–Gerlach analyzer to a new orientation.

To make things clear, let us expand this experiment very slightly, by adding to it a second box. This box is positioned so that it catches the particles after they have passed through the analyzer. The configuration is diagrammed in Figure 8–7(a).

Suppose, for the sake of argument, that the first box in fact contained a superposition. If we apply to this experiment the line of argument that we gave in part III of the previous section, we see that an entanglement develops between the spin of a particle and its trajectory through the Stern–Gerlach analyzer. If this were all that happened, coherence would be maintained between the two beams, and after they were recombined in the second Stern–Gerlach apparatus, the initial state would be recovered. In this case, each particle as it entered the second box would still be described by a superposition.

But, also as we discussed in part III, this does not correspond to a measurement. Let us therefore insert measuring devices into the two paths between the Stern–Gerlach analyzers, each of which registers the passage of a particle (Figure 8–7(b)). These measuring devices terminate the infinite regress via the projection postulate, and they collapse each particle's state to a single term. In this case, as each particle enters the

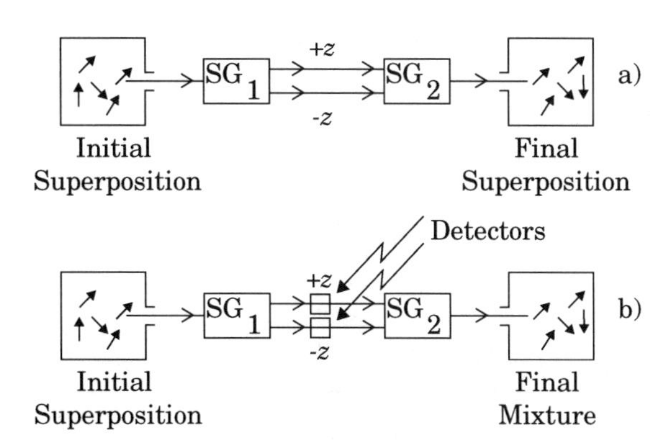

Figure 8–7 *Mixtures and Superpositions*. The box on the left contains particles described by a superposition. They pass through the first Stern–Gerlach apparatus, which separates those with spin $+z$ from those with spin $-z$. If the apparatus contains no measuring device (a) and the two beams are recombined by a second Stern–Gerlach apparatus, they still form a superposition. If, however, we insert measuring devices (b), the superposition is converted into a mixture.

second box, it possesses a definite z-component of spin. So now the second box contains not a superposition but a mixture. *The measuring devices have converted the superposition of the first box into a mixture in the second.*

We showed in the previous chapter that the phenomenon of decoherence effectively converts a superposition into a mixture. Now we see a second way of doing this: simply by performing a series of measurements. Are these the same thing, or are they different? We will return to this question later.

What Is the State of the Photon a Decaying Atom Emits? For our second example of the active role played by measurement in quantum mechanics, we consider an argument due to Jaynes.[3] A single atom is raised to an excited state, and it decays. What is the quantum state of the photon emitted in the decay? Jaynes shows that the answer depends on what sort of measurement we elect to make. Furthermore, this measurement can be made long after the atom has decayed, so that our choice has an influence that appears to act backward in time.

Jaynes is concerned with an atom whose ground state is split into two sublevels labeled h and g, as illustrated in Figure 8–8. The reader will recognize this diagram: it is that of the so-called Type II atoms we considered in Chapter 4, in our discussion of quantum beats. Excite the atom to its upper level a and wait for a long time, until the decay has certainly taken

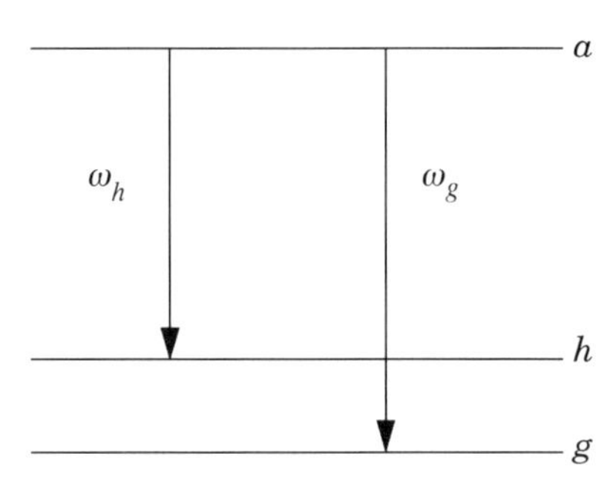

Figure 8–8 *Production of a Photon of Indeterminate Energy* in Jaynes's argument.[3] Depending on what sort of measurement we perform on the atom after the decay, the emitted photon does or does not have well-defined energy.

place. We can write the state of the atom–photon system after the decay is over as

$$\psi = \frac{1}{\sqrt{2}}\left[\phi_h\omega_h + \phi_g\omega_g\right] \tag{8.12}$$

Here ϕ represents the atom's state and ω that of the electromagnetic field. The reader will recognize Equation (8.12) as describing an entanglement: if, after the decay, the atom is left in state h, then a photon of energy ω_h had been emitted; and if the atom is in state g, then the photon's energy was ω_g.

Let us now *measure* the state of the atom. To be specific, our measuring apparatus is designed to determine the atom's energy. The result will either be E_h or E_g. Whichever result we get collapses the wave function: if we measure E_h the state becomes

$$\psi = \phi_h\omega_h \tag{8.13}$$

and if we measure E_g the state becomes

$$\psi = \phi_g\omega_g \tag{8.14}$$

The point we wish to focus on here is that *each of these states contains a photon of well-defined energy.*

But Jaynes then goes on to describe a different sort of measuring apparatus, one that will force the photons to be of undefined energy. He begins by defining a particular linear superposition of atomic and field states:

$$\begin{aligned}
\phi_+ &\equiv \frac{1}{\sqrt{2}}\left[\phi_g + e^{i\theta}\phi_h\right] \\
\phi_- &\equiv \frac{1}{\sqrt{2}}\left[\phi_g - e^{i\theta}\phi_h\right] \\
\omega_+ &\equiv \frac{1}{\sqrt{2}}\left[\omega_g + \omega_h\right] \\
\omega_- &\equiv \frac{1}{\sqrt{2}}\left[\omega_g - \omega_h\right]
\end{aligned} \tag{8.15}$$

where θ is a constant. If Equations (8.15) are substituted in Equation (8.12), we see that the entangled state after the decay can also be written as

$$\psi = \frac{1}{\sqrt{2}}\left[\phi_+\omega_+ + \phi_-\omega_-\right] \tag{8.16}$$

Jaynes then describes a second type of measuring apparatus, one that determines not whether the atom is in the state ϕ_h or ϕ_g, but whether it is in state ϕ_+ or ϕ_-. It turns out that this new apparatus is only a slight variation on the first. The difference merely consists in applying to the atom a pulse of electromagnetic radiation, of a precisely specified intensity and duration, just before measuring its energy. It turns out that, if the atom's state before the pulse is ϕ_+, then after the pulse it will be ϕ_g; and if the atom's state had been ϕ_-, then afterwards it will be ϕ_h. The apparatus then goes on simply to measure the atom's energy in the usual way.

Suppose that, upon making this second sort of measurement, we find the atom's state to be ϕ_g. This means that, prior to the measurement, the joint atom–field state had been

$$\psi = \phi_+\omega_+ \tag{8.17}$$

Conversely, if we find that the atom's state is ϕ_h, then prior to the measurement the state had been

$$\psi = \phi_-\omega_- \tag{8.18}$$

As always, the measurement collapses the wave function. But notice that *in this case, the state to which the collapse leads, if expanded in energy eigenstates, contains a photon whose energy is a superposition of two terms.*

And finally, notice that our measurement of the atom's state can be delayed indefinitely. We could do it a year after the decay. Thus, Jaynes concludes, it is not correct to say that a given decay produces a photon with definite properties. Rather, we must accept the fact that these properties depend on the sort of measurement we elect to make—and that this measurement can be made long after the decay has happened.

We emphasize that the distinction between these two states is not only of conceptual interest. It also has a clear experimental signature: the existence or nonexistence of the quantum beats we discussed in Chapter 4. Indeed, an experiment illustrating this remarkable situation has actually been performed. The delayed-choice experiment of Hellmuth et al.,[4] which we described in Chapter 2, has been performed in a mode in which these beats were made to appear and disappear by choosing, significantly after the decay had taken place, which sort of measurement to perform.

Jaynes's comment on this state of affairs is worth quoting:[3]

> From this, it is pretty clear why present quantum theory not only does not use—it does not even dare to mention—the notion of a "real physical situation." Defenders of the theory say that this notion is philosophically naive, a throwback to outmoded ways of thinking, and that recognition of this constitutes deep new wisdom about the nature of human knowledge. I say that it constitutes a violent irrationality, that somewhere in this theory the distinction between reality and our knowledge of reality has become lost, and the result has more the character of medieval necromancy than science.

The Quantum Zeno Effect As the old maxim goes, a watched pot never boils. In the quantum world, this is not a joke. The act of observing a process can slow that process, and in the limit of continuous measurement, can completely stop it.

The effect is sometimes known as the quantum Zeno effect, named by Misra and Sudarshan[5] after Zeno's famous paradoxes that appear to show that motion is impossible. The idea first arose in connection with the decay of an unstable state. It was argued that, if one were to prepare an atom in an unstable excited state, and then repeatedly observe it to see if it had decayed, the observations would slow the decay. Indeed, Misra and Sudarshan's calculations showed that, as the number of observations increased without limit, the state was predicted *never* to decay.

Although this calculation referred to the spontaneous decay from an unstable state, the same effect should exist for induced transitions. An experiment illustrating this phenomenon has recently been performed by Itano, Heinzein, Bollinger and Wineland.[6] The process Itano and colleagues studied is the excitation of an atom by light. As we discussed above (Figure 8–4), an electromagnetic wave is capable of raising an atom from its ground state to an excited state with certainty if an appropriate electromagnetic pulse is applied. While quantum theory cannot predict just when any individual atom makes the upward jump, it does predict that, after the time T_{ex} illustrated in Figure 8–4, the transition is sure to have happened. In their experiment, Itano et al. showed that this transition probability was reduced if they looked to see whether the transition had in fact occurred.

It is not hard to understand how this remarkable effect comes about. Let us consider an atom with a ground state ϕ_{gd} and excited state ϕ_{ex}. We wrote the atomic state in Equation (8.3), where α_{gd} is the coefficient of the ground state and α_{ex} that of the excited state. These coefficients are graphed in Figure 8–5. We see that initially α_{gd} smoothly drops, while α_{ex} correspondingly rises.

The initial state is $\alpha_{gd} = 1$ and $\alpha_{ex} = 0$. Consider the state after a short time t, where by "short" we mean a time less than that required to make the transition: $t < T_{ex}$. At this time, the coefficient of the ground state has dropped somewhat, and that of the excited state has risen.

We emphasize, however, that this is the state in the absence of a measurement. Let us now ask what happens if we *do* make a measurement. Suppose the measurement finds the atom to be still in its ground state. This collapses the wave function to

$$\psi_{\text{after measurement}} = \phi_{gd} \tag{8.19}$$

But this is just the initial state. The collapse of the wave function has "re-set the clock" from t to 0. It is as if the time interval from 0 to t had simply never happened. Thus we see that in this case the act of observation has slowed the decay rate.

Conversely, if the measurement reveals the atom to be in the excited state, the collapse leads to this state, in which case the measurement has hastened the decay. But if the measurements are frequent, t will be far less than T_{ex}, and the chances of this happening are small. We will shortly show that the net effect is a slowing of the decay.

Let us pursue these ideas in more detail. Working at the National Institute of Standards and Technology, Itano and colleagues made use of new techniques that allowed small numbers of ions to be trapped in an electromagnetic field, far away from the walls of their apparatus. These ions hovered in space, where they were slowed and then manipulated by a sequence of optical and radio-frequency fields. (The experiment by Chu et al., which we described in Chapter 3, used similar experimental methods.) The ions were of beryllium, only three energy levels of which are of interest: we label them 1, 2, and 3 and indicate them in Figure 8–9. Levels 1 and 2 are very close together, and are separated by only 320 MHz, a radio frequency. The transition from 1 to 3, on the other hand, is an allowed optical transition, with a wavelength of 313 nm.

The two states 1 and 2 were connected by a strong applied radio-frequency field, which drove the transition so rapidly that spontaneous decay from 2 to 1 was negligible, and only the stimulated transitions were

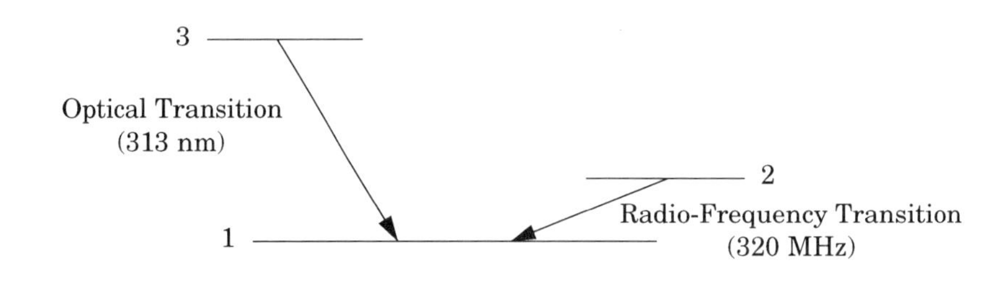

Figure 8–9 *Quantum Zeno Experiment* of Itano et al.[6] made use of the indicated transitions.

of significance. As we have seen, under such circumstances the ions cycle between states 1 and 2 at the Rabi frequency Ω. This implies that the probability of finding the ion in the lower state is

$$P_1(t) = \cos^2(\Omega t/2) \tag{8.20}$$

and that of finding it in the upper state is

$$P_2(t) = \sin^2(\Omega t/2) \tag{8.21}$$

These are simply the quantities sketched in Figure 8–4.

Once again, we emphasize that this is only true if one does not measure the system. If we do observe it, the observation collapses the state to either 1 or 2. In the Itano experiment, the measurement was performed by applying a short probe pulse, this time an optical one precisely tuned to a different transition, that between 1 and 3. It was adjusted to drive the transition with 100% certainty. Thus, had the ions been in the state 1 prior to this pulse, they would be in 3 after it. Conversely, had they been in state 2 prior to the pulse, they would still be in 2 after it.

The final step in Itano et al.'s measurement process was then to wait and search for *the photon emitted when the ion decayed from level 3 back to level 1.* Since this photon could only be emitted had the ion been in the state 1 prior to the pulse, its presence or absence constituted the measurement of the state.

We emphasize that the transition under consideration was that between 1 and 2; the observations of whether it had happened were made by studying a second transition, that between 1 and 3. We now need to consider how these observations affect the probability of induced transitions between states 1 and 2.

First, let us find the time T_{ex}, which is the time it takes for the radio-frequency field to move the ions with 100% certainty from state 1 to 2.

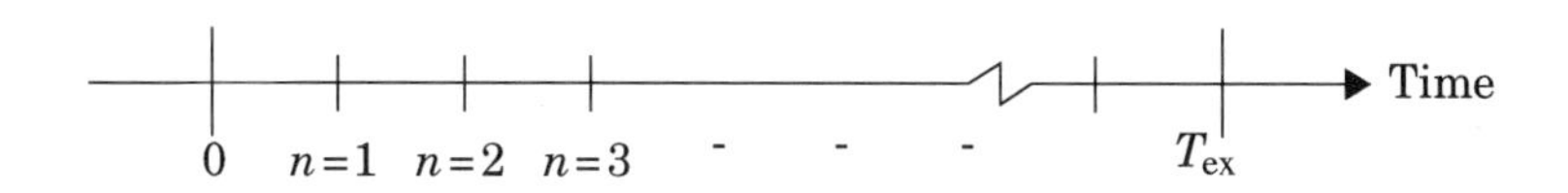

Figure 8–10 *Time Line* indicating T_{ex}, the time required for the atom to make a transition if not observed, and the n observations made by Itano et al.[6] which delayed the transition.

Because it is just $T_{ex} = \pi/\Omega$, a pulse of this duration is called a π-pulse. Putting $t = T_{ex} = \pi/\Omega$ in Equations (8.20)–(8.21), we see that after the time T_{ex}, $P_1(T_{ex}) = 0$ and $P_2(T_{ex}) = 1$, as expected. During the time interval from $t = 0$ to $t = T_{ex}$, Itano et al. then made a series of n measurements of the ion's state, separated in time by $\Delta t = T_{ex}/n = \pi/n\Omega$. Figure 8–10 shows the interval T_{ex} divided up into n such subintervals, each of length Δt.

We now need to evaluate

- the probability for a transition in a subinterval Δt;
- the probability for no transition in a subinterval Δt.

At this point a potential difficulty arises. If the probabilities given by Equations (8.20)–(8.21) were linear functions of the time, then the transition *rate* would be constant in time. But Equations (8.20)–(8.21) are not linear. This means that the rate varies with time, and the probability of transition in any particular subinterval will depend on just *which* subinterval we are considering. Here the collapse hypothesis intervenes to simplify the problem! Since Itano et al. are measuring the ion's state at the beginning of each subinterval, the collapse process "re-sets the clock" at each measurement—to $t = 0$ if the result of the measurement is level 1, and to $t = T_{ex}$ if the result is level 2. Thus we can use Equations (8.20)–(8.21) without asking which subinterval they are being applied to. They show that the probability of the ion making a transition to 2 during the time Δt, if it was in level 1 at the beginning of this interval, is

$$P_2(\Delta t) = \sin^2\left(\frac{\pi}{2n}\right) = \left(\frac{1}{2}\right)\left[1 - \cos\left(\frac{\pi}{2n}\right)\right] \tag{8.22}$$

and the probability of it staying in level 1 during Δt is

$$P_1(\Delta t) = \cos^2\left(\frac{\pi}{2n}\right) = \left(\frac{1}{2}\right)\left[1 + \cos\left(\frac{\pi}{2n}\right)\right] \tag{8.23}$$

If, on the other hand, the ion was in level 2 at the beginning of the subinterval, then the probabilities are given by Equations (8.20)–(8.21) evaluated at $T_{ex} + \Delta t = (\pi/2)[1 + (1/n)]$.

We now evaluate the probability of transition from 1 to 2 after *the entire* interval T_{ex} has passed, having made the n measurements in that time. To see how the calculation is done, begin with the particularly simple case $n = 2$: only two observations are made, one at $t = T_{ex}/2$, and the other at $t = T_{ex}$. There are, in this case, only two subintervals, and there are only two ways in which the ion, having started in level 1, could end up in level 2 at the end of the time T_{ex}:

(a) a transition occurs in the first subinterval, and no transition occurs in the second;
(b) no transition occurs in the first subinterval, but one does happen in the second.

We begin with (a). The probability of a transition in the first subinterval is just $P_2(T_{ex}/2)$. The probability of no transition in the second, given that the state was 2 at the beginning of this subinterval, is given by $P_2(T_{ex} + T_{ex}/2)$. The probability of the course of events (a) is then

$$P_a = P_2\left(\frac{T_{ex}}{2}\right)P_2\left(T_{ex} + \frac{T_{ex}}{2}\right) = \left(\frac{1}{2}\right)\left(\frac{1}{2}\right) = \frac{1}{4} \tag{8.24}$$

Similarly, the probability P_b for the second course of events turns out to be just the same product in reverse order, and therefore is likewise $\frac{1}{4}$. The overall probability of finding the ion in level 2 after 2 measurements in the time interval T_{ex} is therefore

$$P = P_a + P_b = \tfrac{1}{2} \tag{8.25}$$

Notice that, in the absence of measurements, this probability would have been 1: *the act of observing the ions twice has cut the probability of transition in half.*

The calculation can be extended to greater numbers of observations in a similar manner. The following general expression can be derived for the probability of finding the ion in level 2 after a time T_{ex} given n equally spaced measurements:

$$P = \left(\frac{1}{2}\right)\left[1 - \cos^n\left(\frac{\pi}{n}\right)\right] \tag{8.26}$$

This probability is what Itano et al. compared to their experimental data.

In their experiment, about 5000 beryllium ions were loaded into the trap, cooled to about 0.25 K, and prepared in state 1. The radio-frequency field was then turned on for 0.256 s, with an intensity adjusted to make it exactly a π-pulse. If no intervening measurements were made ($n = 1$), then at the end of the 0.256-s interval, all the ions would be in the state 2.

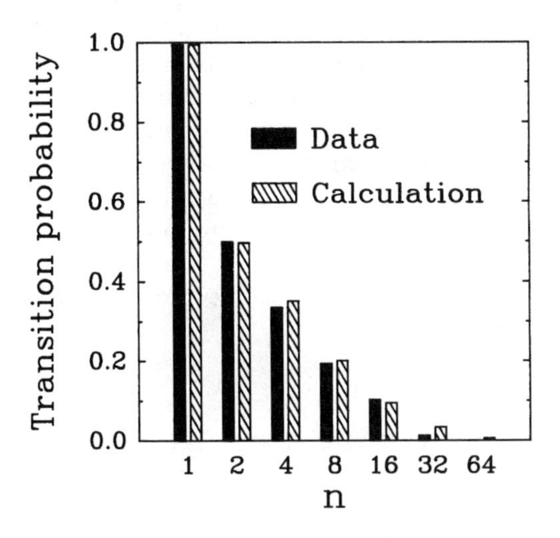

Figure 8–11 *Results of the Quantum Zeno Experiment.* The probability of having made a transition after a time T_{ex} as a function of the number of intermediate observations n. The decrease of the transition probability with n is the quantum Zeno effect. Agreement of the observations (solid bars) and theory (hatched bars) is excellent. SOURCE: Reproduced with permission from W.M. Itano, D.J. Heinzen, J.J. Bollinger and D.J. Wineland, "Quantum Zeno effect," *Phys. Rev. A*, vol. 41, p. 2295 (1990), published by The American Physical Society.

During the radio-frequency pulse, however, n short 313-nm probe pulses were also applied, with n taking on values 1, 2, 4, 8, 16, 32, or 64. The resulting 313-nm decay photons were searched for: these comprised the measurements of the state of the ions. After suitable calibration, Itano et al. were able to compare their experimental results with the predictions of Equation (8.26). Figure 8–11 shows a bar graph of their data for the transition probability from levels 1 to 2 as a function of the number of their measurements n; it also gives the theoretical predictions. The decreasing probability with increasing n is the quantum Zeno effect. The agreement between theory and experiment is excellent.

The experiment is a beautiful one and its results are unambiguous. Unfortunately, however, its interpretation is not. Following Itano et al.'s own description, we have used the language of the collapse of the wave function in analyzing their experiment. Other physicists, however, have argued that this is unnecessary, and they have performed alternative analyses, successfully predicting its results *without resorting to the collapse process*. So at this point, all we can say is that the quantum Zeno effect is real, but its interpretation in support of the collapse hypothesis remains only one option among many.

This lack of clarity is characteristic of the problem of collapse. In every other chapter of this book, we have been able to achieve considerable insight into the details of the theory and the corresponding experiments. The various quantum phenomena we have studied challenge our conventional understanding of the world—but the formalism and the experimental data are relatively straightforward, and though detailed interpretations may vary, the overall implications are generally agreed upon. As soon as we encounter the problem of measurement, however, this clarity gives way. The best we can hope for is to refine our definition of the problem itself. In this way, we can at least become increasingly clear about the source of our confusion.

8.3 Attempts to Solve the Measurement Problem

The measurement problem described in the first section of this chapter has received much attention. We turn now to a description of some of the many attempts that have been made to solve it. We caution the reader that there is no general agreement as to where the actual solution lies, so our discussion will not lead to any definite conclusion.

Small Detectors and Big Detectors: Decoherence Return to our analysis of the infinite regress that develops when we attempt to describe a measurement. Recall our comment that, in going from Equation (8.5) to Equation (8.6), an important new element has entered the situation: *we made a transition from microscopic to macroscopic.* Recall also from the previous chapter that large objects, unless they are of a very special sort, are subject to the process of decoherence. A number of workers in the field have argued that *this solves the measurement problem.* Their claim is that decoherence does away with the need for the projection postulate. We turn now to this claim.

At the close of our discussion of decoherence, we summarized its essential points (Section 7.5). We now repeat that summary, but with one change—everywhere the word "system" appeared before, we now write "macroscopic detector":

> [The essential elements of decoherence are] as follows. (I) The environment in which any macroscopic detector is embedded is constantly and irregularly fluctuating. (II) If a macroscopic detector is described by a superposition, the different terms in this superposition will interact differently with the environment. In particular, they will have different interaction energies. Therefore, (III) the time evolution of each of the terms in the superposition is constantly and irregularly fluctuating—and (IV) this is indistinguishable from a mixture.

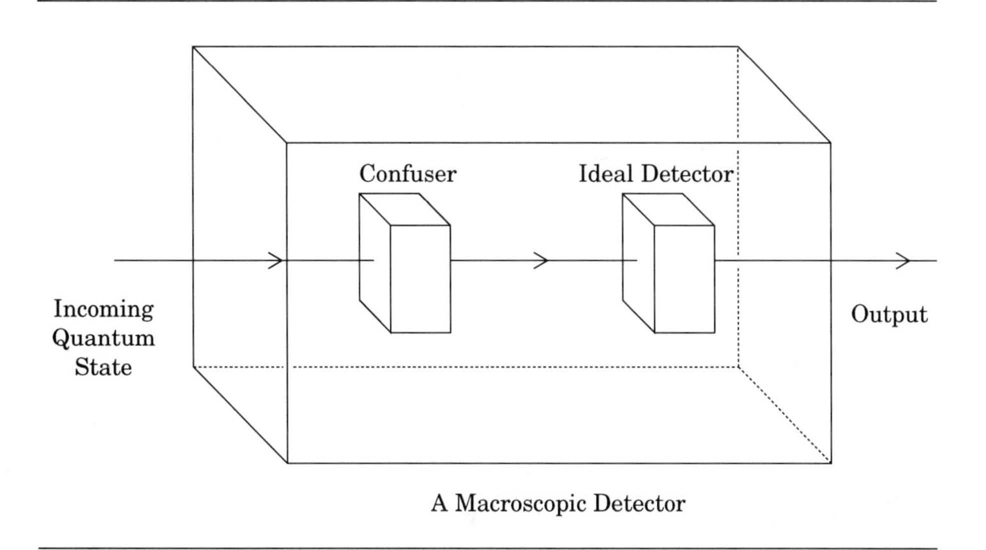

Figure 8–12 *A Macroscopic Detector* consists of an ideal detector connected to a "confuser"—a device that mimics the coupling between a macroscopic detector and its irregularly fluctuating environment.

Up to now in our discussion of measurement, we have tacitly assumed the macroscopic detector to behave in the same way as do microscopic objects such as photons and atoms. But the phenomenon of decoherence shows that this assumption was unwarranted. Let us now correct this error.

We imagine a macroscopic measuring device as being composed of two parts. The first part describes all the imperfections of a real measurement process, one made by a large-scale object. The second part consists of the sort of absolutely perfect device we have been considering up to now. We will call the first part a "confuser," and the second an "ideal detector." Figure 8–12 diagrams the configuration we have in mind.

In this diagram, the confuser represents all the unwanted interactions of the large-scale detector with the environment and with its own internal states, which themselves constitute an irregularly fluctuating intrusion into its behavior. We have no information about these interactions, which means that they cannot be included in the quantum-mechanical treatment of the detector's behavior. We can only treat them as unknown and uncontrollable perturbations.

How does such a two-part measuring device work? As before, decay photons are emitted by our atoms into a certain state. This can be any of the states we treated in our three cases above: an eigenstate, a mixture or a superposition. In any event, the state is well-defined. But now these photons enter the confuser, and at this point everything changes. An element of randomness enters our description, arising from the process of decoherence. Recall that the effect of this randomness is to make a superposition indistinguishable from a mixture. And as case II made clear, *if the state being measured is a mixture, the projection postulate is not required.*

No matter what the input state into the confuser, its output will be effectively a mixture. This state now enters the second component of our large-scale measuring device, the perfect detector. And as we have seen, in this situation we simply do not need the projection postulate. In this way, the argument goes, the phenomenon of decoherence solves the measurement problem by obviating the need for this strange and unsatisfactory postulate.

Does Decoherence Solve the Measurement Problem? The Quantum Eraser Not all workers in the field agree that decoherence solves the measurement problem. At the time of this writing, there is intense debate as to whether the line of argument we have sketched above is valid. There is no debate over the fact that macroscopic detectors are intimately connected to a complex and fluctuating environment; and there is no debate over the fact that a complex, fluctuating superposition state is indistinguishable from a mixture for certain purposes. But there is much debate as to whether this state is *in principle* the same thing as a mixture—and the measurement problem is one of principle, not of practice. The reader may have noticed that our discussion in Chapter 7 of decoherence was somewhat equivocal—it was peppered with phrases such as "equivalent to," "indistinguishable from" and the like, rather than simply "is." This equivocation reflects the lack of consensus in the field at present.

It will not be possible to do justice to the subtle arguments that have been raised in this debate. But we do wish to describe the important concept of the "quantum eraser," which sheds interesting light on the problem. The idea of the quantum eraser was invented by Marlan Scully and co-workers.[7] We will begin by describing an experiment that embodies it,[8] after which we will point out its relevance to the problem of measurement.

The experimental design is so complex that we will approach it in stages, reaching the actual design only in the third stage. Figure 8–13(a) illustrates the first step. It is a simple Mach–Zehnder interferometer. As the phase shifter in one of the paths is varied, the detector D records an interference pattern.

Figure 8–13 (right) *Quantum Eraser* experiment.[8] The experimental design begins with a simple Mach–Zehnder interferometer (a). In (b), nonlinear crystals have been placed in the two arms of the interferometer, and their outputs monitored by two additional detectors d_1 and d_2. Finally, in (c), a beam splitter BS_3 "erases" the which-path information that in (b) had been provided by the crystals, and a coincidence counter between D and d_2 records an interference pattern.

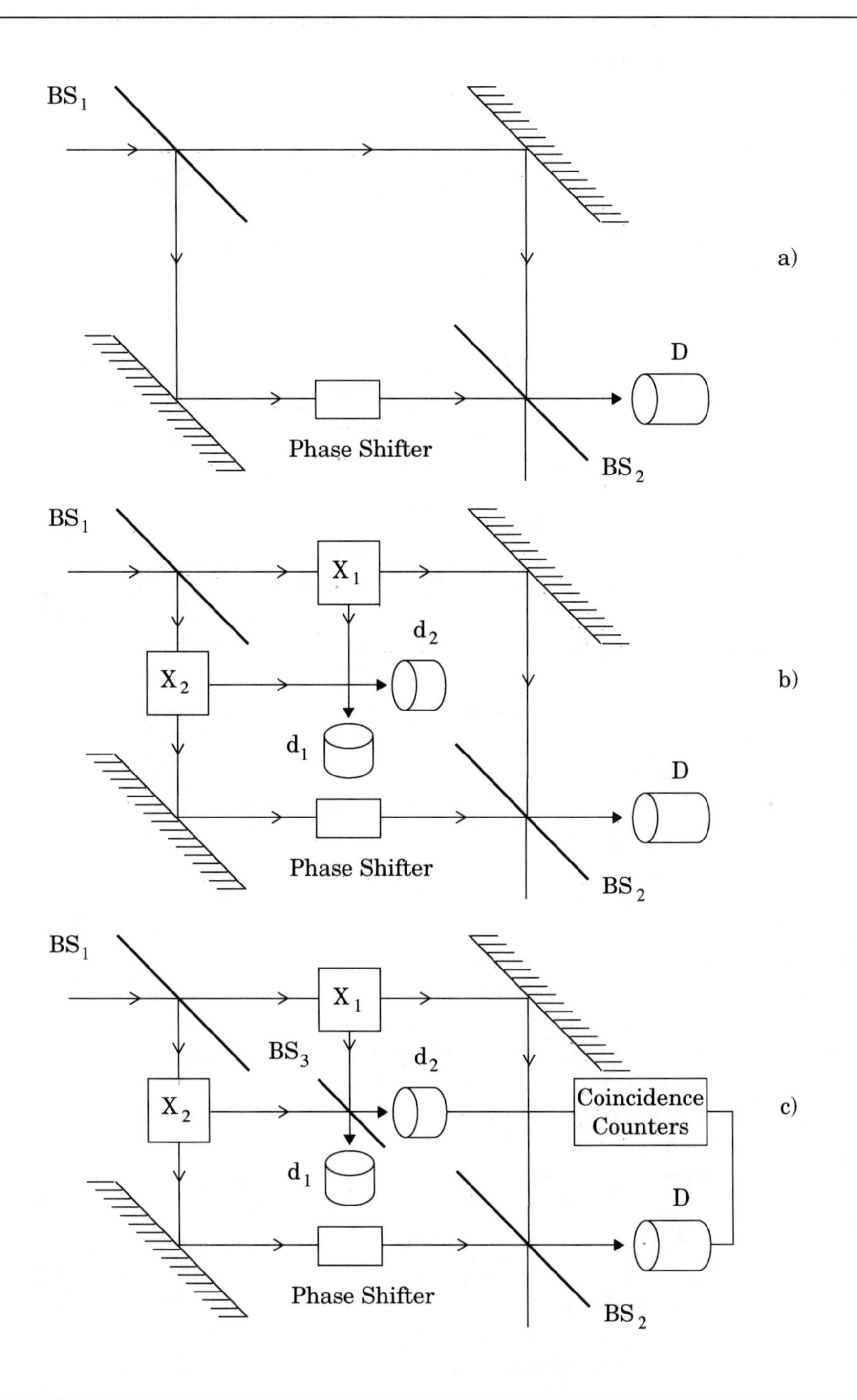

BS$_1$
a)
D
Phase Shifter
BS$_2$
BS$_1$
X$_1$
d$_2$
X$_2$
b)
d$_1$
D
Phase Shifter
BS$_2$
BS$_1$
X$_1$
BS$_3$
d$_2$
X$_2$
Coincidence
Counters
c)
d$_1$
D
Phase Shifter
BS$_2$

Now move on to the second stage of the analysis. We insert two nonlinear down-conversion crystals, X_1 and X_2. Each photon, as it enters a crystal, is split into a pair. These are illustrated in Figure 8–13(b). We have also illustrated in this figure two additional detectors, d_1 and d_2, which record the additional photons.

Will the initial detector D still register an interference pattern as the phase shifter is adjusted? The principle of complementarity shows that it will not. The apparatus illustrated in Figure 8–13(b) is capable of giving us which-path information; therefore it cannot exhibit interference. To see how this comes about, suppose that we send a single photon into the apparatus. We know that it is going to split into two photons, because either path it takes leads to a nonlinear crystal. One of the two additional detectors, d_1 and d_2, is therefore sure to register a count. And if d_1 clicks, we know the initial photon chose the upper path. Similarly, if d_2 clicks, the initial photon chose the lower path. Thus, whenever D clicks, we ask which of d_1 or d_2 also clicks. The answer gives which-path information.

The essence of Scully's concept of the quantum eraser is that this which-path information can be erased—and when it is, the interference pattern can return. This is accomplished in the final stage of the experiment (Figure 8–13(c)), in which we place a third beam splitter into the paths of the secondary photons from X_1 and X_2. Now we have lost the means of knowing which photon it was that made d_2 register a count. By the principle of complementarity, since we have no which-path information, an interference pattern can be seen.

But, as we emphasized in Chapter 6 in our discussion of quantum nonlocality, this interference signal does *not* show up if we record only counts in the detector D. Rather we must connect D and d_2 by a coincidence counter, which fires only if D and d_2 fire simultaneously. It is this coincidence signal that registers an interference pattern as the phase shifter is varied.

The experiment we have described has been performed by Mandel and coworkers at the University of Rochester.[8] They made use of techniques very much like those used in their experiment described in Chapter 6. Two-photon parametric down conversion supplied the secondary photons, in this case twice. Thus, a single ultraviolet photon from a powerful laser was first placed into a one-photon superposition state of the usual kind by passing it through a beam splitter. But then this superposition state passed through two down-conversion crystals, X_1 and X_2, creating thereby a complex two-photon entangled state. Inserting and removing the third beam splitter made this state's interference properties appear and disappear.

What is the relevance of such an experiment to the measurement problem? It lies in the fact that the interference pattern will only be observed if we look at coincidence counts between two detectors. Interference, of course, is the characteristic sign of quantum behavior: *and this quantum behavior will not be seen if we do the wrong experiment.* Looking at only the single detector D is the wrong experiment: it reveals what appears to be classical behavior—the absence of interference.

In the normal single-photon Mach–Zehnder experiment diagrammed in Figure 8–13(a), detector D is "the" detector, and it reveals quantum behavior as the phase shifter is varied. But in the more complex two-photon experiment of Figure 8–13(c), it alone does not. We might be tempted to argue that this is because the full experiment makes use of nonlinear crystals, which are macroscopic devices, subject to all the fluctuations of which decoherence treats. The quantum eraser experiment reveals that this, however, is not the case. In reality the full quantum behavior is still present, but it can only be seen by performing a different measurement.

Indeed, the effect of the nonlinear crystals here is not to wipe out quantum coherence. It is to entangle a photon arriving at the detector D with something else—with another photon arriving at d_2. Similarly, the effect of the incessant, fluctuating interactions to which all macroscopic detectors are subject is also to entangle them with something else. In this case, however, the "something else" is far more complex. It is the rest of the world. The lesson of this experiment is that only if the right experiment could be performed, one which detects all the multitudinous components of this gigantic entangled state, could quantum behavior be seen.

In the decoherence model, the conceptual device that we have termed a "confuser" introduces a complex, random disruption of the quantum state. This leads to a loss of interference. But does the loss of interference mean that quantum coherence has been lost? This is the key issue addressed by the eraser experiment. If this disruption truly destroys quantum coherence, destroys it not just in practice but in principle, then it will be impossible ever to recover an interference signal. On the other hand, if the disruption leads rather to the creation of an entanglement, then the state has become more complex but its fundamental nature has not altered—it is a superposition, not a mixture. In the measurement process, the projection postulate will be unnecessary only if the output of the confuser is truly a mixture: nearly a mixture is not good enough. And, at least in this one experiment, it is clear that the quantum behavior has not been destroyed by decoherence.

Comments In the real world, the detailed analysis of a detector with its attendant confuser is beyond our reach theoretically. For this reason, it is difficult to be sure how much relevance this simple model has to the measurement problem. Complex and subtle arguments have been brought to bear on this issue, with no general agreement at present.

We close by briefly mentioning three other ideas that have been put forward in an attempt to solve the measurement problem. These are not the only such attempts, nor are they necessarily the most significant. Rather, our goal in selecting them is simply to indicate how wide is the net that has been cast in the debate on the subject.

Everett[9] has put forward a re-interpretation of quantum mechanics, commonly known as the many-worlds interpretation, in which the wave function does not collapse. The entanglement of system and observer is never resolved. Instead, each measurement multiplies the number of branches that the system and observer must simultaneously sustain. Each branch represents a real option for the universe. In Everett's interpretation, all universes or worlds are simultaneously present with comparable reality.

Ghirardi, Rimini and Weber,[10] on the other hand, modify standard quantum mechanics in a way that has no effect on microscopic objects, while at the same time changing the quantum dynamics of large objects into a stochastic mechanics that displays all the features of classical physics. They accomplish this by introducing a term describing a continually fluctuating field whose effect is to cause superpositions to rapidly evolve into mixtures.

Finally, Wigner[11] has proposed that a measurement occurs, and the wave function collapses, when a person becomes aware of a detector's state. In this view the brain is described by ordinary quantum mechanics, but the mind is not: it stands outside normal physics, and its workings are not subject to physical law.

The great variety of these suggestions, and the absence of agreement on how the measurement problem is to be solved, are all the more remarkable in that the idea of measurement lies at the very heart of quantum mechanics. It lies at the heart of the prescription that ψ^2 at some point gives the probability that *a measurement* will find a particle there. It lies at the heart of the prescription that

$$\langle O \rangle = \int \psi^* O \psi \, d^3x \tag{8.27}$$

gives the average value of a series of *measurements* of the observable represented by O. Indeed, the concept is essential to every scientific theory, for it is through measurements that theory makes contact with experimental reality.

Finally, it is a commonplace that measurements take place every day, in laboratories throughout the world. Indeed, if Wigner's proposal is wrong and consciousness itself flows from the workings of the human brain, and if quantum mechanics applies to the brain just as well as SQUIDS and macroscopic bits of ferritin—then the very act of looking and seeing is a measurement. How can so prosaic an act be so fraught with difficulty for a theory that has proved so wonderfully successful in every other regard?

Epilogue

Many threads have woven through the fabric of this book. One consistently recurring theme has been the question of whether quantum mechanics is incomplete—whether in reality *things happen* in the microworld: processes that we can picture in our mind's eye and describe theoretically, but which quantum theory fails to discuss. The question was first posed in the context of the enigmatic evidence presented by interference experiments; it gained force with our consideration of the limitations on knowledge imposed by the uncertainty principle and by complementarity, and it reached a stunning climax with Bell's discovery of his famous theorem and the experiments that have tested it.

A second thread running through this book has been a regular progression from one to two to many particles. In our early chapters we concentrated on phenomena involving single quanta. These phenomena were surely rich enough—but entangling a second particle with the first led to entirely new considerations involving "passion at a distance" and the mystery of the EPR correlations. Finally, with our discussion of Schrödinger's famous cat paradox, we made the jump from two to great numbers of particles, a subject whose riches researchers have only begun to mine.

A third thread has been our constant reference to actual experiments. These experiments have only recently become possible, owing to spectacular modern advances in experimental technique, and they have cast the historic debates of the founders of quantum theory in a new light. Some have actualized the famous thought experiments by which Einstein, Bohr and others sought to clarify their new theory's many peculiarities; others have moved far beyond these early considerations, and have taken the field in directions its founders never guessed.

Throughout it all, the concept of measurement has played a central role. Experimentalists, of course, make measurements every day in the lab, but the concept has continually surfaced in our theoretical considerations as well. In our final chapter we turned to a discussion of the utterly remarkable position measurement occupies in quantum mechanics, to its active nature, and to the severe difficulties it poses for the theory.

The universe revealed by modern research on the foundations of quantum mechanics is a strange and wonderful place. In this book we have not succeeded in explaining it. As a matter of fact, our suspicion is that this will prove to be impossible. For surely, to explain something is to reduce it to what is already known. But it may turn out that we will never be able to reduce the quantum universe to our customary ways of thinking. Perhaps we will have to adjust our ways of thinking to it. Perhaps, years from now, people will think in new and unfamiliar ways, ways in which the quantum universe is no longer a challenge, but rather simple everyday reality.

References

Prologue

1. P.A. Schilpp, *Albert Einstein: Philosopher–Scientist* (LaSalle, IL: Open Court), vol. 2, p. 666 (1970).

Chapter 1

1. A. Tonomura, J. Endo, T. Matsuda, T. Kawasaki and H. Exawa, "Demonstration of single-electron buildup of an interference pattern," *Amer. J. Phys.*, vol. 57, pp. 117–120 (1989).
2. G. Moellenstedt and H. Druecker, *Zeit. für Physik*, vol. 145, pp. 375ff (1956).
3. R. Gähler and A. Zeilinger, "Wave-optical experiments with very cold neutrons," *Amer. J. Phys.*, vol. 59, pp. 316–324 (1991).
4. O. Carnal and J. Mlynek, "Young's double-slit experiment with atoms: A simple atom interferometer," *Phys. Rev. Lett.*, vol. 66, pp. 2689–2692 (1991); see also D.W. Keith, C.R. Eckstrom, Q.A. Turchette and D.E. Pritchard, "An interferometer for atoms," *Phys. Rev. Lett.*, vol. 66, pp. 2693–2696 (1991).
5. D.M. Eigler and E.K. Schweizer, "Positioning single atoms with a scanning tunneling microscope," *Nature*, vol. 344, pp. 524–526 (1990).
6. Isaac Newton, *Optiks* (1704) Queries, quoted in *The Scientific Revolution 1500–1800*, by A.R. Hall (Boston: Beacon Press), p. 213 (1962).

Chapter 2

1. W.E. Lamb, Jr. and M.O. Scully, "The photoelectric effect without photons" in *Polarisation, Matière et Rayonnement* (Presses University de France, 1969); see also L. Mandel, "The case for and against semiclassical radiation theory," in *Progress in Optics*, vol. 13 (Amsterdam: North-Holland, 1976), and M.D. Crisp and E.T. Jaynes, "Radiative effects in semiclassical theory," *Phys. Rev.*, vol. 179, pp. 1253–1261 (1969).

2. E. Schrödinger, *Annalen der Physik*, vol. 28, pp. 257–264 (1927); J. Dodd, "The Compton effect—A classical treatment," *Eur. J. Phys.*, vol. 4, pp. 205–211 (1983); J. Strand, "The Compton effect—Schrödinger's treatment," *Eur. J. Phys.*, vol. 7, pp. 217–221 (1986).
3. R. Hanbury-Brown and R.Q. Twiss, "Correlations between photons in two coherent beams of light," *Nature*, vol. 177, pp. 27–29 (1956).
4. J.F. Clauser, "Experimental distinction between the quantum and classical field theoretic predictions for the photo-electric effect," *Phys. Rev. D*, vol. 9, pp. 853–860 (1974).
5. P. Grangier, G. Roger and A. Aspect, "Experimental evidence for a photon anticorrelation effect on a beamsplitter," *Europhys. Lett.*, vol. 1, pp. 173–179 (1986).
6. J.A. Wheeler in *Mathematical Foundations of Quantum Mechanics*, edited by A.R. Marlow (New York: Academic Press), pp. 9–48 (1978).
7. T. Hellmuth, H. Walther, A. Zajonc and W. Schleich, "Delayed-choice experiments in quantum interference," *Phys. Rev. A*, vol. 35, pp. 2532–2541 (1987); see also C.O. Alley, O. Jakubowicz, C.A. Steggerda and W.C. Wickes, "A delayed random choice quantum mechanic experiment with light quanta," *Proceedings of the International Symposium on the Foundations of Quantum Mechanics—Tokyo*, edited by S. Kamefuchi (Physics Society of Japan), pp. 158–164 (1983).

Chapter 3

1. R.L. Pfleegor and L. Mandel, "Interference of independent photon beams," *Phys. Rev.*, vol. 159, pp. 1084–1088 (1967).
2. P.A.M. Dirac, *Quantum Mechanics* (London: Oxford University Press), 4th ed., chapter 1, p. 9 (1958).
3. P.S. Laplace, *A Philosophical Essay on Probabilities*, translated by F.W. Truscott and F.L. Emory (New York: Dover), p. 4 (1951).
4. W. Heisenberg, *Zeit. für Phys.*, vol. 43, pp. 172–198 (1927).
5. M.A. Kasevich, E. Riis, S. Chu and R.G. DeVoe, "Rf spectroscopy in an atomic fountain," *Phys. Rev. Lett.*, vol. 63, pp. 612–615 (1989).
6. A. Abramovici et al., "LIGO: The laser interferometer gravitational-wave observatory," *Science*, vol. 256, pp. 325–333 (1992); M.A. Lewis, "Sleuthing out gravitational waves," *IEEE Spectrum*, vol. 32, pp. 57–61 (1995).
7. R. Henry and S. Glotzer, "A squeezed state primer," *Am. J. Phys.*, vol. 56, pp. 318–328 (1988).
8. C.M. Caves, "Quantum-mechanical noise in an interferometer," *Phys. Rev. D*, vol. 23, pp. 1693–1708 (1981). See also D. Bohm and Y. Aharanov, "Time in the quantum theory and the uncertainty relation for time and energy," *Phys. Rev.*, vol. 122, pp. 1649–1658 (1961).
9. R.E. Slusher, L.W. Hollberg, B. Yurke, J.C. Mertz and J.F. Valley, "Observation of squeezed states generated by four-wave mixing in an optical cavity," *Phys. Rev. Lett.*, vol. 55, pp. 2409–2412 (1985); R.E. Slusher and B. Yurke, "Squeezed light," *Sci. Amer.*, pp. 50–56 (May, 1988).
10. V.B. Braginsky, Y.I. Vorontsov and K.S. Thorne, "Quantum nondemolition measurements," *Science*, vol. 209, pp. 547–557 (1980).
11. K. Bencheikh, J.A. Levenson, P. Grangier and O. Lopez, "Quantum nondemolition demonstration via repeated backaction evading measurements," *Phys. Rev. Lett.*, vol. 75, pp. 3422–3425 (1995) and references therein.

Chapter 4

1. W. Heisenberg, *Physics and Beyond* (New York: Harper and Row), pp. 73–76 (1971).
2. N. Bohr, *Collected Works* (Amsterdam: North-Holland), vol. 6, pp. 11–12 (1972).
3. W. Heisenberg, interview by T.S. Kuhn, 19 February 1963, quoted in Abraham Pais, *Niels Bohr's Times* (New York: Oxford University Press, 1991).
4. N. Bohr, *Collected Works*, vol. 3, p. 458.
5. N. Bohr, *Nature*, vol. 121 (Suppl.), p. 580 (1928); or *Collected Works*, vol. 6, p. 24.
6. N. Bohr, letter to A. Einstein, 13 April 1927, *Collected Works*, vol. 6, p. 418.
7. N. Bohr, *Atomic Theory and the Description of Nature* (Cambridge, England: Cambridge University Press), p. 10 (1961).
8. N. Bohr, *Atomic Theory*, p. 56.
9. J.A. Wheeler and W.H. Zurek, *Quantum Theory and Measurement* (Princeton, NJ: Princeton University Press, 1983).
10. L. Rosenfeld, interview by T.S. Kuhn and J.L. Heilborn, 1 July 1963, quoted in Pais, p. 315.
11. P. Ehrenfest, letter to S. Goudsmit, G.E. Uhlenbeck and G.H. Dieke, 3 November 1927, in N. Bohr, *Collected Works*, vol. 6, p. 37.
12. From a taped discussion with R. Jost of 2 December 1961; quoted in Pais, p. 318.
13. N. Bohr, letter to E. Schrödinger, 23 May 1928, *Collected Works*, vol. 6, p. 464.
14. A. Einstein, letter to E. Schrödinger, 31 May 1928, reprinted in *Letters on Wave Mechanics*, ed. M. Klein (New York: Philosophical Library, 1967).
15. C. Moller, *Fysisk Tidsskr.*, vol. 60, p. 54 (1962).
16. P.A. Schilpp (ed.), *Albert Einstein: Philosopher–Scientist* (Evanston, IL: Library of Living Philosophers, 1949).
17. L. Rosenfeld, in *Proc. 14th Solvay Conference* (New York: Interscience), p. 232 (1968).
18. M.O. Scully, B.-G. Englert and H. Walter, "Quantum optical tests of complementarity," *Nature*, vol. 351, pp. 111–116 (1991); M.O. Scully and H. Walther, "Quantum optical test of observation and complementarity in quantum mechanics," *Phys. Rev. A*, vol. 13, pp. 5229–5236 (1989).
19. S. Haroch, "Quantum beats and time-resolved fluorescence spectroscopy," in *High-Resolution Laser Spectroscopy*, ed. K. Shimoda (Berlin: Springer-Verlag, 1976).
20. T. Hellmuth, H. Walther, A. Zajonc and W. Schleich, "Delayed-choice experiments in quantum interference," *Phys. Rev. A*, vol. 35, pp. 2531–2541 (1987).
21. W.K. Wooters and W.H. Zurek, "Complementarity in the double-slit experiment," *Phys. Rev. D*, vol. 19, pp. 473–484 (1979); B.C. Sanders and G.J. Milburn, "Complementarity in a quantum nondemolition measurement," *Phys. Rev. A*, vol. 39, pp. 694–702 (1989).
22. L.J. Wang, X.Y. Zou and L. Mandel, "Induced coherence and indistinguishability in optical interference," *Phys. Rev. Lett.*, vol. 67, pp. 318–321 (1991); *Phys. Rev. A*, vol. 44, pp. 4614–4623 (1991).
23. N. Bohr, *Atomic Theory*, p. 54.

Chapter 5

1. J. von Neumann, *Mathematical Foundations of Quantum Mechanics* (Princeton, NJ: Princeton University Press, 1955).

2. J. Bell, "On the Einstein–Podolsky–Rosen paradox," *Physics*, vol. 1, pp. 195–200 (1964); "On the problem of hidden variables in quantum mechanics," *Rev. Mod. Phys.*, vol. 38, pp. 447–452 (1966).
3. S. Kochen and E.P. Specker, "The problems of hidden variables in quantum mechanics," *J. Math. Mechanics*, vol. 17, pp. 59–87 (1967); and see especially D. Mermin, "Hidden variables and the two theorems of John Bell," *Rev. Mod. Phys.*, vol. 65, pp. 803–815 (1993); "Quantum mysteries revisited," *Amer. J. Phys.*, vol. 58, pp. 731–734 (1990); "What's wrong with these elements of reality?" *Physics Today*, vol. 43, pp. 9–11 (June 1990); *Boojums All the Way Through* (New York: Cambridge University Press), chapters 10–12 (1990).
4. L.E. Ballantine, Resource Letter I.Q.M.2, "Foundations of quantum mechanics since the Bell inequality," *Amer. J. Phys.*, vol. 55, pp. 785–792 (1987).
5. A. Einstein, B. Podolsky and N. Rosen, "Can quantum-mechanical description of physical reality be considered complete?" *Phys. Rev.*, vol. 47, pp. 777–780 (1935).
6. From *Niels Bohr: His Life and Work as Seen by his Friends and Colleagues*, ed. S. Rozental (Amsterdam: North-Holland), pp. 128–129 (1967).
7. D. Bohm, *Quantum Theory* (New York: Prentice-Hall, 1951).
8. Various proofs of the BKS theorem can be found in Mermin's paper in *Rev. Mod. Phys.*, vol. 65, pp. 803–815 (1993).
9. J.F. Clauser and A. Shimony, "Bell's theorem: experimental tests and implications," *Rep. Prog. Phys.*, vol. 41, pp. 1881–1927 (1978); D.M. Greenberger, M.A. Horne, A. Shimony and A. Zeilinger, "Bell's theorem without inequalities," *Amer. J. Phys.*, vol. 58, pp. 1131–1143 (1990).
10. N.D. Mermin, "Is the moon there when nobody looks?" *Physics Today*, vol. 38, pp. 38–47 (April 1985).

Chapter 6

1. E. Schrödinger, "Discussion of probability relations between separated systems," *Proc. Cambridge Phil. Soc.*, vol. 31, pp. 555–563 (1935).
2. A. Aspect, P. Grangier and G. Roger, "Experimental tests of realistic local theories via Bell's theorem," *Phys. Rev. Lett.*, vol. 47, pp. 460–463 (1981).
3. A. Aspect. P. Grangier and G. Roger, "Experimental realization of Einstein–Podolsky–Rosen–Bohm Gedanken experiment: A new violation of Bell's inequalities," *Phys. Rev. Lett.*, vol. 49, pp. 91–94 (1982).
4. A. Aspect, J. Dalibard and G. Roger, "Experimental test of Bell's inequalities using time-varying analyzers," *Phys. Rev. Lett.*, vol. 49, pp. 1804–1808 (1982).
5. M. Lamehi-Rachti and W. Mittig, "Quantum mechanics and hidden variables," *Phys. Rev.*, vol. 14, pp. 2543–2555 (1976).
6. L.R. Kasday, J.D. Ulman and C.S. Wu, "Angular correlation of Compton-scattered annihilation photons and hidden variables," *Nuovo Cimento*, vol. 25B, pp. 633–661 (1975).
7. J.F. Clauser, M.A. Horne, A. Shimony and R.A. Holt, "Proposed experiment to test local hidden-variable theories," *Phys. Rev. Lett.*, vol. 23, pp. 880–884 (1969).
8. S.J. Freedman and J.F. Clauser, "Experimental test of local hidden-variable theories," *Phys. Rev. Lett.*, vol. 28, pp. 938–941 (1972).
9. R.L. Liboff, *Introductory Quantum Mechanics*, 2nd ed. (Reading, MA: Addison-Wesley), pp. 546–553 (1992).

10. D. Bohm and Y. Aharonov, "Discussion of experimental proof for the paradox of Einstein, Podolsky and Rosen," *Phys. Rev.*, vol. 108, pp. 1070–1076 (1957).
11. E.M. Purcell, "The principle of certainty: philosophical reflections on quantum mechanics," lecture delivered at Harvard University, 20 March 1987.
12. D. Bohm, "A suggested interpretation of the quantum theory in terms of 'hidden' variables. Parts I and II," *Phys. Rev.*, vol. 85, pp. 166–193 (1952).
13. D. Bohm and B.J. Hiley, *The Undivided Universe* (London: Routledge, 1993); D. Bohm, B.J. Hiley and P.N. Kaloyerou, "An ontological basis for the quantum theory," *Phys. Lett. A*, vol. 128, pp. 323–348 (1987).
14. D.C. Brunham and D.L. Weinberg, "Observation of simultaneity in paramagnetic production of optical photon pairs," *Phys. Rev. Lett.*, vol. 25, pp. 84–87 (1970).
15. R. Ghosh and L. Mandel, "Observation of nonclassical effects in the interference of two photons," *Phys. Rev. Lett.*, vol. 59, pp. 1903–1905 (1987).

Chapter 7

1. E. Schrödinger, "Discussion of probability relations between separated systems," *Proc. Cambridge Phil. Soc.*, vol. 31, pp. 555–563 (1935).
2. From *Quantum Theory and Measurement*, J.A. Wheeler and W.H. Zurek (eds.) (Princeton, NJ: Princeton University Press, 1983).
3. J. Summhammer, G. Badurek, H. Rauch, J. Kischko and A. Zeilinger, "Direct observation of fermion spin superposition by neutron interferometry," *Phys. Rev. A*, vol. 27, pp. 2523–2532 (1983).
4. G. Gamov, *Zeit. für Physik*, vol. 51, p. 204 (1928).
5. R.W. Gurney and E.V. Condon, *Nature*, vol. 122, p. 439 (1928).
6. A.J. Leggett, "Schrödinger's cat and her laboratory cousins," *Contemporary Physics*, vol. 25, pp. 583–598 (1984). See also S. Das Sarma, T. Kawamura and S. Washburn, "Quantum interference in macroscopic samples," *Amer. J. Phys.*, vol. 63, pp. 683–694 (1995).
7. C. Kittel, *Introduction to Solid State Physics*, 4th ed. (New York: John Wiley & Sons), pp. 737–743 (1971).
8. J. Clarke, A.N. Cleland, M.H. Devoret, D. Esteve and J.M. Martinis, "Quantum mechanics of a macroscopic variable: The phase difference of a Josephson junction," *Science*, vol. 239, pp. 992–997 (1988).
9. D.D. Awschalom, D.P. DiVincenzo and J.F. Smyth, "Macroscopic quantum effects in nanometer-scale magnets," *Science*, vol. 258, pp. 414–421 (1992); S. Gider, D.D. Awschalom, T. Douglas, S. Mann and M. Chaparala, "Classical and quantum magnetic phenomena in natural and artificial ferritin proteins," *Science*, vol. 268, pp. 77–80 (1995).

Chapter 8

1. G. Greenstein and A.G. Zajonc, "Do quantum jumps occur at well-defined moments of time?" *Amer. J. Phys.*, vol. 63, pp. 743–745 (1995).
2. J. von Neumann, *Mathematical Foundations of Quantum Mechanics*, translated by R.T. Beyer (Princeton, NJ: Princeton University Press), chapter 6 (1955).

3. E.T. Jaynes, "Quantum beats," in *Foundations of Radiation Theory and Quantum Electrodynamics*, A.O. Barut (ed.) (New York: Plenum Press, 1980).
4. T. Hellmuth, H. Walther, A. Zajonc and W. Schleich, "Delayed-choice experiments in quantum interference," *Phys. Rev. A.*, vol. 35, pp. 2532–2541 (1987).
5. B. Misra and E.C.G. Sudarshan, "The Zeno's paradox in quantum mechanics," *J. Math. Phys.*, vol. 18, pp. 756–763 (1977).
6. W.M. Itano, D.J. Heinzen, J.J. Bollinger and D.J. Wineland, "Quantum Zeno effect," *Phys. Rev. A*, vol. 41, pp. 2295–2300 (1990).
7. M.O. Scully and K. Druhl, "Quantum eraser: a proposed photon correlation experiment concerning observation and 'delayed choice' in quantum mechanics," *Phys. Rev. A*, vol. 25, pp. 2208–2213 (1982); A. Zajonc, "Proposed-quantum beats, quantum-eraser experiment," *Phys. Lett. A*, vol. 96A, pp. 61–65 (1983).
8. Z.Y. Ou, L.J. Wang, X.Y. Zou and L. Mandel, "Evidence for phase memory in two-photon down conversion through entanglement with the vacuum," *Phys. Rev. A.*, vol. 41, pp. 566–568 (1990); and comments by A. Zajonc, L.J. Wang, X.Y. Zou and L. Mandel in *Nature*, vol. 353, pp. 507–508 (1991).
9. H. Everett, III, "Relative state formulation in quantum mechanics," *Rev. Mod. Phys.*, vol. 29, pp. 454–462 (1957); Y. Ben-Dov, "Everett's theory and the 'many worlds' interpretation," *Amer. J. Phys.*, vol. 58, pp. 829–832 (1990).
10. G.C. Ghirardi, A. Rimini and T. Weber, "Unified dynamics for microscopic and macroscopic systems," *Phys. Rev. D*, vol. 34, pp. 470–491 (1986).
11. E.P. Wigner, "Remarks on the mind–body question," in *The Scientist Speculates*, I.J. Good (ed.) (London: Heinemann), pp. 284–302 (1962).

Index